FRONTIERS IN SCIENCE

Basic Books · *New York*

FRONTIERS

IN SCIENCE

A Survey

EDITED BY EDWARD HUTCHINGS, JR.

WITH EDITORIAL COMMENTARIES BY

L. A. DuBRIDGE, GEORGE W. BEADLE,

HARRISON BROWN, AND HUNTER MEAD

ALL OF CALIFORNIA INSTITUTE OF TECHNOLOGY

Contents

FRONTIERS IN SCIENCE

Frontiers in Science

Some time ago I was asked to address a large group of teachers representing all subjects. Eager, as a scientist, to impress on them the value of studying science, I chose to talk about it as "The Endless Adventure." The speech (reprinted in this volume) was not intended to be a profound discourse; rather, it was an attempt to convey to nonscientists some of the intense excitement attached to scientific discovery.

For science is a continuous advance to new frontiers. We recognize the adventure of life on a geographic frontier, as in the Old West in America; the laws to be obeyed are not clear, the unexpected happens at every turn, the conflicts between "good" and "evil" forces—between order and anarchy—become fierce. But out of such conflicts new nations arise and new social structures are built.

The frontiers of the mind offer analogous adventures. There, too, the unexpected is always found. The conflict between good and evil is analogous to the conflict between knowledge and ignorance. And out of this conflict a new area of human understanding will some day be built, which may intimately affect the structure of our own society.

The geographic frontiers are disappearing. But the frontiers of the mind are never-ending. Ignorance remains an infinite, unconquered wilderness, and the adventure of this conquest will mount in interest as the centuries go by.

Is it possible in a book such as this—in any book—to give some hints of this great adventure? One can probably hope for only partial success; yet here, in the language of the adventurers themselves, are stories of conquest, of battles now being fought on various salients of the advancing front of science. In one story the salient is the farthest reaches of space—the most distant objects that the Palomar telescope can "see." In another the frontier is the submicroscopic world—the genes, viruses, huge molecules that the electron microscope can "see" only barely. Or the frontier may be far beyond the visible—molecules, atoms, and nuclei which, because of the very nature of light itself, can never be seen—and yet can be understood!

If there is a particular lesson to be learned from these adventures, it is that the various intellectual frontiers they describe are not disconnected from each other. The physicist's electron spin and exclusion principle help unravel the structure of the protein molecule, and this helps the biologist to see how genes are made and how viruses reproduce. The discovery of radioactivity led eventually to nuclear fission and a vast new supply of energy. It led also to understanding the source of the heat in the sun and stars and enabled us to determine the age of the earth's rocks. The stars and the genes contain the same atoms, obey the same laws of physics. Thus, as Max Mason, a trustee of the California Institute of Technology, once remarked, "The study of astronomy might save your life."

It is no accident that this group of adventurers—with such diverse but overlapping interests—happens to be working at a single institution. Any university, by its nature, brings together men from various areas of learning and encourages the cross-fertilization of ideas. But often, too, a university, by its very size, will build barriers between the various disciplines. The chemistry building houses such a large group of people that they tend to become self-sufficient. And then, too, the physics and biology and mathematics buildings are a long way off—and one doesn't pass them on the way to and from the parking area!

The leaders who converted a small technical college in Pasadena into the Caltech of today capitalized on the supposed disadvantages of a small campus. They deliberately made it an intimate one in order to keep physicists, chemists, engineers, and biologists together. The buildings were designed so as to prevent a great expansion of the student body and faculty which could force the departments apart, force a diversion of effort from the prime tasks of scholarship.

Thus it has come about that a faculty of 400 has associated with it an undergraduate student body of only 600, a graduate group of 475. And no campus laboratory is more than four hundred yards from any other.

But intimacy does not of itself guarantee either individual productivity or group collaboration. Two more things are required: high individual talent and a spirit of unity of purpose. Through energy, foresight, and fine judgment (plus fine persuasive powers) the men of great ability were assembled. Through the magic of catalytic leadership, the group spirit was engendered.

The results in breaking down interdisciplinary barriers have been spectacular. A former physicist is now director of the Mount Wilson and Palomar Astronomical Observatories; another is head of the laboratory of virology; a third and a fourth headed, in succession, the Guggenheim Laboratory of Aeronautics. A chemist is leading a brilliant attack on the problems of mental disease; another chemist heads an important research group in geology. Two mathematicians play key roles in the engineering division. A Caltech student recently did brilliant undergraduate work in physics, then earned his Ph.D. in chemistry. He is now on the faculty—as a geologist.

The unity of science appears not only in individuals but in group efforts as well. When chemists, physicists, geologists, and astronomers combine forces to present a graduate course on "The Nature and Evolution of the Earth," the resulting lecture series becomes really exciting. This same group is also tackling the problem of understanding the evolution of the universe, the origin of the elements, the energy sources of the stars. A geologist and a microchemist use the techniques of isotope analysis to help locate ore bodies and to determine the temperature-history of the oceans. One electronics expert has revolutionized

5

the techniques of seismology, and another is undertaking a similar task in optical astronomy. A roomful of electronic computer equipment, under the supervision of an electrical engineer who also designed much of it, serves the needs of all sciences, of engineering, and of industry. A great group of chemists and electrical and aeronautical engineers, headed by a physicist, does research on rockets and jet propulsion in a laboratory sponsored by the United States Government.

Thus, science and its engineering applications move forward more rapidly as first-class men are brought into intimate contact and given adequate time and facilities to pursue their scholarly inquiries. An astonishing number of their students are inspired, too, and eventually join as full-fledged members of the group —keeping it always youthful in outlook and enthusiasm.

Granted that the attack on the unknown is going on actively on many fronts, how does one distill out of a vast mass of technical reports and put into more popular language the essence of this work? It is not easy. Many would say it is impossible. There are too many projects under way to be summarized. To select but a few is arbitrary. Even when a few are selected, the act of translating the results and the ideas into everyday English may make sharp statements appear fuzzy and oversimplified. Many a science writer has met his Waterloo in attempting this task of translation.

The answer, of course, is to ask the research men themselves to perform both the distillation and the translation, for they should be able to express their own ideas in simple language without risk of distortion. Not all research men are able or willing to attempt the task, of course. But the few who will can turn out documents of great importance. For, in this age of science, there is a profound need to bring the discoveries of the specialist to the nonspecialist—who, in the last analysis, is the one to reap the benefits.

Over the years, the editor of *Engineering and Science* has persuaded certain key scientists to set forth their ideas in fairly nontechnical form. This book is a collection of a few of the best of those articles. Although it was never intended that they should form a unified whole, the unity of science is such that they do fit together in astonishing ways.

L. A. DuBridge
President
California Institute of Technology

January 14, 1958

George W. Beadle:

This has been a swift-moving and revolutionary decade in the biological sciences. Because we have made enormous strides toward understanding life at the molecular level, not only can we now speculate sensibly about the origin of living systems, but we even seem to be on the verge of synthesizing living molecules in the laboratory.

We have long known in principle how organic evolution takes place through mutation and natural selection. We have known, too, that all organisms are built out of giant molecules. But the process by which these molecules achieve their specific

8

THE BIOLOGICAL SCIENCES

structure is no longer as mysterious as it was a few years ago. Knowledge of the inner structure of the gene promises to tell us how mutations occur, how high-energy radiation increases their frequency, and how mutant genes modify the organisms that inherit them.

Even more remarkable is the possibility that biochemists will soon know how to synthesize, from nonliving molecules, a very primitive kind of life—molecules capable of being replicated from an assortment of simpler molecules, of directing the synthesis of other species of large molecules, and of undergoing mutation. If one defines life in terms of this kind of self-duplication and the capability of giving rise through evolution to living systems of greater complexity, one may appropriately call such structures "living."

The mystery of life is indeed being replaced by understanding.

The following essays on biology were not written with the thought that they would be brought together as parts of an account of the science of biology as we know it today. Nevertheless, assembled as they are here, they become integral parts of a more general account. The following discussion indicates their relationship to the story as a whole.

The Origin of Life. Professor Horowitz, who has made important contributions to our understanding of how organic evolution may have taken place at a stage when only virus-like systems existed on earth, describes how simple molecules, such as hydrogen (H_2), water (H_2O), ammonia (NH_3), and methane (CH_4), in the absence of free oxygen and in the presence of a source of energy such as an electric discharge, interact to produce molecules of amino acids that are identical with some of those out of which the proteins of our bodies are constructed.

These are reactions that occur regularly and predictably when the conditions are right. And there are good geophysical, astrophysical, and physical chemical reasons for believing that conditions were "right" on earth a few billion years ago. Hence it is highly probable that there arose spontaneously, as a result of myriads of such inevitable reactions, not only amino acids but also a vast array of complex "organic" molecules of other kinds.

It is not difficult to believe that, in such an environment, there would have arisen by natural chemical reactions a molecule endowed with the life-giving properties of self-reproduction and mutability. And it is not too difficult to believe that this may have happened repeatedly during the thousands of millennia during which the chemical stage for life was properly set. The nucleic acids possess properties suggesting that they could have served to bridge the important evolutionary gap between the nonliving and the living world.

Molecular Evolution. Supposedly there then followed organic evolution at a molecular level, during which societies of "living" molecules were formed, and the members of these societies acquired diversity through mutation. If these were, indeed, nucleic acids, it seems reasonable to assume that early in the process of evolution they acquired protein coats that served both to protect them from the harshness of the environment and to catalyze the reactions by which they would synthesize their necessary building blocks from simpler substances.

Professor Horowitz has pointed out elsewhere how such a system could gradually acquire the ability to synthesize systematically all its subunit molecules from the simpler inorganic molecules that were present in abundance. The Horowitz hypothesis assumes only phenomena that we know about in today's organisms. It requires that no single step in the organic evolutionary process need have been larger than a single gene mutation which made the new organism one step less dependent on rare spontaneous chemical reactions and thus gave it a selective advantage.

Viruses. Are there still present on earth organisms as simple as the assumed early stages of the Horowitz hypothesis? The viruses come close to it, although there are reasons for believing they are simple systems derived from more complex parasitic organisms through retrogressive evolution rather than direct descendants of primitive forms. Whatever the evolutionary history of viruses, they serve as models that tell us how primitive organisms might have been constructed.

Some viruses consist of little more than self-duplicating mutable molecules surrounded by protective coats of protein. Their cores are nucleic acid of either the DNA (deoxyribonucleic acid) or the RNA (ribonucleic acid) type. Their coats may be removed and discarded without destroying the "living" characteristics of the cores—that is, the ability to be replicated and to mutate. In the proper environment (so far found only in the

11

interior of living host cells of the proper kind), replicas of the nucleic acid cores are built and new coats are made that are specific to the virus from which the cores come.

Nucleic Acids. In addition to knowing that the material that bridges the gap between generations of viruses is nucleic acid, we also have evidence that viruses contain units remarkably like the genes of higher organisms. These facts, plus the observation that all cellular organisms contain nucleic acids, make it quite clear that these substances must be biologically important in a very basic way.

Nucleic acids are of two main varieties, ribonucleic acid (RNA) and deoxyribonucleic acid (DNA). Except for some of the viruses, DNA appears to be the primary genetic material in all organisms.

Within the past several years a great deal has been learned about DNA—enough to show how and why it plays such an important role in all living things.

All higher forms of life—bacteria, protozoa, algae, mosses, flowering plants, and higher animals—have nucleic acid in the nuclei of all cells capable of reproduction. This is of the DNA variety and it seems to carry the primary genetic information through which daughter organisms are directed to develop like their parents.

In 1953 Watson and Crick proposed a molecular structure of DNA that beautifully accounts for its remarkable biological properties. Details of the Watson-Crick model cannot be described here, but it can be said that it assumes DNA to be a double molecule made of two parallel chains, each built of four kinds of units. The two chains are complementary in that the units are paired in fixed ways. If the units are designated A, B, C, and D, a four-unit segment of the molecule can be symbolized as follows:

$$\overline{A}\ \overline{B}\ \overline{C}\ \overline{D}$$
$$.. \ .. \ \ .. \ ..$$
$$\underline{B}\ \underline{A}\ \underline{D}\ \underline{C}$$

in which an A unit in one chain (a half-molecule) is always paired with a B unit in its partner. Similarly, a C is paired with a D. There are thus four pairs of units. If these can be arranged in any order (and there is no obvious mechanical reason why this should not be true), the number of ways a molecule of a given length can be constructed is 4^n, where n is the number of paired units in the chain. Thus a 4-unit piece can be put together in $4 \times 4 \times 4 \times 4 = 4^n = 256$ ways. A 10-unit segment could be built in 4^{10} (1,048,576) ways. These orders are responsible for the specificity of particular segments of DNA. In other words, DNA is a molecular code which carries information in much the same way as do specific arrangements of the letters of our alphabet, or as do dots and dashes in a telegraphic code.

Replication is believed to occur by the halves separating, followed by the building of a new complementary half by each old half. This can be represented as follows:

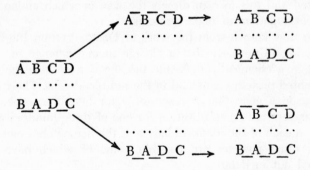

The nucleus of the fertilized egg of man contains about 200 million A:B, B:A, C:D, or D:C units. The number of possible arrangements of these is essentially infinite. The total DNA of a particular arrangement in an egg is a kind of genetic recipe that says what type of individual will develop from that cell in a proper environment and with an adequate supply of raw material (food).

In the case of tobacco mosaic virus, it is known from the work of Doctor H. Fraenkel-Conrat and Professor Robley Williams of the University of California that nucleic acid cores, which are RNA in this virus, will spontaneously recombine with partially "disassembled" protein coats to reconstitute viable and stable virus units. In an essentially similar manner, DNA may be capable of directing the construction of specific protein coats, a possibility of considerable interest in speculations about the early steps in organic evolution.

Changes in the order of units of DNA may occur during replication through errors that are analogous to typographical errors made in copying a written message. Such changes are the basis of gene mutation. If such a new order is advantageous, it will be likely to replace the parental form by natural selection.

Protein Synthesis. The mechanism by which DNA transfers specificity to protein molecules is the subject of important studies now being made in biochemistry. In higher forms of life the transfer seems to be indirect. One current working hypothesis assumes that DNA determines how RNA is constructed and this in turn directs the way in which amino acids are put together to make proteins.

It is now known from the work of Doctor Vernon Ingram of Cambridge University that a change in one gene in man will result in a chemically definable modification of hemoglobin, a pigmented protein compound in the red blood cells. The specific change in a gene that is responsible for hereditary sickle cell anemia results in a substitution for one of three hundred amino acids in each of the identical halves of the hemoglobin molecule. Many other changes are possible, some of which have been worked out in detail.

Although it has been known for many years that proteins are long chains of amino acids joined together through peptide linkages, it was only recently demonstrated that these polypeptide chains in many "native" proteins are arranged helically in very specific ways. One of these is called the alpha helix and was first worked out in terms of detailed spacing of atoms by Professor Linus Pauling and his collaborators. The manner in which this advance was made and its significance to biology are described in the paper on protein structure that is a part of the following series.

Biosynthetic Autonomy. In the early course of evolution, a number of lines of descent became independent of prefabricated organic building blocks by "learning" to make them from inorganic precursors. The most successful of these gave rise to the green plants of today—among them algae, mosses, ferns, and flowering plants—that contain the pigment chlorophyll. They are able to use light energy to break water molecules into hydrogen and water and to convert carbon dioxide into energy-rich carbohydrates. Typically, green plants are able to live successfully on purely organic raw materials such as CO_2, H_2O, NO_3, SO_4, PO_4, and a series of similar molecules and ions.

Professor Arthur Galston tells us, in his brief section on chlorophyll, a little of the wonders of this remarkable pigment that plays such an important role in the capture of light quanta.

Societies of Cells. From the first single-celled green alga to a present-day flowering plant there transpired a tremendous period of evolution—certainly hundreds of millions of years. In the process, colonial forms—that is, societies of cells—evolved. In these, there was division of labor among cells. This specialization of cells is termed "differentiation." It involves specialization in both structure and function.

Differentiation is one of the great unsolved problems of biology. It is commonly believed that the genetic material in all cells of a multicellular organism is the same. With the same set of directions, how is it that cells become so different in appearance and in function?

We do not know the answer in any detail. But there are suggestions in many instances that environmental differentials are important. Thus, in a Siamese cat, a pigment cell in the extremities, where the temperature is a few degrees below body temperature, will form pigment, whereas a genetically identical pigment cell in the main part of the body fails to manufacture pigment. It is known, in fact, that a special "Siamese" gene specifies that a temperature-sensitive pigment-forming enzyme will be inactivated at body temperature, but not at a temperature a few degrees lower. This simple case

15

is a very small beginning toward understanding the enormously complex general problem of differentiation.

Cancer.. The problem of cancer may well be synonymous with that of differentiation, for cancer seems to be a kind of de-differentiation. There are cases known in animals in which virus infection causes cells to become malignant. A classical virus-caused cancer is the Rous sarcoma of the chicken. As Dr. Harry Rubin makes clear in his review of the subject, other cancers, including some of those known in man, may eventually be shown to be caused by viruses.

The Nervous System. Whatever is the basis of differentiation, it is responsible, in the animal line of descent, for the evolution of the nervous system. This remarkable system had its evolutionary beginnings way back in the early multicellular organisms. Even the lowly sea anemone has a simple network of nerve cells—but has no suggestion whatever of a brain.

Cultural Inheritance. In the degree of development and specialization of the nervous system, man outstrips his ancestral forms by a tremendous gap. In him, the nervous system makes possible a highly developed capacity to reason and to remember. These, in turn, make possible communication and learning, indispensable fundamentals to the evolution of culture. Unlike biological inheritance through information coded in DNA, culture is passed from one generation to the next by way of words, written or spoken, or instruction by demonstration. It is cumulative from generation to generation and is responsible for the evolution of religion, music, art, literature, agriculture, technology, and science.

The Mind. Through knowledge of science man is capable of freeing himself of the limitations of mutation and natural selection in his future evolution. Achievement of this freedom will not be easy. It will require wisdom, courage, and faith far beyond anything man has so far displayed.

All this is possible because of the mind. What is the mind and how does it work? We are only beginning to make progress in this enormously complex and difficult field. The most elaborate computing machine that can be imagined is nothing beside the mind of man. The mind can invent the machine, but the machine can do only what the information fed into it orders. And the mind of man must formulate the information and must tell the machine what to do with it.

Through a series of ingenious and delicate experiments on the brains of fish, frogs, salamanders, rats, cats, and monkeys, Professor Roger Sperry and Doctor John Stamm give us a tiny glimpse of what the psychobiologist of the future might be able to learn about this mind which makes man unique among all living things and can give him mastery of himself, the world, and all the vast space that lies beyond.

Cultural inheritance is not separable from biological inheritance. The first cannot exist without the second. It follows that, while man is nurturing his cultural inheritance, he must not let his biological inheritance regress. And this it will surely do if care is not taken. Relaxation of natural selection, or natural selection for the wrong characteristics, can lead to a degeneration of the biological capacity for continued cultural inheritance.

An increase in mutation rate beyond a certain level can have the same effect. Unfortunately, we do not know the level that constitutes a serious threat. But we do know that the increased exposure to high-energy radiation that accompanies the explosion of nuclear weapons in testing or war, the use of unshielded power reactors, the use of X-rays for diagnostic or therapeutic medical purposes, and the use of radioactive isotopes in industry and medicine will increase mutation rates in proportion to the exposure.

Present levels of man-made radiation in the United States, including that used medically, is perhaps enough to increase the natural mutation rate by 10 percent. We do not know how serious this percentage increase is. We ought to find out as rapidly as possible and, until we know more, should keep radiation exposures to the germ lines of persons who have not yet passed the reproduction period at the lowest practicable levels. Professor A. H. Sturtevant, discoverer of the linear order of the genes, states this problem clearly and authoritatively.

Populations. If man's lot on earth is to be a happy one, he must either find a way to keep his numbers within some reasonable bounds or find ways to speed up the application of the science and technology that enable him to harness energy, gather raw material, and grow or synthesize food.

As Professor Henry Borsook points out, there is no reason that, with the knowledge and resources he now has, man cannot adequately feed the present world population. The plant hormones that Professor Bonner writes about will help by giving him greater control than he now has over his crop plants. But if populations continue to grow at anything like their present rates, it is inevitable that eventually Thomas Malthus will be proved to have been right.

The gloomy side of man's population problem is presented by Sir Charles Galton Darwin, noted grandson of a noted grandfather. He has warned that, whereas it is easy to be concerned about the welfare of one's children and grandchildren, concern for generations further removed falls close to the zero level. And many others have made the point that overcrowded, underprivileged men with empty stomachs do not easily tell right from wrong. Man must, he says, find some effective way of controlling total population size. Any solution that does this in a nonuniform way will, in the end, be no solution at all, for the slow breeders will be replaced by the fast breeders, and the latter will again outrun their food supplies and other resources.

Astronomer Fred Hoyle is not prepared to accept these pessimistic conclusions completely, and he explains why. It is fitting that the section on biology should end on this note of reserved optimism.

Man can, if he will, intelligently control his future biological and cultural evolution. The reward for success can be a world better beyond imagination. The price of failure could be the destruction of civilization and a return to savagery.

NORMAN H. HOROWITZ

The Origin of Life

A COLORFUL ACCOUNT OF THE STUDIES MAN HAS MADE IN HIS
ATTEMPT TO DISCOVER THE FUNDAMENTAL CHARACTERISTICS
OF LIVING MATTER.

From the earliest times it has been believed that living things
can originate spontaneously from nonliving material. For centuries it was thought, for example, that worms, frogs, insects
and scorpions could originate in mud, or from dew or decaying
meat, without parents. Known as the doctrine of spontaneous
generation, this was the view of the classical Greek authors—
Aristotle, Lucretius, and others who influenced Western thinking for 2000 years. It was the generally accepted view all through
the Middle Ages and well into the 17th century.

The following quotation from the works of a well-known physician and chemist named Van Helmont, who lived from 1577
to 1644, is typical:

"Furthermore, if a dirty undergarment is squeezed into the
mouth of a vessel containing wheat, within a few (say 21) days
the ferment drained from the garments and transformed by
the smell of the grain, encrusts the wheat itself with its own
skin and turns it into mice. . . . And what is more remarkable,
the mice are neither weanlings, nor sucklings, nor premature;
but they jump out fully formed."

It is important to note that Van Helmont was not making
this up; he actually carried out the experiment and this is the
way he says it worked.

19

Two hundred years later Pasteur commented on this quotation from Van Helmont. "What this proves," he said, "is that to do experiments is easy; but to do them well is not easy." One can see now how careless Van Helmont must have been when he set up this experiment. But the result came out just as he had expected; it was in keeping with the view of the times, and he did not feel like being very critical about it. It is still true today, as it was then, that the easiest thing to do in a laboratory is to find the result you expect to find.

In 1668 an important discovery was made. An Italian physician named Redi decided to test the idea that worms were generated spontaneously in rotting meat. He put some rotting meat and fish in open jars, and he watched them. In time, he noticed that flies came and laid their eggs in the meat and that maggots hatched from the eggs. When he covered the jars with muslin he found that flies came and laid their eggs on the muslin, but as long as the eggs did not get to the meat, no "worms" ever developed in it—and that was the beginning of the end of the theory of spontaneous generation of higher plants and animals. From this point on, this belief gradually died out among educated people.

A few years later, however, in 1675, another discovery was made which was to reopen the whole question at a different level. This discovery was made by Leeuwenhoek, a Dutch microscopist. Leeuwenhoek was the greatest microscopist of all time; he discovered a whole new world—the world of bacteria and protozoa. Nearly one hundred years later they were to form the subject of another controversy on the theory of spontaneous generation.

Leeuwenhoek is probably the most original figure in the history of biology. He was not an educated man; he was only an amateur scientist, and his true calling was the haberdashery business. Fortunately, he was able to spend a great deal of his time at his hobby, which was making microscopes. He made the best microscopes that were known up to that time. Actually, they were not what we call microscopes; they were magnifying glasses of remarkably high power and resolution. One of them is known to have had a magnification of 270 diameters.

Leeuwenhoek learned how to blow glass and how to grind and polish lenses by going to the fair in Delft and watching professionals. Then he went home and practiced by himself, and in this way he learned to make excellent lenses. But he never gave his secrets away; he never told anyone how he made the lenses. He never lent his best instruments or sold any or showed visitors his best glasses.

All of Leeuwenhoek's scientific discoveries were communicated in the form of letters to the Royal Society in London. The Royal Society had only recently been formed, and was in search of people doing interesting scientific work. Somebody from Holland told them that Leeuwenhoek was doing interesting things with microscopes, and he was invited to communicate his discoveries. So he wrote a long series of letters which were sent to London, translated, and published. He was elected to membership in the Royal Society in 1680. In a way, this was the climax of his career. Elected to the company of people like Newton, Hooke, Robert Boyle, Halley, and other great names of his day, Leeuwenhoek was deeply touched. On his death he left 26 of his best microscopes to the Royal Society. Unfortunately, these have all been lost.

BACTERIA AND DECAY

The next important date in the history of our subject was 1745, when a Scottish minister named Needham, also a microscopist, published observations and arguments which led him to believe that bacteria were generated spontaneously from decaying organic matter. People no longer believed that worms and mice were generated in this way, but bacteria were so small and primitive, so simple, that it seemed they were really on the threshold of nonliving and living matter. It seemed quite reasonable to believe that bacteria were generated spontaneously, especially since it could be demonstrated that they were found wherever decay or putrefaction was going on.

Needham's paper started a controversy. In 1765 an Italian by the name of Spallanzani published a report of an investigation which he thought disproved the claims of Needham. Spallanzani said that if he took mutton gravy, or any other medium suitable for the growth of bacteria, and heated it for a long enough time in a sealed vessel at the boiling point of water, it would no longer give rise to bacterial growth. Needham argued that what Spallanzani had done was to destroy some vital element of the air—some substance which was necessary for spontaneous generation—and that this experiment therefore did not disprove Needham's view.

ORIGIN OF CANNED FOOD

This actually was to some extent true; years later, after oxygen had been discovered, it was shown by the French chemist, Gay-Lussac, that in Spallanzani's experiment the oxygen had, in fact, been used up. What Spallanzani had done was to fill the jar nearly to the top and heat it for 45 minutes; the oxygen was consumed by reacting with the organic material in the jar. So the controversy was not settled at that time. (One important thing did come out of it though. In one of Spallanzani's experiments he used garden peas as his growth medium, and he found that the peas kept indefinitely without spoiling. This was the first time that anything was canned, and it was directly from this observation that the canning industry started.)

The argument was finally settled a hundred years later in a famous series of experiments by Pasteur. Pasteur proved, once and for all, that bacteria are not generated spontaneously—any more than Van Helmont's mice were. He showed that bacteria are not the product of decay but the *cause* of decay. He communicated his results to the general public in a famous lecture which he gave at the University of Paris 92 years ago and in which he demonstrated three important experiments.

In the first experiment, Pasteur showed that if you destroy the bacteria in a suitable medium by boiling, and allow only sterile air to enter the flask, you get no subsequent growth of bacteria.

In his next experiment he proved that growth of bacteria

would start in the medium if it was inoculated with dust collected from the air.

STERILE SOLUTION

The third experiment—and the one of which he was obviously most proud—was one in which he prepared his broth in an ordinary flask which he then pulled out in a flame so that it had a gooseneck. He boiled the medium in the flask for three or four minutes, allowing the steam to go up the gooseneck. Then he simply turned off the burner and let the flask sit there until it cooled. Then, without sealing it, and without any other precaution, he put the flask in an incubator and left it there. Nothing grew in it. The flask was completely open to the air, and there was no question of the oxygen being depleted because oxygen had free access to the flask. Yet the broth remained sterile. If you visit the Institut Pasteur in Paris today you will still see such flasks which, it is said, were put there by Pasteur. There is still nothing growing in them.

The explanation which Pasteur gave for this experiment is this: When the broth is boiled, the steam comes out the gooseneck and, of course, drives out the air. When the flame is turned off, air re-enters the flask, but it comes in contact with the liquid which is almost at its boiling point—hot enough to kill bacteria. As the broth cools down, the stream of air entering the flask slows down very much, to the point where dust particles in the air can no longer make the trip; they get caught in the moist gooseneck, so that they never reach the surface of the broth after it is cool.

This experiment, and the others that preceded it, settled once and for all the question of spontaneous generation of bacteria. Of course, many people repeated these experiments after Pasteur, and many failed; but it was a question of technique. Nowadays, it is commonplace to prepare a sterile solution that will remain bacteria-free indefinitely.

Researches that have been carried out since Pasteur's day have shown that bacteria are not nearly so simple as had been assumed up to that time. Although they are very small, they have a very delicate organization and very complicated chemical processes go on in them. They are just as complicated chemically as the individual cells that make up the bodies of higher plants and animals, and the idea of such complicated structures originating by chance in a medium containing nothing but organic chemicals is quite fantastic. As a recent writer has said: "Imagine a factory with smokestacks, machinery, railroad tracks, buildings, and so on springing into existence in a moment—following some natural event like a volcanic eruption. The same sort of event is assumed when one assumes that something as complex as a bacterial cell can originate in a pot of gravy."

ATTRIBUTES OF LIVING MATTER

It was shown by Pasteur, and by others, that bacteria arise only from other bacteria. This property, which we call self-reproduction, is a very important and fundamental attribute of living matter, true of all cells. There is another attribute of living matter which we must consider: mutability. By mutability we mean the property of undergoing an hereditary change.

For example, if we take a culture of bacteria growing in broth and add some penicillin to the broth, we will destroy most of the bacteria, but there may be a few bacteria—a few mutants —which are resistant to the penicillin. They will continue to grow, and they and all their descendants will be penicillin-resistant. We say that these bacteria are mutated. This represents an elementary step of evolution. These bacteria have evolved to a certain extent; they have changed one of their fundamental properties, and they are a different kind of bacteria than their parents were. These two qualities—the ability to self-reproduce, and the ability to mutate—are probably the most fundamental characteristics of living matter, and the problem of the origin of life as we see it today is that of finding the simplest chemical structure which exhibits these two fundamental attributes.

We think that if we can find a molecule that exhibits these two qualities, we shall have found a simple form of life. Imagine, if you can, a chemical substance that is capable of reproducing itself and that is capable of blindly mutating in various directions. By mutating, our molecule will try out new ways of existence, and after a few generations it will be very different from the thing that it started from. In time, everything else that we associate with living matter will follow by logical necessity. For this reason we feel that these are the two qualities that we must look for when we examine the question of the origin of life.

What are the simplest systems which exhibit these qualities?

About thirty years after Pasteur's experiments—around 1900—organisms were discovered which are even smaller than bacteria. These are the viruses, and they have played an important part in considerations of the origin of life.

The first virus to be discovered, the tobacco mosaic virus, has been very much studied, especially by Stanley and his collaborators at the University of California. This virus causes a disease of tobacco plants—a disease causing the mottling of the leaves—and in producing the disease the virus multiplies in the plant. If you inoculate the plant with a few particles of the virus, you will find, after a week or two, that the plant contains a great deal of the virus, and you can isolate from the plant juices many times as many virus particles as you put in. The interesting thing about these virus particles is that they are not only much smaller than bacteria—but they really seem to be simpler than bacteria. Viruses do not have a very complicated chemical structure; they do not carry on all the chemical activities of ordinary cells. It appears that the only activities viruses are capable of are reproduction and mutation. The viruses are very close to being particles which possess just the two elementary attributes of living matter.

The chemical composition of the tobacco mosaic virus has been studied, and it has been found to consist of only two parts —an outer jacket of protein and an inner core of nucleic acid. Recently two workers—Fraenkel-Conrat and Williams—at the Virus Laboratory of the University of California succeeded in separating the protein part from the nucleic acid part and then putting them back together again, reconstituting the infective virus. See Plate I.

On looking at this experiment more closely, a very interesting thing appears. Fraenkel-Conrat and Williams, of course, tested the solution of protein to find out if it had any virus activity by itself, and found that it does not. When they carried out the same test with the nucleic acid, they found a slight infectivity which, at first, they assumed was due to contamination by active virus particles that had not been disintegrated by the chemical treatment. On repeated tests, it appeared that they could not remove the small amount of infectivity from the solution of nucleic acid—and it has now been proven that the nucleic acid by itself has infective properties.

This means that the properties of self-duplication and mutability reside not in the whole virus particle but just in the nucleic acid part.

This finding is in accord with other experiments done on other organisms which indicate that nucleic acids have infective properties and are capable of reproducing themselves and of mutating.

Some biologists now think that the nucleic acids—perhaps combined with proteins—were the original forms in which living matter first appeared on the earth. These molecules are very much simpler than bacteria, and Van Helmont's mice. There is a chance that, given enough time and given the right conditions, a nucleic acid molecule could be spontaneously generated in the proper chemical medium. Plate II illustrates several forms of highly purified molecules.

Geophysicists think there were about two billion years between the origin of the earth and the first signs of living matter. That is a long time, of course, and many improbable things can be accomplished in that long a stretch. The conditions of the earth at that time, we are told, were quite different from now. The atmosphere consisted not of oxygen, nitrogen, and carbon dioxide, but of hydrogen, ammonia, methane, and water. Quite recently Dr. Stanley Miller, a post-doctoral fellow at Caltech (now at the University of Chicago), tried the experiment of passing an electric discharge through an atmosphere consisting of these four gases to see what would happen. He was simulating on a small scale the conditions that the geophysicists say existed on the earth some two billion years ago. He found a large number of organic compounds at the end of the experiment, including a number of amino acids. He found no nucleic acid or nucleic acid building blocks, but he did find amino acids, which are the building blocks of protein.

There are about 20 different amino acids in an ordinary protein. In Miller's experiment, he found glycine, alanine, aspartic acid, glutamic acid, and about 20 others which do not occur in protein. These four amino acids are very far, of course, from a protein, and they are even much farther from a living cell, but that is where this problem stands today—and I guess that is where I had better leave it.

ROBERT B. COREY AND
LINUS PAULING

The Structure of Proteins

RESEARCHERS DISCOVER THE FUNDAMENTAL MOLECULAR
CONFIGURATION OF PROTEINS—THE SUBSTANCE THAT
CONCERNS ALMOST EVERY ACTIVITY OF A LIVING ORGANISM.

Because of the dominant role that proteins play in man's physiology, health, and industrial economy, the constitution and properties of proteins have long been a subject of intense interest and investigation. More than 50 years ago the German chemist Emil Fischer showed that proteins consist of long polypeptide chains composed of many amino acid residues. The properties of proteins are determined in part by the chemical character of the amino acid residues and by the sequence of these residues in the polypeptide chains composing the protein molecule.

During the past few years great progress has been made in the determination of the sequences of amino acid residues in the polypeptide chains of proteins, especially through the work of Sanger and his collaborators at the University of Cambridge. The complete sequences of the amino acid residues in two proteins—insulin and the anterior corticotropic hormone ACTH —have already been determined, and information about many others is rapidly becoming available.

Thus, one can now write the chemical formulas of several proteins, in whole or in part, just as one can write the structural formulas of simpler organic compounds. But this chemical information is not enough for understanding the specific properties of proteins, such as denaturation, serological reactions, enzymatic and hormonal activity, and the like. These properties depend to a large extent upon the spatial configuration of the polypeptide chains and even on the relative positions in space of their component atoms.

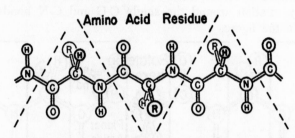

Fig. 1.—A diagrammatic representation of the polypeptide chain; dotted lines divide the chain into the various amino acid residues of which it is composed. The letter R represents the chemical side chains which are characteristic of the different residues.

Investigations of the structure of proteins were begun at the California Institute of Technology 20 years ago. Chemists had already described the polypeptide chain in proteins as composed of residues of glycine, alanine, serine, and other amino acids, connected by peptide bonds between the carbon and nitrogen atoms (Fig. 1), but attempts to discover the probable spatial configuration of polypeptide chains were at first unsuccessful. What was needed was more accurate knowledge of the molecular dimensions of amino acids and simple peptides. Our attack on the structure of proteins therefore began with thorough X-ray diffraction studies of crystals of many of the amino acids and simple peptides of which protein molecules are composed.

From these accurate crystal structure determinations, carried out by more than a dozen investigators at Caltech, many pertinent data were derived. The bond lengths and bond angles associated with the carbon and nitrogen atoms forming the important peptide bond, the central structure of the amide

29

group, were determined. In addition, the amide group was found to be planar, as predicted from chemical theory.

With its fundamental dimensions known, the polypeptide chain could be considered from a structural rather than a chemical point of view. As shown in Fig. 2, it could be considered to consist of an array of alternating planar amide groups and tetrahedral carbon atoms; its configuration could be altered only by rotation around the single C-C and C-N bonds indicated in the figure.

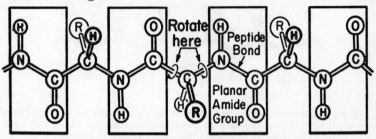

Fig. 2.—A representation of the polypeptide chain emphasizing its structural rather than its chemical features.

The crystal structure studies also showed that amino acids and peptides tend to form the maximum number of N-H $\cdots$ O hydrogen bonds between nitrogen and oxygen atoms and that these bonds are generally linear and about 2.8 A. in length. In all the simple peptides that were studied, except a cyclic dipeptide, the amide groups were found to have the *trans* configuration shown in Fig. 2.

In 1950 all of this structural information was used to derive two new and specifically defined configurations for polypeptide chains. In the derivation of these configurations the following basic assumptions were made: (1) the dimensions of the polypeptide chain are those derived from crystals of amino acids and simple peptides; (2) the amide group is planar and is in the *trans* configuration; (3) the maximum number of N-H $\cdots$ O hydrogen bonds are formed, they are nearly linear, and they have dimensions compatible with those found in crystals of simple substances. The additional condition was imposed that, except

30

for the nature of the side chains, all amino acid residues were to be structurally equivalent.

The most general set of operations that will convert an asymmetric element into its geometrical equivalent is a rotation around an axis and a translation parallel to that axis. Repetition of this operation generates a helix, so that structures developed in this way would be helical structures. When this investigation was carried out, only two configurations were found that were compatible with the assumptions.

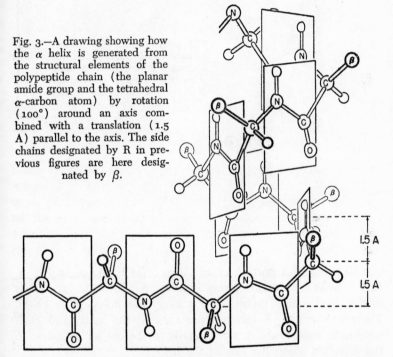

Fig. 3.—A drawing showing how the α helix is generated from the structural elements of the polypeptide chain (the planar amide group and the tetrahedral α-carbon atom) by rotation (100°) around an axis combined with a translation (1.5 A) parallel to the axis. The side chains designated by R in previous figures are here designated by β.

1.5 A

1.5 A

One of these configurations was designated the alpha helix. The way in which the alpha helix is generated from the polypeptide chain is illustrated in Fig. 3. The elements of the chain, each element consisting of a planar amide group together with a tetrahedral alpha-carbon atom, are successively rotated 100° around a vertical axis and translated 1.5 A. parallel to the axis.

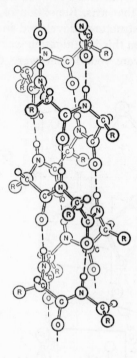

Fig. 4.—A drawing of a portion of an α helix. Small circles are hydrogen atoms. Dashed lines show the position of vertical N-H · · O hydrogen bonds.

A drawing of a portion of an alpha helix is shown in Fig. 4. In this helix each amide group is connected by hydrogen bonds to the third amide group from it along the polypeptide chain. There are about 3.6 residues per turn of the helix, and each residue is spaced about 1.5 A. above or below its neighbor in the direction along the axis of the helix.

The second possible configuration for the polypeptide chain that resulted from this investigation was designated the gamma helix. In this configuration each amide group is hydrogen-bonded to the fifth amide group beyond it in the chain, and there are about 5.1 residues per turn of the helix. One feature of this structure is a hole about 2 A. in diameter extending along the axis of the helix. There are good theoretical reasons for believing that a hole of this sort, too small to admit even a water molecule, would make the helix so unstable that it would not occur in nature. This conclusion seems to be confirmed experimentally; there appears to be no X-ray evidence that supports the occurrence of the gamma helix in proteins.

Strong evidence for the occurrence of the alpha helix in polypeptides and proteins has been provided from several sources. Indeed, in the case of synthetic polypeptides the evidence may be considered to be conclusive. Workers in the Courtaulds Research Laboratory in England synthesized polypetides such as poly-L-alanine and poly-gamma-methyl-L-glutamate and formed them into fibers and thin films in which the molecules were arranged with remarkable regularity. These specimens produced rather elaborate X-ray diffraction patterns. A very satisfactory interpretation of these patterns was given by workers at the Universities of Cambridge and Glasgow, who derived a theoretical expression for the calculation of the intensities of X-ray scattering by a helical molecule. The theoretical scattering which they calculated for the alpha helix was found to be in good agreement with the observed X-ray patterns. There now seems to be general agreement that the alpha helix is the fundamental structural component of polypeptides in the alpha configuration.

As for the proteins of the so-called alpha-keratin group—unstretched hair, wool, horn, etc.—there are good indications that the polypeptide chains of these proteins are also in the alpha-helix configuration. In X-ray photographs of these materials reflections have been discovered which correspond to the spacings characteristic of the alpha helix, but the chemical complexity and natural disorder of the samples have prevented the accumulation of X-ray data comparable to those obtained from synthetic polypeptides. Although there is evidence supporting the presence of alpha helixes in proteins of the alpha-keratin type, the detailed arrangement of the helixes in any specific protein has not been established. Some evidence also exists for the presence of the alpha helix in globular proteins, such as hemoglobin, but as yet it has to be considered suggestive rather than conclusive.

After the investigations leading to the discovery of the alpha helix, a new study was made in which the problem of the possible configurations of the polypeptide chain was attacked in a somewhat different way. Essentially the same structural assumptions were made about the dimensions and planarity of the amide group and the length and directional characteristics of the hydrogen bonds. However, in this study structures were considered to be acceptable if all hydrogen bonds were either formed between atoms of the same chain or so directed as to make satisfactory bonds to adjacent chains having the same configuration. In order to reduce this investigation to a systematic basis, an additional assumption was also made, namely, that the orientation of the amide group be restricted to certain preferred orientations with respect to the alpha-carbon atom, this preferred orientation being in agreement with that found in known structures of simple substances. This restriction limited the number of possible configurations to 36 in all.

When the 36 configurations were constructed, only 4 were found to be compatible with the criteria concerning hydrogen-bond formation. Two of them represent the alpha helix, one constructed as a right-handed helix, the other as a left-handed helix. The third possible configuration is the completely extended polypeptide chain similar to that already shown in Fig. 2. Many of these chains arranged side by side might be expected to be held together by N-H · · · O hydrogen bonds to form a planar sheet. However, if an attempt is made to construct a sheet in this way, it is found that the side chains, R, interfere with one another, so that this planar sheet cannot constitute a possible configuration of the polypeptide chains in a protein.

The fourth configuration is shown in Fig. 5. As in the fully extended chain, the hydrogen and oxygen atoms are well situated for the formation of good hydrogen bonds with adjacent chains, but in this new configuration the planar amide groups are tilted back and forth so that the side chains, R, extend on opposite sides of the main chain in a perpendicular direction

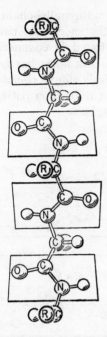

Fig. 5.—A diagrammatic representation of a polypeptide chain in the pleated sheet configuration. Hydrogen and oxygen atoms are well situated to form N-H $\cdots$ O hydrogen bonds on both sides of the chain. The side chains, R, extend forward and backward perpendicular to the plane of the drawing.

and therefore do not interfere with each other or with the formation of hydrogen bonds. Polypeptide chains having this configuration can thus be arranged side by side so that they build up a structure which is called a pleated sheet. A diagram of an antiparallel-chain pleated sheet, in which adjacent polypeptide chains run in opposite directions, is shown in Fig. 6.

The presence of antiparallel-chain pleated sheets in fibrous proteins has been definitely established. A thorough investigation of the structure of silk was made at Caltech a few years ago. This study, based on the best obtainable X-ray diffraction data, demonstrated very definitely that in fibers of commercial silk the polypeptide chains are arranged in the form of antiparallel-chain pleated sheets; it even succeeded in establishing the way in which the sheets were packed together, and the relative positions of individual atoms in the structure. The silk from wild silk worms was also investigated and, like commercial

35

silk, it was shown to be made up of antiparallel-chain pleated sheets; however, the way in which the sheets are packed together differs significantly from that found in commercial silk. The determination of the structures of silk fibers has been possible because silk is a protein of relatively simple chemical composition and one which gives excellent diffraction patterns containing many well-defined X-ray reflections.

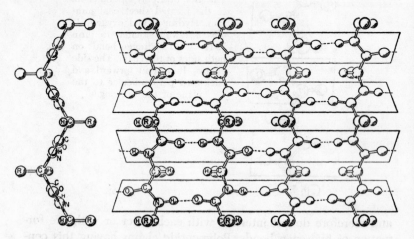

Fig. 6.—A drawing of the anti-parallel-chain pleated sheet, an arrangement of polypeptide chains that has been found in the protein of silk fibers.

X-ray diffraction studies have also been made of other fibrous proteins: stretched hair, wool, and feathers. Although it is probable that their structures are also based on the pleated sheet configuration, their chemical compositions are so complex and their X-ray diffraction patterns are so poor that no definite confirmation of this probability has been made. More numerous and more difficult problems of protein structure still remain to be solved.

ARTHUR W. GALSTON

An Uncolored View of Chlorophyll

A PLANT PHYSIOLOGIST CASTS A CRITICAL EYE ON
THE RECENT CHLOROPHYLL CRAZE.

I should make it clear at the outset that I have nothing against chlorophyll per se. As a plant physiologist I am aware that my livelihood depends upon the fact that plants are green, upon the fact that there is a substance known as chlorophyll which possesses certain wonderful—one might say even magical—properties.

Chlorophyll, as you know, is the green pigment of plants. It is universally distributed in green leaves and stems, but is absent from most roots and the white areas of variegated leaves.

Chemically speaking, there are at least two chlorophylls, differing from each other in only minor respects. They are both composed of carbon, hydrogen, oxygen, nitrogen and magnesium, and the organic chemist knows them as substituted tetrapyrroles grouped around a central core of magnesium.

In the plant, chlorophyll does not occur randomly dispersed throughout the leaf but, rather, is localized in little bodies called chloroplasts, which are about the size and shape (but not the color) of our red blood corpuscles. Chlorophyll in the chloroplasts is closely bound to other chemicals which are important to its stability and function.

Now, every student of elementary plant physiology knows how to get chlorophyll out of the chloroplasts and out of the

37

leaf. He merely immerses a leaf in some appropriate solvent such as methyl alcohol or acetone, and the green pigment readily passes out into the solvent. The solvent may then be evaporated away, leaving the chlorophyll-containing pigments behind.

The chlorophyll thus extracted is quite unstable, especially in light, and is also insoluble in water. It may be readily converted into a stable water-soluble derivative known as chlorophyllin by first treating it with alkali to remove the long-chain phytol substituent, and then by replacing the magnesium core of the molecule with copper or nickel. It is these simple procedures, long known to plant physiologists, which have resulted in the booming new multi-million-dollar chlorophyll industry.

What is it about chlorophyll that is so exciting and interesting? We know, in the first place, that it is chlorophyll which absorbs the light energy that makes possible the fixation and reduction of atmospheric carbon dioxide to sugar. This process of photosynthesis is of basic importance to all of us, for without it, animal life on earth would be impossible.

The sugars and other organic materials formed by green plants constitute the basic fuels for all of us, for when we walk, pound a typewriter, or sing a lullaby, we are using the energy released by the combustion of sugars in our body. Thus we are all essentially machines operating on solar energy. The green plant is the gear that makes that solar energy available to our bodies, and chlorophyll, in some way that we do not yet completely understand, is a key component of this gear.

It has become quite clear that what chlorophyll does is, in a way, magical. Everyone knows what a stable material water is. You can apply great quantities of heat to water and you do not decompose it; all you do is vaporize it. If you take hydrogen and oxygen, which are the components of water, they will ignite explosively to make water. If you want to tear water apart, you must expend just as much energy to do it as was liberated by that explosion. You have to electrolyze it or do something else very drastic.

It has now been found that chlorophyll does, in fact—with the aid of light energy—tear this stable water molecule apart.

The oxygen produced from this disruption of the water molecule is released into the air. This, incidentally, is very fortunate for us because we all require oxygen, and if plants did not release it, we would run out of it eventually. The hydrogen which is left behind after the release of oxygen furnishes a sort of reservoir of reducing power which somehow gets funneled to the carbon dioxide, converting it eventually to sugar.

WHAT CHLOROPHYLL DOES IN A PLANT

I do not mean to deliver a lecture on elementary plant physiology, but I should like to sum up here again what chlorophyll does in a plant. It dismembers a water molecule, using light energy to do the job. This results in the liberation of oxygen and eventually in the formation of sugar, both of which products make our existence possible. We may not actually eat sugar, of course; we may eat, instead, the protein of a cow. But, after all, the cow in turn has eaten a plant product to make the meat we eat. Ultimately, as the Bible says, all flesh is grass.

Chlorophyll does not accomplish this tremendous job by itself. In the chloroplasts there is an abundance of protein and fat, and the chlorophyll cannot function, so far as we know, without being firmly attached to the protein and fat. This fact immediately makes us a bit suspicious of so-called water-soluble, unattached chlorophyll—which is added to toothpaste, for instance.

An analogous situation exists in the red pigment of our blood, which we call hemoglobin. The heme, or the red part of this compound, is chemically very similar to chlorophyll—but it is attached to a protein, or globin, to make hemoglobin. In the same way, you have a chlorophyll protein which is completely analogous with the hemoglobin, and unless the protein is there you get no chemical activity.

We know, then, that chlorophyll is necessary for green plants. What does it do to animals? There are—I am pleased to state—at least two recognized medical uses for chlorophyll—though I had to do a good deal of digging in the literature to find them.

First, chlorophyll is known to stimulate the production of healing tissues—so-called granulation tissue—in certain types of lesions. If you have a peptic ulcer, for instance, some doctors will recommend a preparation of chlorophyll, together with aluminum hydroxide and magnesium trisilicate. This is mixed up into a paste, which you take into your stomach and, if you are lucky, you will lose your ulcers.

I do not speak from personal experience, but I would guess that there are probably better things to take for ulcers. However, this is a use of chlorophyll which has in the past been recommended, and one can claim that it has medical validity.

The second accepted use is the one that has given rise to the current fad. Gangrene, as you may know, is essentially a rotting of the flesh in deep-seated wounds. Certain gangrenous lesions, usually incurred as a consequence of military activity, may become rather foul-smelling. It was found some years ago that the application of chlorophyll pastes to this particular type of lesion would decrease the unpleasantness of the odor associated with them.

You now have the necessary background for understanding the chlorophyll boom and for seeing how a bright brain, in an effort to "make an honest buck" could launch an attempt to deodorize the American public. You begin with two scientific facts:

1. Certain kinds of lesions that smell bad are made less obnoxious if you smear chlorophyll poultices on them.

2. Chlorophyll in the plant results in the production of oxygen, thus "purifying the air."

CLEARING THE AIR

The manufacturers of air-purifiers were the first to take advantage of these facts. I think you are familiar with the use of these products. You take the magic bottle and put it in the corner of the room in which, let us say, you are cooking onions. Now that magic little bottle, containing miracle-working chlorophyll, absolutely kills the odor of the onions in the room.

How does this magic bottle work? As a matter of fact, it operates on a very old principle: If you can't lick 'em—join 'em. They can't really lick that onion odor, but they *can* prevent you from smelling it—or from smelling anything else, as it turns out. What they accomplish is the deadening of your sense of smell by means of a volatile anaesthetic, such as formaldehyde. The job is done, and *you* won't smell any onions, but the smell is still there. Thus chlorophyll appears to have nothing whatever to do with the deodorizing effect of this preparation.

After the air-purifiers came the production of water-soluble chlorophyllin from alfalfa—apparently by the classical methods well known to students of elementary plant physiology. It is this water-soluble product which has now found its way into soaps, toothpastes, gargles, hair tonics, inner soles for shoes, dog food, baby diapers, and other products almost too numerous to mention.

Frankly, I don't think any of these products containing either chlorophyll or chlorophyllin do what they are represented as doing. But my feeling definitely represents a minority opinion, for about $100,000,000 worth of chlorophyll-containing products were sold during one fiscal year. I think that our most charitable appraisal must be that we have here a case of a little bit of truth going a very long way.

Recently, the American Medical Association and the American Dental Association felt called upon to issue statements on this subject. Cautiously, and in diplomatic language, they have said that present evidence does not indicate that the claims made for these various products are in fact justified. To my knowledge, no refutation of this statement has ever been made by any company manufacturing a chlorophyll product.

A QUESTION OF ETHICS

This brings up a question of ethics—and perhaps a question of the duties of government. Here are the American people willingly parting with a good deal of money for products that are, to put it mildly, not what they are represented as being. Should this waste be permitted?

I do not know whether most people would feel they were being imposed upon if such products were compulsorily withheld from the market until their claims were proved. Americans are very jealous of their freedom, and probably the freedom to be gypped is one of the freedoms we all treasure. However, we do have a Pure Foods and Drugs Administration and a Federal Trade Commission, and these organizations do have some jurisdiction over such matters.

You may remember back to the days when a certain "vegetable compound" was sold as a cure for almost any feminine ailment. A lot of extravagant claims were made for the compound, but the only effective principle in it turned out to be ethyl alcohol. Eventually, as a result of the intervention of federal agencies, the manufacturers were required to state this fact.

Many extravagant claims have similarly been made by cigarette manufacturers—and are now being made by manufacturers of chlorophyllin-containing products. Perhaps, if we are going to have a Pure Food and Drugs Administration, we ought to support it to the extent that it can conduct policing operations effectively.

GET YOUR CHLOROPHYLL HERE

What if I am wrong in this one man's appraisal of chlorophyll? Suppose that chlorophyll does all these things that manufacturers claim for it? If that is the situation, I have a very simple recommendation. You undoubtedly have some green plants growing around your home; there is abundant grass on the Caltech lawns; and there is lots of spinach in the market. Just buy some, or pick some, and eat it. You will get more chlorophyll that way than you will in any of the chlorophyll products.

I think the best summary and conclusion that I can make of this problem is contained in a little poem that appeared recently in *Chemical and Engineering News*. It went like this:

"Why reeks the goat on yonder hill
Who seems to dote on chlorophyll?"

HARRY RUBIN

Viruses and Cancer

A REPORT ON RESEARCH IN PROGRESS AT CALTECH ON THE VIRUSES THAT—INSTEAD OF KILLING CELLS—CAUSE THEM TO MULTIPLY AT A FASTER RATE AND IN A DISORGANIZED MANNER.

Poliomyelitis and influenza are two of the most familiar virus diseases. In both these cases, the virus produces disease symptoms by damaging or killing cells. It seems strange then that there are other viruses which not only fail to kill cells but actually may cause them to multiply at a faster-than-normal rate. This multiplication occurs in a very disorganized manner, and the result is a cancer which ultimately kills the host.

Most of these cancer-causing viruses have been found in chickens. The common leukemia of chickens is due to a virus; that is, we can make a cell-free extract from the tumor tissue which will cause a similar growth when inoculated into another chicken. This was discovered almost half a century ago. Similarly, many other chicken cancers, particularly those of connective tissue origin, are caused by viruses. One of these that has received a good deal of attention is the Rous sarcoma virus. This was discovered by Dr. Peyton Rous in 1910 at the Rockefeller Institute. He observed a large tumor in the breast muscles of a laboratory hen and found that this could be very easily transplanted to other chickens by transferring intact cells. Then he found that cell-free extracts of the tumor, which were passed

43

through filters of small-enough porosity to hold back the smallest bacteria, were just as efficient in transmitting the growth. More recently, it has been found that the same virus can also cause a completely different type of cancer, a carcinoma or epithelial cancer, if inoculated into the proper tissue of the chick embryo.

What distinguishes cancer viruses from ordinary viruses? In size and gross chemical composition there are no distinguishing characteristics. Yet one group causes cells to multiply malignantly, and the other group causes cells to die. This problem has been investigated in the Biology Division at Caltech. Rous sarcoma cells were removed from afflicted chickens and grown in tissue culture. In this way, the number of cells was always known, and the rate of virus production could be studied.

These cells were found to produce infectious virus at a very slow but constant rate—approximately one virus particle per cell every day or two. Compare this with a poliomyelitis-infected cell which may produce 1000 virus particles within a few hours. This simple quantitative finding may indicate why such differences in pathological manifestation of the two groups of viruses are found.

A cell which only has to produce a single virus particle every day may have its normal metabolism upset somewhat—perhaps to the extent of being liberated from the normal regulating mechanisms of the animal and thereby becoming cancerous—but it will not be destroyed. A cell which has to produce a thousand virus particles in several hours has to divert all its metabolic machinery to this function. Not being able to carry on its own essential functions, it soon dies. Thus we have the first hint of an explanation for the distinctive pathologies.

SPECULATIONS ON STRUCTURE

It was once thought that the Rous sarcoma virus contained normal unaltered host protein as an integral and functional part of its structure. This seemed to be a very important and exciting thing, since it suggested that this virus was very closely related to the cells which it parasitized, in contrast to the ordinary cell-killing viruses, such as polio, which have no such relation to the cells in which they multiply.

It seemed reasonable to speculate that cancer viruses originated in their host cells where the cell-killing viruses were of foreign origin. However, some recent work at Caltech has indicated that the evidence for the postulated relation was misleading. It was based on the finding that the addition of antiserum to normal cells seemed to neutralize the virus. It has now been shown that the serum acts, not on the virus, but on the cell infected by the virus. Thus the basis for the speculation has been removed.

One of the more perplexing aspects of this problem is the ease of finding cancer viruses in chickens, contrasted with the great difficulty in demonstrating them in mammals. The first mammalian cancer virus was not isolated until 1936. In that year, John J. Bittner found that the common breast cancer of mice was ordinarily transmitted by a virus found in the milk of nursing mothers from a strain of inbred mice which had a very high incidence of breast cancer. However, to demonstrate the agent, Bittner had to infect mice within a few days after birth. Then he had to wait until these mice became mature nursing mothers themselves—a matter of almost a year—before the cancer appeared. Compare this with the Rous sarcoma virus of chickens, which can be inoculated at any age and will produce cancer in less than a week. In addition, Bittner had to have another inbred strain of mice which had a very low incidence of cancer, in order to convincingly demonstrate the effect of the virus. With chicken cancer viruses such complications did not exist.

Since 1936, only two more mammalian cancers have been shown to be of viral origin. In one of these, mouse leukemia, the difficulties in demonstrating the virus encountered with the breast cancer were multiplied. This suggests that the failure to isolate causative viruses from mammalian cancers may arise from such complications rather than from the absence of a virus.

Therefore the critical question—are all cancers, and particularly human cancers, caused by viruses?—must remain unanswered for the present. Certain aspects of the origin of even such thoroughly-studied viruses as those which infect bacteria are quite obscure.

Even in such well-defined systems the line between viruses as foreign invaders and as altered cell components is not clearly drawn. Thus it is difficult to distinguish, even theoretically, between the most prominent alternatives for the origin of cancer.

Two crowning difficulties in the study of the relation of viruses to human cancer must be kept in mind. The first is that some of the known cancer viruses are produced in such small quantities that they cannot be readily demonstrated by physical methods such as electron microscopy. The second is that they can generally cause cancer only in animals of the same species and frequently, as in the case of the mouse tumors, only in very closely related strains of the same species.

To carry this to perhaps a not too absurd extreme, demonstration of a tumor virus in humans by the methods now known could involve inoculating newborn babies of known genetic constitution with tumor extracts and waiting 30 or 40 years until maturity was reached to see if cancer developed. Even then, a large enough group would have to be included to make the results significant when compared with the normal incidence of cancer in a control group, since we have no genetically pure strains to work with.

THE PROMISE OF FUTURE RESEARCH

This perhaps dramatizes the difficulties. There are some bright spots on the horizon of basic research. Perhaps the most promising is the great flowering of tissue culture work—growing cells, human as well as animal, outside the body—within the last few years.

Three developments along this line are of special significance to research in cancer. The first was the development of a technique for the precise assay of virus infectivity in tissue culture by Dulbecco at Caltech. The second was the application of this technique to the assay of the Rous sarcoma virus by Manuker and Groupé at Rutgers. And the third was the demonstration by Puck at Colorado that single animal cells could be grown up into a colony of cells in tissue culture, thus allowing work with cells of a clearly defined background.

With these tools, it is likely that there will be a rapid unfolding of knowledge on the relationship between viruses and cancer.

R. W. SPERRY

Brain Mechanisms in Behavior

SOME EXPERIMENTAL OBSERVATIONS ON THE WORKINGS OF
THAT BAFFLING MECHANISM—THE BRAIN.

The vertebrate brain, with an organizational complexity far
surpassing that of any other natural or man-made system and
possessing in certain of its parts the puzzling property of conscious awareness, will probably continue to remain a challenge
to man's understanding for many decades to come. At the
present time, the cerebral events underlying even the simplest
forms of mental activity remain quite obscure. Although it
should someday be possible to start correlating subjective experience with the corresponding brain process—perhaps even to
comprehend the basis and derivation of the "mental" properties
—we have to be satisfied, for the present, to work at many re-
moves from this ultimate goal.

How *far* removed can be judged from the following series
of experimental observations that will serve to illustrate some of
the things our psychobiology group has been doing and will
also serve to indicate the general status of some of the current
problems in brain organization.

I will start with some early work dealing with nerve growth
and regeneration, the results of which have been interpreted
broadly to mean that brain function in the vertebrates generally
is predetermined by inheritance to a much greater degree than

48

formerly had been supposed. The findings also give us some ideas about how the inherent patterning of the brain circuits is achieved in embryonic development.

Our information on the developmental patterning of brain pathways has been obtained mainly from fishes and amphibians because the early developmental stages in these lower vertebrates are accessible to surgery and because the central nervous system, in the larval and adult stages, retains a capacity for regrowth after surgical intervention that is almost entirely lacking in higher forms.

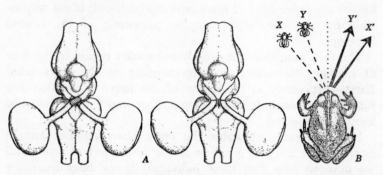

Fig. 1.—Connecting eyes to wrong side of brain results in an illusory right-left reversal of visual field. However, the relationships of X to Y and of X to any and all other points within the same visual field are restored to normal patterns.

As shown in Fig. 1, it is possible in these animals to cut the nerves of the eye where they cross and to reunite them surgically in such manner that, when they regenerate, the eyes become connected to the wrong sides of the brain. Under these conditions, the animals respond thereafter as if everything seen through one eye were being viewed through the opposite eye. For example, when a fly moves within the field of view of a frog's left eye, the frog will strike out at a corresponding point in the right field of view. This right-left reversal of visual reactions persists indefinitely, with no evidence of correction by re-education.

The sensory surface or retina of the eye in all vertebrates

is projected through the optic nerve fibers onto the brain in an orderly, topographic, or map-like fashion. In the foregoing experiment the behavioral tests (and other evidence) indicate that this orderly topographic projection is restored with systematic precision in the regeneration process—despite extensive intertangling of the regenerating fibers. In Fig. 1, for instance, the the relationships of X to Y and of X to any and all other points within the same visual field are restored to their normal patterns. The fact that this occurs, despite the maladaptive functional effect produced by crossing the optic nerves, means that learning, or any other kind of functional readjustment, is not responsible for the orderly topographic patterning of the central hook-ups.

The fact, also, that this orderly restoration occurs in the face of random intermixing and intertangling of the regenerated fibers—particularly in the region of the nerve transection—has forced us to conclude that the optic fibers must differ from one another in quality.

In the lower vertebrates the optic fibers number around 25,000 (there are over a million in the optic nerve of man), and we have to infer that these individual fibers differ from one another in their biochemical constitution according to the particular points of the retinal field from which they arise. The further inference here is that the ingrowing fibers, on entering the brain, establish their central hook-ups in a selective, discriminative manner, governed by specific chemical affinities between the different types of ingrowing fibers and the central cells on which they terminate. This inference requires the corollary conclusion that a similar topical specificity exists among the nerve cells of the optic centers.

There is good reason to think that the qualitative specificity of the optic fibers is achieved in development through a polarized chemical differentiation of the retina. First, a naso-temporal, or front-back gradient of differentiation is laid down, and later—superimposed at right angles on top of this—an up-down gradient. This would mark each retinal locus with a latitude and longitude, so to speak, expressed as a unique ratio of chemical properties. We don't know the exact chemical or physico-chemical nature of these neuronal specificities as yet any more than we know the chemical basis for most of the cellular differentiations that occur throughout the organism during development.

By rotating the eye surgically in the orbit, or by transplanting the eyeball from one orbit to the other, with different degrees of rotation, one may produce various other types of visual inversion and distortion. These inversions and distortions are always correlated directly with the orientation of the eyeball in the orbit; and, like the right-left reversal, they too persist without functional correction.

Leon Stone at Yale and George Szekely in Hungary have since carried these eye transplantations into prefunctional embryonic stages and have found that inverted vision results in just the same way as it does in the later stages. It would appear that the perception of visual direction is built into the vertebrate brain and, contrary to earlier opinion, does not have to be learned.

In some related work on cutaneous sensibility it was found that if one crosses the major nerve trunks of the left hind foot in the rat into the opposite leg and reunites them with the corresponding nerves of the right hind foot, then, after regeneration of the fibers into the skin of the opposite foot, all sensations aroused in the right foot are falsely referred to the left foot, from which the nerves originally came. For instance, an electric shock applied to the sole of the right foot causes the animal to withdraw the left foot.

The surgery was done in these rats during the fourth week after birth—before the animals could have had much experience in localizing cutaneous stimuli. The resultant reversal of reflex-reaction with the false reference of cutaneous sensibility persisted indefinitely, despite prolonged efforts to retrain the reactions by conditioning techniques and other methods. The results suggest that the mechanism for locating points on the body surface, like that for sensing visual direction, is built into the nervous system and, common assumption to the contrary, is not a product of experience and training.

This interpretation received further support in later experiments like the one carried out by Dr. Nancy Miner in which a flap of skin was peeled off the trunk region of a frog, lifted, and cut completely free of all nerve and other connections, rotated 180 degrees, and reimplanted (Fig. 2). The operation was done in early larval stages. When the tadpoles had grown up and undergone metamorphosis into the adult, we found that tickling these frogs on the back, within the graft region, caused them to scratch the belly with the foreleg. Conversely, stimulating them on the belly caused them to swipe at the back with the hind leg.

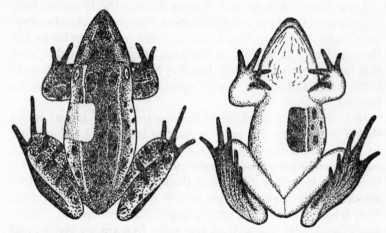

Fig. 2.—Skin grafts, rotated 180 degrees, result in a reversal of localizing reflexes. When back is stimulated in graft region, frog rubs belly—and vice versa.

These and related experiments have confirmed the preceding inference that the mechanism for locating points on the body surface is organized in the growth process itself—ultimately, of course, under genetic control. This neural apparatus for locating points on the skin is not a simple thing: I am told that our engineering is not yet developed to the point where we could build a machine to do nearly so well—particularly one in which the points to be localized are on its own mobile parts.

The further interpretation of how the neural mechanism is put together and developed in the growth process—based on the foregoing, and similar, studies—goes something like this: The skin, like the retina of the eye, must undergo a refined local differentiation during development—probably also on a basic, biaxial plan. The local specificity of the skin is then stamped or imprinted upon the nerve fibers at their terminal contacts. This induced chemical specificity in the nerve fibers, after spreading centrally along the fibers into the spinal and cranial nerve centers, then determines the type of reflex hook-ups formed —again, presumably on the basis of specific affinities between the peripheral fibers and central cells with which they connect.

It was shown further by Dr. Miner that if an extra hind limb

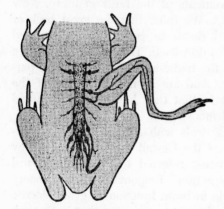

Fig. 3.—Trunk nerves growing into transplanted limb form limb reflex connections instead of normal trunk reflexes.

bud is transplanted into the trunk region of the frog (Fig. 3.), the same trunk nerves that were involved in the preceding graft experiment—and which normally form belly, back, and side-wiping reflex patterns—now form entirely different patterns of central connections, suited in each case to the particular patterns of the transplanted limb with which the fibers connect. By stimulating different points in the extra limb we get knee-wiping, thigh-wiping, and various types of kicking reactions. This means that cutaneous nerve fibers destined normally to form central hook-ups appropriate for the belly, flank, and back skin of the trunk formed instead connections appropriate for the digits, heel, and knee of the limb.

All these responses, incidentally, are made by the normal limb on the same side as the transplant; the transplant itself has no motor function. The important point is that here again the local quality of the skin with which the fibers connect in the periphery, and not the functional effects for the organism, determines the patterns of synaptic hook-ups formed in the central nervous system.

It used to be thought that the nervous system was first laid out in embryonic development pretty much as a random equipotential network that was gradually channelized through experience and training. The training effects were presumed to start way back in the early movements of the fetus in utero. Now our picture is quite different. We think that the great bulk of the neural circuits are laid down in precise, predetermined patterns in the growth mechanism itself. The effects of learning are presumably confined to the highest association centers, particularly the cerebral cortex, and are so minute a part of the total central nervous structure that they have thus far eluded any direct morphological demonstration.

Another part of our work deals with a brain theory of perception that developed out of the Gestalt school of psychology and is perhaps most commonly referred to as the "electrical field theory of cerebral integration." Proponents of field theory have ascribed a primary role in brain function to gross electric currents that spread through the cortex *en masse;* that is, through the cortical tissue as a volume conductor. Most aspects of perception appear to be more readily correlated with these gross electric currents in the brain than with the more orthodox type of nerve impulses that travel in scattered discontinuous patterns along discrete fiber pathways.

In an experiment aimed at testing this electrical field theory, the visual area of the cortex in the cat was filled with metallic inserts of tantalum wire. The aim here was to short-circuit, and hence to distort, the normal patterning of DC current-flow in the cortex during visual form perception. These numerous metallic inserts, which are biologically inert and remained in the brain for months without any deleterious effects, proved to have no measurable effect on any visual reactions—including previously-trained high-level pattern discriminations.

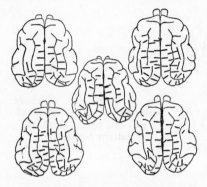

Fig. 4.—Dielectric mica plates inserted in visual cortex to distort the patterning of brain currents during perception.

In another experiment aimed at testing the electrical field theory the approach was just the opposite. Dielectric or insulating plates of mica were inserted vertically into the cortex, in the patterns shown in Fig. 4, in an attempt to distort—this time by blocking instead of by shorting—the postulated patterns of DC flow in the visual area during pattern perception. Although some functional impairment was found in this series, it was shown in controls to be correlated with the tissue damage produced by the inserts rather than with their dielectric effects, and the conclusion was the same as in the previous experiment.

The outcome of these two studies has rather discouraged any inclination, on our part at least, to forsake the traditional fiber conduction doctrine of brain function in favor of the newer electrical field hypothesis.

Any brain theory of perception, we believe, must square also with the following observation: The visual area of the cortex, in the cat again, was sliced with numerous subpial knife cuts in crisscross patterns, as shown in Fig. 5. When these cuts—in the top two cases—proved to have only negligible effects upon pattern perception, we decided—in the third case—to carry this slicing procedure to an extreme, making the cuts as numerous and as close together as possible. After four weeks, this third animal was performing again on our test scales at a level only one or two notches below its preoperative standard.

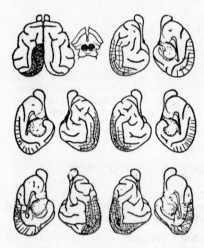

Fig. 5.—Visual area of cortex, partitioned with numerous sub-pial cuts to test effect on pattern perception.

The best discriminations that this animal was able to perform several months later are shown in (A) of Fig. 6. It could discriminate the central triangle when paired with any of those surrounding it. And the animal also readily learned the size discrimination shown in (B). The lack of any marked functional disturbance after such slicing of the cerebral cortex seems to eliminate as an important factor in perceptual integration any tangential or horizontal spread of nervous conduction within the cortex itself—that is, on any scale large enough to mediate so-called relational or structuring effects in the perception of pattern.

In another group of studies we have been concerned with the function in perception of long fiber connections in the mammalian cortex. The largest of the fiber bundles in the brain of higher mammals is the corpus callosum which unites the two cerebral hemispheres. It has been somewhat embarrassing to our concepts of brain organization that complete surgical section of this largest fiber tract has consistently failed in human patients to produce any clear-cut functional symptoms. In checking this observation in animal experiments, however, we have been able in recent years to demonstrate definite integrative functions for this structure.

Fig. 6.—With its visual cortex subdivided by multiple crisscross cuts, test animal could discriminate central triangle in A, above, when it was paired with any of those surrounding it—and also learned size discrimination in B.

In these experiments, carried out mainly in cats, we first section all crossed optic fibers at the chiasma, in order to restrict the input from each eye to the same side of the brain. The animal is then taught a few simple visual discriminations with a mask covering one eye. After the habit has been stabilized by overtraining, the mask is shifted to the other eye.

With this procedure it was shown originally by Dr. Ronald Myers that the trained performance transfers readily to the untrained eye, if the corpus callosum is intact; but if the corpus callosum has been sectioned prior to training, there is no transfer at all. Without the callosum, such animals apparently have no recollection with one eye of what they have been doing with the other eye. In fact, it is possible to train opposing incompatible discriminations to the separate eyes concurrently without getting any interference. Work in progress shows the same to be true in the monkey.

In collaboration with Dr. John Stamm, we have obtained similar results for the contralateral transfer from one forepaw to the other of tactile discriminations. Cats are trained to push the correct one of two pedals which they can reach with only one forepaw and which they are unable to see and must distinguish entirely on the basis of touch. One gets 70 to 80 percent transfer of learning upon shifting to the untrained paw in unoperated animals. When the callosum is sectioned, the transfer is zero.

Perceptual learning and memory thus seem to proceed independently in the two hemispheres of the brain in the absence of the corpus callosum. It is interesting that, in spite of this independence, the learning curves for the two separated hemispheres are remarkably similar in character, suggesting that the individual variability in perceptual learning is predetermined to an unexpected degree by the intrinsic structural and functional organization of the cerebral hemisphere. This was found to be true in cats for both tactile and visual discriminations, but seems to be much less characteristic of the monkey, the difference here reflecting perhaps an important species difference in learning.

Attempts to localize in the brain the memory traces for particular habits have generally failed. The memory traces, or engrams, appear to be extremely elusive and diffuse and so far have not been specifically localized or demonstrated. In the case of the memory traces ingrained for the visual discriminations in the foregoing experiments, it was possible to show that they are not confined to the directly trained hemisphere. One can remove the visual and the neighboring association cortex on the trained side in these animals before switching the mask and still get the transfer to the untrained eye through the callosum. Further, one can still get this transfer even if the entire callosum is sectioned after the completion of training but before testing for the transfer. Some kind of mnemonic carryover into the opposite hemisphere is evidently effected via the corpus callosum.

At the present time we are investigating the functional capacities of small islands of cerebral cortex. In these studies we put to use the above-mentioned functional independence of the two hemispheres in what we have come to call the "split-brain preparation." This is an animal in which the brain has been split down the middle by sectioning the corpus callosum, hippocampal commissure, and the optic chiasma and, frequently also, some of the lower-level connecting systems. To casual examination, these split-brain animals after recovery are indistinguishable from normal in their general cage behavior.

In such animals the brain-lesion analyses can be carried out in one hemisphere alone, the other hemisphere being kept intact to maintain generalized background functions. In the test hemisphere, instead of the customary small lesions in the critical area, it becomes possible in such preparations to use the opposite approach—that is, to remove the greater part of the cortex and to leave intact only the small critical area, the functions of of which one wishes to investigate.

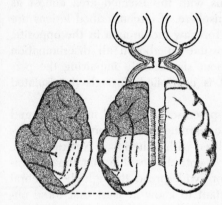

Fig. 7.—Removal of nonvisual cortex with preservation of visual area abolishes visual functions for reasons still undetermined.

To what extent would visual perception be possible, for example, if all parts of the cerebral cortex were removed excepting just the visual area itself? We have found that vision is practically absent on the test side when the visual area is isolated in cats to the degree shown in Fig. 7.

If the nonvisual parts are removed in two or three separate operations, starting with the cortex immediately surrounding the sector to be preserved, it is not until the final removal of

59

frontal or temporal lobes, as the case may be, that we get the really severe visual impairment.

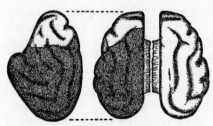

Fig. 8.—Small island of intact cortex retains capacity to remember and to learn new tactile discriminations almost as well as the whole hemisphere.

Similar isolation of the cortical area for touch perception, as shown in Fig. 8, has yielded quite different results. In this case the cats, after operation, are still able to perform, at a high level, previously-trained tactile discriminations. They also are able to learn new discriminations with the isolated area almost as well as with the whole hemisphere. If circumscribed lesions are subsequently placed in the forepaw tactile area in the opposite, intact hemisphere, it is possible to abolish all discrimination with the affected paw without significantly impairing the performance of the paw that is controlled through the isolated remnant of cortex.

It would appear that the processes of cortical integration and reintegration involved in the learning and memory of these tactile discriminations are localized within the intact cortical island. Under normal conditions it is entirely possible that the integrative processes are much more widespread through the cerebral hemisphere, but it is important to know at least that these unknown cerebral mechanisms are of such a nature that they *can* be handled with a rather small, isolated sector of the cortex.

This is about where we stand on these projects at the moment. As can be seen, we are still a very long way from being able to blueprint the circuit diagrams for perceptual integration, learning, or memory. Nor have we the vaguest notion of the general type of circuits needed, for example, to build into a machine so simple a thing as pain sensation. We don't know enough to say in theory even that it can—or ever could—be done.

JOHN S. STAMM

Hoarding

HAMSTERS DO IT, RATS DO IT, AND HUMAN BEINGS DO IT.
BUT WHY? RECENT STUDIES AT CALTECH SUGGEST THAT
PHYSIOLOGICAL AND GENETIC FACTORS MAY BE INVOLVED.

Hoarding, or the collection of more materials than can be an-
ticipated to be needed, can be easily observed with many animals
and with men in most cultures. We have all seen the squirrel
busily engaged in collecting and burying food; the pack rat is
famous for carrying and hoarding many objects; and the hamster is, of course, the prime example of a hoarder. As a matter
of fact, in the German language the words for hamster and
hoarding are synonymous, and this animal has been known to
accumulate such vast amounts of grain that during times of
famine in Europe his hoards have been raided to supply human
food.

In our society, all of us are acquainted with hoarders—people
who collect food, fuel, valuable objects, or often ridiculous ones
to a far greater degree than they can be expected to be used in
the reasonable future. In many, but not all, primitive societies
this "irrational" activity has also been observed.

Unfortunately, we do not know much about the conditions
which bring about this activity, either in animals or humans.
Naturalists and zoologists have little to say about hoarding activity other than to mention it when it occurs. Similarly, psy-

chologists and anthropologists know little about human hoarding—although they do have a number of theories about it.

Recent investigations at Caltech have been concerned with the biological basis of hoarding. In order to clarify some of the innate mechanisms which underlie hoarding behavior in rats, the physiological and genetic bases of hoarding were investigated. These studies yielded some interesting results about the control of hoarding activity by a specific area of the brain, and about genetic differences in hoarding. Before discussing these findings, however, it may be of interest to describe some of the experimental conditions which have been found to influence the hoarding performance.

EXPERIMENTAL CONDITIONS

1. *Apparatus.* The hoarding apparatus has been pretty well standardized. The common one is a "closed" alley—a runway 4 inches wide and about 3 feet long, enclosed by about 8-inch-high boards. This connects at one end to the cage, which has a door that can give the rat access to the alley. At the far end is a bin in which the material to be hoarded (usually food pellets) is stored.

2. *Onset of Hoarding.* When a rat is allowed access to this apparatus, it will usually not begin hoarding right away. Even under the most favorable hoarding conditions, several days will elapse before the rat will leave the cage and commence to hoard.

There is always a hoarding schedule which permits the rat a certain period of time daily in the apparatus. This may be one half-hour daily, twice a day, 12 hours daily, or continuously. In all cases pellets are counted at regular intervals and then returned to the bin.

Even though animals may not exhibit hoarding behavior for many days after the experiment has begun, the amazing thing is that once a rat begins to hoard, it does so very abruptly. On the first day of hoarding, it collects many pellets—the number usually depending on how late in the trial it commenced to hoard. On the following few days the hoarding scores reach a peak, and as many as 120 pellets may be returned in a one-half hour period. After this peak has been reached, the daily hoarding scores may decline slowly and then reach an average which will be maintained for a long time. During this period of hoarding there are often marked day-to-day variations in hoarding scores, but very rarely does a rat stop hoarding altogether.

3. *Deprivation.* One of the most important factors affecting hoarding is deprivation of the material to be hoarded. Although it has been shown that deprivation is not necessary in order to elicit this behavior, it always both facilitates the onset of hoarding and increases the amount of material collected.

Deprivation consists in putting rats on limited feeding schedules. Usually about 15 grams of pellets are given the rat before each hoarding trial. If half an hour is allowed for this feeding period, the rat soon learns to finish eating before the hoarding trial begins. If the rats are not fed immediately before the trial, they will take time to eat the first pellets they return to the cage, in order to satisfy their hunger. Under these conditions, of course, hoarding does not proceed as well as when feeding precedes the trials.

4. *Extinction.* Hoarding may be extinguished or sharply reduced by placing the rats on continuous food supply. The high level of hoarding may persist for several days after the satiation period has been started, but then it will drop off sharply, usually to a lower value.

5. *Recovery.* If, after hoarding experiments have been discontinued for some time or rats have been under satiation conditions, deprivation conditions are re-established, rats will immediately resume their high hoarding activities. In general, during this recovery period, each rat will duplicate its original hoarding curve. Rats which had high hoarding scores will again have high scores, and rats which hoarded less previously will again do the same.

6. *Pre-hoarding activity.* Very few rats will begin their hoarding activity by running to the bin and returning a pellet. In general, rats will at first very slowly stretch out of the cage, then enter the alley and thoroughly explore it near the cage. During this period they frequently attempt to escape by reach-

ing to the top of the alley walls. Some rats will only spend several minutes on this pre-hoarding activity, whereas others will take days, or even weeks, before they begin to hoard in an orderly manner.

7. *Familiarity with the hoarding apparatus.* A rat feels most comfortable, of course, in its home cage, and therefore deposits the hoarded pellets in it. When rats which have hoarded for a number of days are then put into different cages, their hoarding activity is markedly changed. The number of hoarded pellets is greatly reduced; rats were found to hoard only about one tenth as many in a new, strange cage. It was found, however, that they dropped a good many pellets into the alley in front of the cage. Though there was never any alley hoarding when the home cage was available, this was found to be the case in about 58 percent of the trials when the strange cage was substituted.

During the first days after the substitution of a strange alley, rats again spent considerable time in exploring the new alley and consequently hoarded much less. After several days, however, the daily hoarding scores again reached the same magnitude as they had before the substitution.

Even when the pellets in the food bin are changed to new ones, rats will hoard less for one or two days, until they become familiar with the smell of the new pellets. It was found that on the first day after the introduction of new pellets, average hoarding scores dropped to one third—after which they rose again.

These experiments point to the importance of "familiarity" as a factor in hoarding. Although a hoarding drive always exists, the hoarding activity cannot be demonstrated until the animal has become familiar with all elements in the situation. Any change of the rat's environment will therefore temporarily reduce or abolish the hoarding activity.

8. *Stereotypes.* An interesting observation is that there is a good deal of difference in the patterns of behavior of individual rats during hoarding experiments *and* that individual rats maintain their stereotyped behavior throughout the experimental period. Some rats, for example, always make a dry run before

64

they begin hoarding during each trial. Another rat may circle the food bin or sit on the pellets in the bin for a while before hoarding.

The persistence of this stereotyped hoarding behavior is a marked phenomenon, although the amount of hoarding will vary greatly in successive trials.

9. *Preference of hoarding material.* In one interesting experiment rats were deprived of water, but not food, and then were allowed to hoard water-soaked cotton pellets. It was found that water hoarding proceeded in the same manner as pellet hoarding usually does—a maximum number of pellets being hoarded during the first few days of hoarding, and then fewer pellets in every trial.

When comparative groups of rats showed the same hoarding behavior for water and for food pellets, the two groups were alternated for food and water hoarding. All the rats then hoarded more of the material of which they were deprived. However, both groups hoarded about two and one-half times more food pellets than they hoarded water pellets.

When rats were given the choice of hoarding food pellets or saccharine-sweetened mash, which was placed in bottle caps, they all hoarded the sweet mash to the exclusion of the food pellets.

When, however, wooden blocks, which looked and smelled like the pellets, were mixed with pellets, the rats refused to hoard the wooden blocks. And when only blocks were put into the bin, there was no hoarding at all.

10. *Hoarding of the hamster.* The hamster is, of course, a much better known hoarder than the rat, and one may question whether the conditions for hoarding in rats also apply to the hamster. In a number of experiments with hamsters it was found that all the conditions and influences which affect hoarding in rats are equally applicable to the hamster—the only difference being that hamsters hoard more. This fact offers assurance to the experimenter that the findings of experiments with rats—which are experimentally much more flexible—are also valid for other animals.

The experiments which have been reviewed here clearly establish hoarding as an experimental behavior which can be regularly studied. It is a motivated, unlearned, and complex behavior that must compete with other activities which the rat will "instinctively" practice, such as avoiding strange situations (i.e., leaving the alley, exploration, and escape).

GENETIC FACTORS

Several investigators, working with different strains of rats, have noted differences in the amount of hoarding done by the rats. At Caltech an investigation was conducted to determine some of the genetic factors underlying the hoarding activity of rats. Simultaneous hoarding tests were given to three homozygous strains of rats (i.e., each strain has been highly inbred and is known to be biologically different from the other strains). Two of these strains showed marked differences in their hoarding performance; a black-hooded strain gave a median score of 47 pellets per rat for each trial, whereas an Irish strain had a median of only 7 pellets (see Fig. 1).

The hooded rats also started to hoard earlier than did the Irish; the median trial for the beginning of hoarding was the fourth day for the hooded and the twelfth day for the Irish rats.

When the hoarding activity was reduced by placing a pile of pellets in the rats' cages at all times, the hooded rats still hoarded some pellets after 16 days, whereas the Irish rats had virtually stopped hoarding on the fifth day.

Subsequent studies were concerned with verification of the genetic differences. Rats from the high-hoarding strain were mated with the low-hoarding rats and the offspring (the F_1 generation), when mature, were given hoarding tests. They performed like their high-hoarding parents.

These F_1 rats were then mated with rats from the original low-hoarding strain and the offspring (the F_b generation) gave hoarding scores which were widely distributed. The mean score for the group fell between the means for the original grandparent strains. The distribution of the scores for the F_b group showed a bimodal tendency, with maxima points near the means of the original low- and high-hoarding groups.

These results lead to the conclusion that there are indeed genetic factors underlying hoarding activity and that probably a dominant gene is involved.

PHYSIOLOGICAL FACTORS

1. *The cerebral cortex and hoarding.* Recent investigations at Caltech on the neural basis for hoarding have yielded some interesting results. By removing small pieces of tissue from different parts of the brain's cortical surface, the investigator found hoarding activity was greatly reduced when the lesions had been applied to the cingulate cortex—a strip of cortex along the median

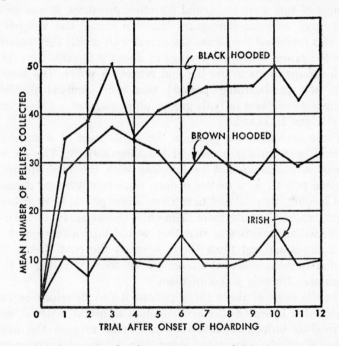

Fig. 1.—Hoarding scores for three pure strains of rats. Investigations indicate that genetic factors underlie hoarding activity. This chart shows the results of simultaneous hoarding tests given to three homozygous strains of rats. The black hooded strain has a median score of 47 pellets per rat in each test; the Irish strain has a median of only 7 pellets. The hooded rats also started hoarding earlier than the Irish.

line of the brain. In one experiment small lesions (averaging about 13 percent of the cortical surface) were applied to a group of 15 rats whose hoarding activity had been determined before and after the operation. As a result of these lesions the hoarding scores (the number of food pellets collected during a series of 20-minute trial periods) of the rats were reduced by an average of 73 percent of the pre-operative scores.

As a control experiment, lesions of the same size (13 percent of the cortical surface) were applied to the lateral cortical surfaces of 8 rats. There was no appreciable change in the hoarding scores of this group as a result of the operation. When the two groups of rats were compared for other measures, it was found that there were no differences between them. The weights of the rats remained the same. The speed with which they hoarded was the same; it took an average of about 7 seconds for rats in both groups to go to the bin and retrieve a pellet. The latency (i.e., the pre-hoarding period) was also identical for both groups; it took rats in both groups an average of 4.5 days until they began to hoard.

These investigations point to the importance of a restricted cortical area for the control of hoarding activity. The cortical lesions were shown not to interfere with the rats' ability to retrieve pellets. As a matter of fact, since rats were on deprivation feeding, they all had to retrieve a few pellets to their home cages, where they ate them. The chief characteristic of the rats with median lesions was that they would take a few pellets to their cages and eat them there; whereas the control rats, like normal animals, collected a large pile of hoarded pellets in their cages and ate only a few of them.

On the basis of these investigations it can therefore be concluded that hoarding—the accumulation of useful material, such as food—is indeed regulated by a specific area in the brain. Removal of the cingulate cortex also interferes with certain other types of "instinctive" behavior patterns—such as mating and maternal behavior.

2. *Metabolic factors in hoarding.* It has been observed by other investigators that changes in environmental temperature

have marked effects on the amount of pellets collected by rats. Hoarding scores have been found to increase with lowered temperatures and to decrease when it gets warmer. These investigators then altered the metabolic functioning of the animals by injections of epinepherine, insulin, and glucose—none of which altered the hoarding behavior. When the thyroid metabolism was altered by feeding rats thiouracil, injecting thyroxine, or by total removal of the thyroid glands, it was again not possible to show any changes in hoarding activity of rats.

HOARDING—LEARNED AND UNLEARNED

We can say, then, that at the present time hoarding can be demonstrated under the proper experimental conditions. It is a relatively complex type of behavior, involving both unlearned responses and learned activity, because the rat has to perform an act which conflicts with other drives, such as avoidance of strange situations and attempting to escape from a restrictive environment.

Hoarding seems to be motivated by some unlearned drive which will persist for a long time and under adverse conditions after it has once been reinforced. This drive is, moreover, related to certain biological factors. The genetic basis of hoarding has been demonstrated by marked and consistent differences between hoarding scores of different strains of rats. Finally, the hoarding drive seems to be controlled by a specific area in the cerebral cortex, removal of which will greatly reduce, or altogether eliminate, hoarding.

A. H. STURTEVANT

The Genetic Effects of High Energy
Irradiation of Human Populations

HOW MUCH OF WHAT IS HAPPENING TO HOW MANY PEOPLE?
A CONSIDERATION OF THE EFFECTS OF RADIATION ON EXPOSED
INDIVIDUALS—AND THEIR DESCENDANTS.

Human populations are now being subjected to increases in
high-energy radiation, through the explosion of A-bombs and
H-bombs and through the widespread medical use of X-rays.

The genetic effects of such exposures have recently been the
subject of some public discussions. Since the matter is of public
concern and is also of considerable complexity, it seems desirable to elaborate somewhat on previous comments.

Two types of radiation hazard may be distinguished—those
to the exposed individuals, and those to their descendants.

The present discussion is based on the latter class of effects
—the genetic results, which will come to expression in the descendants of the exposed individuals.

It is not to be inferred that the direct effects on exposed individuals are negligible. In particular, there is evidence that
irradiation does increase the incidence of leukemia and other
malignant growths. These are difficult to estimate quantitatively,
and there may perhaps be a dosage threshold, such that low
doses of the sort here considered are ineffective. However, no
such threshold has been demonstrated, and the safest course

at present is to suppose that it does not exist—i.e., that even at very low doses there is a real, though small, hazard to the exposed individual.

The genetic effects of irradiation arise through effects on the germ cells of exposed individuals. These germ cells, like the other cells of the body, contain numerous separate hereditary elements, or *genes*, which are responsible for the inherited properties of individuals. The genes in any one individual are of many different kinds, but each particular kind is ordinarily transmitted unchanged from one generation to the next. On rare occasions, however, a gene may *mutate*—i.e., undergo a change to a new kind of gene, which is then transmitted to the following generations in the new, changed form. The genetic interest in high-energy irradiation arises from the fact that it increases the frequency of such mutations.

As previously formulated, the basic facts here are:

1. High-energy irradiation produces mutations.

2. The frequency of induced mutations is directly proportional to the dosage of irradiation. There is almost certainly no threshold value below which irradiation is ineffective.

3. The effects of successive exposures are cumulative.

4. The effects are permanent in the descendants of the affected genes. There is no recovery.

5. The overwhelming majority of these mutations is deleterious; that is, they seriously affect the efficiency of individuals in later generations in which they come to expression. These deleterious effects may lead to early death or to any of a wide variety of defects, often gross ones.

6. There is a store of such undesirable genes already present in any population. What irradiation does is to add to this store.

A further elaboration of these facts falls naturally under two major headings. First, what are the quantitative relations between irradiation dosage and genetic damage? Second, to what dosages are people being exposed? Unfortunately, both of these questions are inherently difficult to answer and only very rough approximations are possible. No scientist interested in exact quantitative results would touch the subject, were it not that

71

its social significance leaves us no alternative. We must, like it or not, try to get some sort of idea as to how much, of what, is happening to how many people.

IRRADIATION AND MUTATION

The quantitative determination of the relation between irradiation and mutation requires careful and elaborately controlled experiments, which must be carried out on a very large scale. It is quite impossible to get significant data directly concerning man, so we are forced to turn to other organisms, and it is also clear that our criteria for mutations in other organisms leave out of account some of the more important kinds that are to be expected in man—more especially those having to do with behavior. The most satisfactory data concern the small fly, Drosophila, and were collected by Spencer and Stern. Their data lead to the conclusion that 1 standard "Roentgen unit" of irradiation (written 1 r) will induce 1 lethal mutation per 10,000 treated germ cells of Drosophila (sperm cells, in this experiment).

It has recently been suggested that there is a much greater effect in mice, and presumably in people, but I cannot agree that this evidence is convincing. It would seem safest to assume —and it must be recognized that this *is* only an assumption— that the rate in man is roughly the same as that in Drosophila. In any case there appears to be no reason to suppose that man has a lower response to irradiation.

The above rate refers to lethal mutations. In general, according to the usual scheme, such a mutated gene has no effects on an individual that carries it—unless one of the same kind was received from each parent. (It may be estimated that, in man, something like 3 percent of the mutant genes will be expressed in males who received them only from their mothers; i.e., will be "sex-linked"). The result would be that an induced mutation of this type would not usually come to expression until numerous generations had passed. However, Stern *et al.* have recently shown that, in Drosophila, even the individuals with only a single "dose" of a lethal mutation have, on the average, about a 4 percent impairment of efficiency, so the undesirable effects from these genes must be supposed to begin appearing in the generations immediately following irradiation.

TIME AND MUTATION

Some of the induced mutations will also be substantially the same as (in genetical terminology, will be allelic to) some of those already present in the population; these may come to expression before there is intermarriage among the descendants of a single exposed individual. This consideration does not lead to any change in the probable average amount of damage due to induced mutations, but it does lead to a decrease in the estimate of the probable average time interval between exposure to radiation and the expression of the effect of the induced mutations.

There are other, nonlethal, types of mutations that are induced by irradiation. The measurement of their frequencies is difficult, and it may be doubted whether their frequency, relative to that of lethals, will be the same in man as it is in Drosophila. In the latter organism the evidence is that nonlethal mutations leading to the production of clearly distinct changes in the structure of viable individuals are distinctly less frequent than lethals; mutations leading only to a somewhat lowered efficiency of the individual are roughly twice as frequent as lethals.

On the whole, then, it seems a reasonable guess that the rate of induction of lethals in Drosophila may be used as a very rough index of the probable rate of induction of undesirable mutations in man—an index that is more likely to be too low than too high. This rate—1 in 10,000 germ-cells per r unit—will be used here without attempting any corrections.

The physical measurement of radiation has been developed to a high degree of refinement. But the estimation of the effective doses received by man is a complex matter, and at best can yield only approximate values. We are all of us receiving radiation in small amounts all the time, from cosmic radiation and from naturally occurring radioactive elements in the ground, in the walls and floors of rooms, in the air, and in our bodies. Further, the amount of this radiation varies from time to time and from place to place. We can, at most, get an approximate average value for irradiation per unit time. Since altitude is an important variable in the cosmic ray component of this normal "background" radiation, I have given two values—one for approximately sea-level, and one for an elevation of 6000 feet.

FALL-OUT FROM BOMBS

It is especially difficult to arrive at a value for the increase in irradiation due to fall-out from the bombs, since this varies erratically from one place to another, since the activity from any one explosion rapidly decreases with time, and since the effectiveness of a radioactive element will be greater if it happens to become incorporated in the tissues of the body. It is for these reasons, rather than because of any policy of secrecy, that it is very difficult to obtain from the published accounts any very satisfactory figure for the average increase in background. The value I have taken from AEC reports appears to represent an estimate for an average locality in the United States in September 1954.

In the following table I have included (from the summary by Plough, 1952, *Nucleonics* Vol. 10) some figures for dosages resulting from a few types of X-ray exposures to which people are sometimes exposed in medical practice. These again are averages, and there is much variation in the output of different machines. There is some scattering of radiation in any X-ray treatment, so that areas other than those intentionally treated will get some effect. The amount of such scattering is difficult to estimate. Accordingly I have included in the table only those treatments involving areas close to the ovaries or testes and have not included the two exposures to which the largest numbers of people are subject—dental and chest examinations.

From a genetical point of view, what we are interested in is the product of the dosage received multiplied by the mutation rate per unit dose. In other words, what will be the frequency of deleterious mutations resulting from the various radiation sources to which people are subjected?

Considering first the natural background, 3.0 to 4.5 r per gen-

74

eration would yield from 3 to 4.5 mutations per 10,000 germ cells. This is probably less than the amount of mutation that would be present if it were possible to screen people from all irradiation of any kind. In Drosophila only a small fraction of the normal mutation rate is due to natural background irradiation; but the proportion due to that cause in man is presumably much larger because the length of a generation is hundreds of times greater and the total background irradiation per generation is greater by the same factor, whereas the number of mutations not due to irradiation is probably proportional more nearly to the number of cell-generations than to time—and man and Drosophila do not differ greatly in this factor.

Irradiation, in r-units

Background, at sea level	0.1 per year, 3.0 per generation
Background, at 6000 feet	0.15 per year, 4.5 per generation
Increase in background due to bomb fall-out	0.0035 per year, 0.1 per generation
X-ray examinations—	
lumbar, spine, anterior-posterior	1.5 per treatment
lumbar, spine, lateral	5.7 per treatment
pregnancy, anterior-posterior	3.6 per treatment
pregnancy, lateral	9.0 per treatment
gastro-intestinal fluoroscopy	10 to 20 per minute
Irradiation of ovaries to induce fertility	200 or more
Recommended maximum permissible for radiological workers	0.3 per week, 15 per year
Average, Oak Ridge and Hanford workers, 1949	0.2 per year

Incidentally, many discussions of irradiation and mutation emphasize the natural rate and start with an attempt to determine the amount of irradiation necessary to double this rate. This seems to me a wrong approach, since the natural rate is not known and will not be easy to determine, and since the induced mutations are added to the natural ones and the two types do not have any fixed proportionality. The natural mutation rate is no more relevant than is the death rate from bacterial infection.

NATURAL BACKGROUND RADIATION

The natural background radiation is something that is always present, and discussion of whether it is a good thing or a bad one is pointless, since nothing can be done about it. The other sources here listed, however, are man-made, and it is legitimate to inquire what they may be expected to do to human populations.

If the increase due to bomb fall-out persists at current levels it may be expected to give about 1 deleterious mutation per 100,000 germ cells per generation—or, since each individual arises from two germ cells, 1 per 50,000 conceptions.

It may seem that this is a negligible proportion, and it should be emphasized that it is such a low number that no individual should be particularly disturbed about the probability that his immediate descendants will be affected.

But, according to the Population Division of the United Nations, there are something like 3,900,000 births per year in the United States, and about 90,000,000 per year in the world. This means that, if the increase in irradiation due to fall-out continues at the estimated present rate, it will lead to the functioning of about 78 mutated germ cells every year in the United States; and, if the same level of irradiation occurs in the rest of the world, of about 1800 per year in the population of the world. These will go on arising at this rate, year after year, as long as the irradiation continues and the number of births stays in this same range.

Another calculation may be made that is of some interest. The Pacific tests of 1954 apparently gave an average total of about .0035 r for any one locality in the United States. It may be estimated that the people now living in the United States will produce, during their lifetimes, over 100 million offspring; i.e., over 200 million of their germ cells will ultimately function. The estimate then is that 70 of these offspring will carry deleterious genes induced by this one series of tests.

A CONSERVATIVE ESTIMATE

It may still seem that these numbers are too small to be

seriously considered, but there are several points to be made. I have made every effort to be conservative; the numbers given should be considered minimal ones—the true value could possibly be 100 times greater. And there is a possibility that the irradiation of the germ cells may sometimes be much greater than is here estimated if there is a heavy fall-out, especially if some of the radioactive elements become incorporated in the tissues. Finally, from a humanitarian point of view, any increase at all in the number of individuals that are defective either mentally or physically is not to be lightly dismissed.

In any case, it is inexcusable to state, as has been done, that no hazard exists. One might agree that the hazard is slight when weighed against the possible benefits; and I would agree that the hazard to any one individual remote from the site of an explosion is so small as to be disregarded. But the fact remains that there *is* a hazard, and that it may become a significant one in terms of large populations.

The "maximum permissible" exposure has been set, by the International Commission on Radiological Protection, evidently on the basis of probable effects on exposed individuals themselves, without regard to genetic effects. If one imagines a situation where an entire population should be exposed to this amount of irradiation continuously, the dose per generation would add up to about 450 r—corresponding to about 4.5 percent of all germ cells undergoing mutation—i.e., every year about one-third of a million infants would be born with newly-arisen deleterious mutations in the United States alone.

This is an amount that some authorities believe might endanger the survival of the race if it were repeated in every generation, and even if the race survived its members would probably decrease in efficiency. It does not seem likely that any such general level of irradiation will be reached—unless possibly in the event of all-out atomic warfare—but to describe an exposure this large as "permissible" is misleading, to say the least, when one thinks in terms of populations.

The "maximum permissible" exposure will become a matter for careful consideration if nuclear reactors come to be widely used as power sources, since under those conditions also there will be an increase in the background radiation. The amount and character of such increases will depend in part on the type of reactors used and on the details of their design and operation—and it is a matter of public concern that this factor, as well as economic ones, be taken into account in a program for the non-military development of atomic energy.

The figures for the medical uses of X-rays run higher than those we have been considering, and there can be no doubt that in much of the world this is a far more effective cause of muta-tion than is radioactive fall-out. The published dosage values are in some respects misleading, since many irradiations—espe-cially among the more drastic therapeutic ones—are most often given to patients who are unlikely to have any further children. But in such cases as the pregnancy examinations here listed it must be remembered that not only the mother's ovaries but also the germ cells of the child are being exposed. If all members of the population were to receive even 1 r-unit just before birth, as would be possible here, the expected result would be that about one in 5000 of the next generation would carry a new mutation due to the treatment. In the case of the irradiation of the ovaries of a sterile woman to induce fertility it may be calculated that the resulting child has at least 1 chance in 50 of carrying a new mutation due to the treatment.

MEDICAL USE OF X-RAYS

In general, the conclusion seems warranted that the medical use of X-rays is dangerous and should be applied with caution and with full realization of the genetic hazards involved. In any given case the potential gains should be weighed against the potential damage; and in order to do this intelligently it is necessary to get as good an estimate as possible for the weight to be assigned to each side of the balance.

The medical use and the fall-out danger are different not only in the amounts of irradiation involved but also in some ethical respects. An individual does not usually have to submit to an X-ray examination or treatment, and when he does so the irradiation is administered for his own personal advantage. But we are all of us submitted, willy-nilly, to fall-out, and although it may be argued that some of this is for our ultimate advantage, it must be recognized that we get fall-out from Russian bombs as well, and that the rest of the world gets it from Russian and American bombs alike.

HENRY BORSOOK

We Could Feed the World

RISING POPULATION NEED NOT MEAN POTENTIAL STARVATION ON A WORLDWIDE SCALE.

We have the tools and the technology to feed everyone in the world with our present resources. And yet it has been estimated that 80 percent of the world population normally suffers from undernutrition or malnutrition.

One hears any number of explanations for this ironic situation —but at the bottom of them all is the simple fact that we still think of food in terms of the nineteenth century.

As long as we persist in thinking of food in terms of bushels of wheat, we will never have enough to go around. As soon as we learn to consider food as a conveyor of essential nutrients— and look for the cheapest and best way to get these nutrients— we will find we have enough for all.

According to the standard definition, only natural, or unprocessed, food deserves the name. Processed foods, generally considered to be the opposite of unprocessed, are by the same token "unnatural." Processing foods is "tampering with nature" —an odd objection when you consider how willingly we accept such "tampering" in every other branch of science.

There is a general impression, even in nutrition circles, that processed and unprocessed foods are competitors. But I know of no case where this is really true, if the circumstances in which the different foods are intended to be used are taken into account.

The novelty in the present situation is that, thanks to great advances in nutritional science and food technology, many more foods can now be improved. There is good reason to process a number of foods which we are accustomed (erroneously) to think of as natural foods—that is, unprocessed foods. No one raises an eyebrow any longer at dehydrated vegetables and fruits. Iodized salt and Vitamin D milk are an old story. So is margarine—ever since manufacturers and nutritionists began adding Vitamin A to it.

During the war, flour in this country was enriched by the use of vitamins and, in some cases, iron and calcium. Opponents of the idea of improving natural foods either forget or like to pass over the fact that during the war, in Britain, the dark flour which they had to use was enriched with calcium—to neutralize the deleterious effects of phytic acid in the bran of the high-extraction flour.

During the war, in this country, orange juice concentrated for export was fortified with synthetic Vitamin C, in order to give it a reasonable Vitamin C content. Recently there has been talk of including a certain amount of Vitamin C in canned tomato juice, for the same reason. If any such measure is finally decided upon, it will be necessary to add synthetic Vitamin C to nearly all of the tomato juice canned in the United States—except that coming from California and Arizona.

Surely this is evidence enough that the processing of foods is an old story—and that it is a natural and reasonable application of scientific progress to extend this kind of processing to foods wherever they can be improved nutritionally without significantly increasing the price.

My interest is in the nutritional aspect of processing foods. From a nutritional point of view, I repeat, a food is only a conveyor of certain essential nutrients. I am aware that there are other important considerations, such as taste and eye appeal, which are of great practical importance; but they, I think, look after themselves pretty well.

81

The great discoveries in nutrition in this century have enabled us to define the nutritional value of foods in quantitative terms. One important item among these great advances was the discovery and proof that, as far as the physiology of the body is concerned, the source of an essential nutrient is immaterial. It doesn't matter whether it is grown or synthesized in the factory. The economic and social implications of this finding are enormous. In fact, no one can see how the present world shortage of essential nutrients can be solved without taking advantage of this great scientific advance and the great modern technology to which it gave rise.

The essential nutrients are, briefly, *calories*, which may be obtained from proteins, fats and carbohydrates and from nitrogen in the form of protein (as far as human beings are concerned). Here the content of the ten indispensable *amino acids* determines whether the protein mixture is adequate or not, for these substances provide all the material from which proteins are built. For nearly all practical purposes, the only *mineral* about which we need to be concerned is calcium. As far as the *vitamin* content of human food is concerned, at least in this country, we need take into account only Vitamins A, B_1, B_2, Niacin, C, and D.

Let me review briefly some of the things we need to take into account in the use of processed and synthetic foods, with regard to the provision of the different essential nutrients.

Where there is a food shortage, we must never forget the need of calories. We learned during the war that a deficiency in calories is what is felt first and most acutely. This, no doubt, applies today in semi-famine areas. A low caloric requirement for sedentary work is 2,000 calories a day. Taking an average value for a mixture of protein, fat, and carbohydrate as five calories per gram, this requirement will call for 400 grams (dry weight) of these food materials; in other words about nine-tenths of a pound.

This disposes at once of the notion one meets every once in a while that it may be possible some day to supply all the food requirements in a few pills. It is simply impossible to squeeze nine-tenths of a pound into a few pills. The fundamental laws relating matter and energy exclude the possibility of our providing our caloric needs with less than this amount of food.

The minimum protein requirement of an adult is in the neighborhood of 50 grams a day or, shall we say, roughly two ounces (dry weight). So little protein, if it is to maintain nitrogen balance, must all be first class. In other words it must contain adequate amounts of the ten amino acids which the body cannot synthesize from others; hence their designation "indispensable." In most cases, where the protein eaten daily is so low, it is for economic reasons; and hence vegetable proteins are used rather than animal proteins. In general, vegetable proteins tend to be low in two of the indispensable amino acids, lysine and methionine. But by mixing some vegetable proteins, proteins relatively rich in these amino acids (though they may be low in others) would convert the whole mixture into a first-class protein. Flour, which is deficient in lysine, is relatively high in methionine. Among the vegetable proteins, those in legumes are, on the whole, of the best quality. But they are low in methionine. This deficiency could be met easily by the use of bread.

As far as calcium is concerned, the experimental nutritionist Henry Clay Sherman showed many years ago that the calcium in such salts as calcium carbonate (chalk) or calcium sulfate (plaster of paris) is used as effectively as the calcium in milk. The British, during the war, added calcium carbonate to flour.

With regard to the vitamins, I need only say that it doesn't matter whether we use vitamin concentrates from natural sources or synthetic vitamins. They are in every respect identical with those in the foods as they come from the field.

Vitamins have two characteristics which set them apart from the other substances the body uses—the small amount necessary to preserve health, and the complete inability of the human body to make them itself. They are formed for the most part by green plants on land and by algae and other smaller organisms in the sea. Until recently we had to get the necessary vitamins directly from plants or indirectly from animals. Now, of course, the synthesis of vitamins has progressed to the point where 11 of the 13 known vitamins are being produced commercially. The naturally occurring vitamins will, for a long time, be the main sources of vitamins for us human animals. But synthesized ones are invaluable in treating vitamin-deficiency diseases and in supplementing diets with inadequate supplies of them. And it is cheaper to manufacture many of them than to grow the plants that provide them.

Present technological knowledge and production facilities can, I would guess, supply all the vitamins and minerals needed for optimal nutrition of all the people in the world, including the billion very poor of Asia. But there can be no question that more calories and protein need to be produced.

As for calories, modern technology cannot compete with the sunlight of the tropics and semi-tropics. The photosynthesis of carbohydrates is still the cheapest and best method of obtaining sugar, and thence calories. What the 1,000,000,000 poor people of the world need is money to get it. That takes us out of the field of food and nutrition into economics, and on that subject I have nothing to say.

One billion people of the world today need more and better proteins. We cannot yet manufacture or synthesize protein. As far as we can see, for a long time to come it will have to be grown, whether as animal or vegetable protein. The production of animal protein is costly and inefficient. Animal protein is a luxury, which is fine if you can afford it. Most of the people of the world cannot afford much of it. Vegetables, with a few exceptions such as the legumes, are not rich sources of protein. And vegetable protein as a class is not first-class protein.

The prospect is not hopeless. I can see two things that can be done which would help a great deal. First, we should use far more of the protein now grown for human consumption. Today most of it is used as animal feed or is simply thrown away. During the war we threw away large amounts of the soybean protein. We are not doing that now; but too little is going to human consumption. There are large amounts of protein in oil cake and residues in the fermentation industries. We should and could use more of it.

A large fraction of fish protein goes to fertilizer or animal feed. Fish protein is first-class animal protein; it is cheaper than terrestrial animal protein; and I know it can be processed so as to be palatable. One of the necessary measures in the solution of the world protein problem is, then, less waste and the diversion of more protein to human consumption.

The other necessary step is education. Processors and consumers need to be taught to so blend incomplete proteins that they will cover each other's deficiencies in essential amino acids. This can be supplemented in a few instances by enrichment with synthetic amino acids.

As an example, and only as an example, of the kind of thing I have in mind, I will discuss briefly a food I had a hand in developing. It has received considerable publicity, and you may know it by the name of Multi-Purpose Food. The specifications which were given me in the devising of this food ran somewhat as follows: Three servings were to supply the Recommended Daily Allowances of protein, minerals, Vitamins A, B_1, B_2, and Niacin. The food was to be palatable, to blend readily with other foods when other foods were available, to be eaten by itself when they were not. The meal had to be quickly cooked, in not more than 10 minutes, and require only the most rudimentary cooking equipment. It had to keep from six months to a year, packaged in a dry state. It was to cost not more than three cents a meal. It could not offend the religious principles of any people. It had to be transported easily. It could not draw on those foods which Americans eat to a large extent.

The major ingredient chosen finally was soy grits, with a low fat content. The soy protein was chosen because it was the best cheap protein from a nutritional point of view. It is cheap because it is a by-product. Soy was grown chiefly for its oil, which has a variety of uses, including the manufacture of paints and lacquers.

Why did I choose the soy grits? The mistake that had been

made and may still be made with regard to the use of soy protein for human consumption was that it was used as a flour and invited comparison with flour. It is not a good substance for flour. It doesn't cook or bake as flour does. The grits, however, have a good texture, and this quality at once determines their use in a different way than flour. One need add only water to make a good soup. If only a little water is added, it is stew. It can be used as a meat extender.

To the grits were added Vitamins A, B_1, B_2, and Niacin, so that one serving of 2¼ oz. would supply one-third of the Recommended Daily Allowances of protein and these vitamins. Vitamin C was not added because it is largely destroyed in the cooking. Certain spices were added. These are of such a character that the food blends readily with any other food. For example, if it is used with a little fish it takes on the character of, shall we say, fish-balls; with cabbage, of a cabbage dish. As it stands, it is low in methionine and in calories. The deficiency of these two essential nutrients is met by bread. It is cheap compared with any other protein food used for human consumption.

The Multi-Purpose Food is only an example, I reiterate. I refer to it here as a very simple example of what can be done by the application of the science of nutrition and modern food technology. A food such as Multi-Purpose Food, is, of course, not intended to replace the habitual American diet wherever people can afford it. All of us would prefer a steak at any time.

The use of foods of this character should be considered in two extreme situations or conditions. One is semi-starvation, in which even the objection of monotony is removed; the other and more common occurrence is where people have some food but for budgetary reasons cannot afford enough first-class animal protein. They need vitamins and minerals in an enriched protein food because fruits and vegetables are dear too. The objection that a processed food cannot supply all of the yet unidentified vitamins and the trace elements is again not valid, because these people will be getting them from the rest of their diet. The common objections to food such as the Multi-Purpose Food is that people would not want to eat it alone every day, three times a day. They are not expected to.

It is this example I have in mind when I say that we have in our hands the scientific tools and the technology to prepare foods to meet almost any situation. The use of industrial and agricultural by-products insures their low cost; vitamin concentrates, synthetic vitamins, and commercial minerals will make them as nutritious as an expensive diet scientifically selected from natural fresh foods. In no other way can the needs of such countries as China, India, and even portions of Europe today be met. It isn't necessary to force people to eat brown bread if they prefer white. It isn't necessary for people to get scurvy if the good food sources of Vitamin C—citrus fruits, tomatoes, cabbage, potatoes, and a few green leafy vegetables—are not available or are too costly. Freedom to eat what we like and still be well nourished is one of the new freedoms which science and the technology of foods offer to the world if it will only take it. That offer has not yet been accepted.

JAMES BONNER

Plant Hormones

BASIC STUDIES ON PLANT HORMONES HAVE RESULTED IN
THE DEVELOPMENT OF A NEW SCIENCE—THE SCIENCE OF
THE CHEMICAL CONTROL OF PLANT GROWTH.

Through basic work on the plant growth hormones the concept
has become available to us that particular substances may be
applied to the plant to accomplish particular useful purposes—
to make the leaves drop off, to make the fruit stay on, to induce
flowering, to inhibit flowering, and even to kill undesired plants.

The different chemicals which are used for the supervision
of these varied aspects of plant development are also, without
exception, substances whose biological effectiveness is based
upon structural similarity to one or another of the native plant
growth hormones. Since a great many substances have been
investigated or screened as to ability to evoke this or that plant
growth response, we have today what is almost a pharmacology
of plants.

It is, of course, well known that the growth of the plant depends upon the process of photosynthesis by which the carbon
dioxide of the air is transformed into the manifold materials of
which a plant is made. The growth of the plant is dependent,
too, on the water and on the varied mineral constituents of the
soil which are ordinarily taken up by the root and incorporated
into plant materials.

As photosynthesis, mineral uptake, and the chemical trans-
formations of metabolism proceed, the plant increases in size
and in mass and, in due course, proceeds from the vegetative
state to a reproductive one. The total increment of plant which
occurs as a result of synthetic reactions must be apportioned
between the several organs, leaves, stems, and, ultimately, the
flowers and fruits.

It is the harmonious integration of the development of the
several plant organs and tissues in space and in time which
appears to be the primary function of the plant hormones. Each
of these materials is produced in a particular organ in minute
amounts and is then transported to other organs where it brings
about a specific effect on growth. It is through the growth hormones that the individual parts of the plant interact with one
another and mutually regulate one another's growth.

That the growth of the root is dependent upon specific chemical substances which are normally supplied by the aerial organs
can be shown simply and elegantly by the cultivation of the
excised tips of roots. If we remove a tip a few mm. long from a
growing root and place this in an appropriate nutrient solution,
the tip will grow into a whole root. If the nutrient solution has
been correctly selected, the excised root will, in fact, grow in
length as rapidly as it would have done had it remained attached to the intact plant.

We may now ask ourselves what chemical substances must
be added to the nutrient solution used for the culture of excised
roots in order to bring about continued root growth. One knows
a priori that an appropriate nutrient solution must contain a
carbohydrate, which may be used by the root tissue as a respira-
tory substrate and which may serve as a source of building blocks
for the synthesis by the root of the many substances of which
roots are made.

The nutrient solution must also contain the inorganic nutrients which plants require for their growth. A nutrient solution
containing only mineral salts and sucrose, however, is inadequate
for the cultivation of excised roots. An excised root tip of flax,
for example, cultivated in such a nutrient, ceases its growth in

a few days or a few transfers. In order to cause excised flax roots to grow at the normal rate, it is necessary to add a small amount of thiamine to the nutrient solution. All of the species of excised roots which have been studied up to the present time require thiamine and, in general, one or both of the vitamins pyridoxine and niacin in order to continue growth as isolated roots.

It is possible by simple plant physiological experiments to show that these three vitamins of the B complex are produced in mature green leaves, primarily in the light. They are then transported from the leaf, through the stem to the root. Since roots cannot produce these vitamins, and since these materials are required for root growth, thiamine, pyridoxine, and niacin constitute root growth hormones.

OTHER TYPES OF GROWTH HORMONES

The same basic kind of experiment used for the demonstration of the presence in the plant of root growth hormones may be used for the demonstration of the existence of other types of growth hormones as well. Thus, we know of leaf growth hormones, stem growth hormones, fruit growth hormones, and hormones for the initiation of flowering.

We must then visualize the growing plant as containing many currents of transport of a variety of growth regulating substances. The mature leaves produce the vitamins of the B complex which are transported to and used in the regulation of root growth. The same leaves produce the leaf growth factors such as adenine, as well as the hormones which regulate flower initiation and reproductive development—hormones which are possibly protein in nature.

Still other factors produced in the roots are required for the growth of the aerial parts. And to this array of known or suspected correlational carriers we will doubtless add, in the future, further hormones whose existence is not even suspected today.

A major portion of our knowledge of plant growth substances has been derived from the study of one particular group of materials, known collectively as the auxins. This term is a physiological one, and the auxin concept is physiological rather than chemical. An auxin is a substance produced in the apical bud and young leaves of the plant and transported from this point to the growing region of the stem, where it is used in the support of stem elongation.

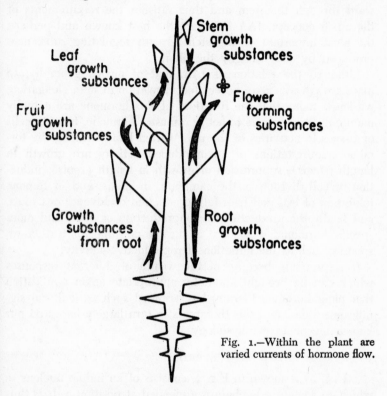

Leaf growth substances

Stem growth substances

Flower forming substances

Fruit growth substances

Growth substances from root

Root growth substances

Fig. 1.—Within the plant are varied currents of hormone flow.

It can be simply demonstrated that special chemical substances have to do with the regulation of stem elongation. If we excise sections from the growing region of, say, a seedling oat plant and place the sections in a nutrient solution containing only sugar and mineral salts, they grow but little. However, if we add a small amount of indole acetic acid (IAA) to the nutrient solution, the rate of growth of the sections is greatly increased and may in fact achieve or surpass the rate normally attained in the plant.

That IAA is a naturally occurring plant material has been shown by isolation from a variety of plant products. It is produced in the apical bud and young leaves and transported downward through the stem and thus satisfies the requirements of the auxin concept. IAA is in fact the best known and perhaps the most important of the stem growth regulating substances produced by and used by the plant.

Although the relation of IAA, and of auxins generally, to plant growth was first appreciated in relation to stem elongation, we know today that the functions of this hormone are actually manifold. IAA appears to act as a master hormone, inciting cells or tissues to activities of the most varied kinds. Among the terminal manifestations of auxin-induced activity are growth in length (stems), suppression of growth in length (roots), induction of cell division in the cambium, in callus, and in tumors, inhibition of leaf and fruit fall, production of adventitious roots, and finally the production or nonproduction of other and more specific hormones which are in turn responsible for further responses, such as the initiation of reproductive activity.

It is precisely because of the wealth of different responses which can be brought about by appropriate auxin application that plant hormone therapy has assumed such agricultural significance today, and this therapy is in turn largely based on our knowledge of auxin physiology.

AUXINS: NATIVE AND SYNTHETIC

IAA, as is shown in Fig. 2, consists of an indole nucleus to which an acetate side chain is appended at position 3. It is thus related in structure to the amino acid tryptophan and is in fact synthesized in the plant from trytophan by a series of reactions mediated by an enzyme system which is found in apical buds and other centers which possess the ability to generate the hormone.

Approximately 15 years ago it became known through the work of Haagen-Smit and Went of Caltech that IAA is not alone in its ability to regulate the stem growth of plants. Certain related chemical substances, not necessarily naturally occurring, were found to be able to duplicate the effects of IAA in causing the elongation of excised sections of stems of oat coleoptiles. Naphthalene acetic acid is not a naturally occurring plant material. It is a chemical substance which is able to simulate the effects of a plant hormone, although it is not itself a plant hormone. In the years since 1935 a very great number of compounds have been tested for their ability to replace IAA in the induction of plant growth responses. So much study has been put into this matter that at present our knowledge of the relation of chemical structure to biological activity among the auxins is one of the best documented studies of this nature. Let us therefore see what new insight into auxin physiology these intensive chemical studies have given us.

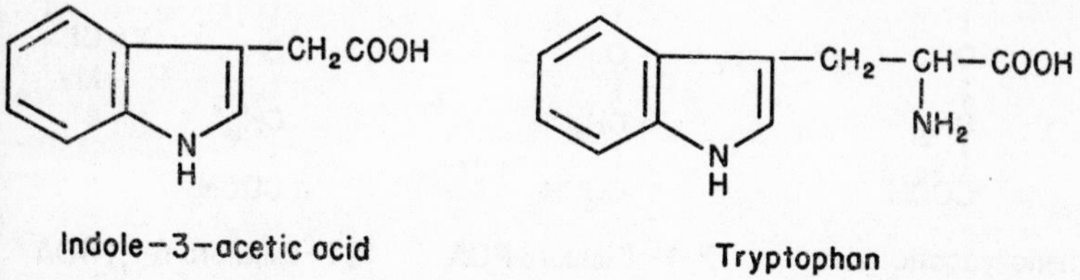

Indole–3–acetic acid

Tryptophan

Fig. 2.—Indole acetic acid is related to—and derived from—the amino acid tryptophan.

The conclusions which we draw from the study of the activity or nonactivity of a great many different substances may be summarized in the empirical rules that a compound, in order to manifest auxin activity, must possess the following minimum qualifications: (1) A ring system containing at least one double bond; (2) A side chain ending in a carboxyl group; (3) Ability to assume a certain configuration in which the carboxyl group is suitably arranged relative to the ring system.

It has recently become possible to define more closely the role of the cyclic unsaturated nucleus in relation to auxin activity and from this to learn more concerning the biochemistry of auxin action.

Muir, Hansch, and Gallup (1949) of Pomona College have shown that a compound, to be active as an auxin, must possess in its cyclic nucleus a substitutable hydrogen or other group of a minimum critical reactivity. This reactive position is in general either of the two positions ortho to the carboxyl group containing side chain. This is shown by the example in Fig. 3. The ortho reactivity of phenoxyacetic acid is increased by halogen substitution in the 2 and 4 positions and 2,4-D is active as an auxin. Blocking of both ortho positions renders the molecule inactive.

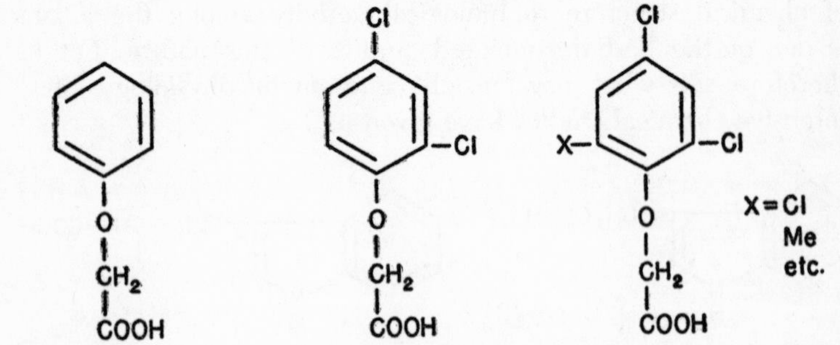

Phenoxyacetic acid (POA)	2,4-Dichloro POA (2,4-D)	2,4-Dichloro 6-X POA
INACTIVE	ACTIVE	INACTIVE

Fig. 3.—Growth substance activity can either be increased or decreased by proper ring substitution.

It appears, then, that a molecule, in order to be an auxin, must possess not only a carboxyl group but also a cyclic nucleus with an ortho group of some critical reactivity. These two functional groups must further be capable of assuming some suitably spatial relationship with one another. All of our present knowledge of structure and activity among the auxins appears to be qualitatively encompassed by this generalization.

TWO-POINT ATTACHMENT

The fact that auxins act at low concentrations suggests at

once that they may perform their work in promoting growth by acting as prosthetic groups of an enzyme or enzymes—that, in short, they may be bound to protein in the plant.

It has long been known that auxin is in fact bound to protein within the plant and that auxin thus bound may be again released by proteolytic hydrolysis. This suggests that the carboxyl group of the auxin molecule may be involved in the binding, perhaps through the formation of peptide-like linkages. That the ortho group is also involved in chemical reaction within the plant, and that this is also related to binding, is indicated by both chemical and kinetic studies.

We may suggest, therefore, as a tentative working hypothesis, not only that the auxin molecule possesses two reactive functional groups but also that the molecule, in carrying out its growth-promoting task, reacts with and binds to two suitable receptor sites within the plant.

This concept—the two-point attachment concept—has served as a fruitful basis for, and is strongly supported by, further experimentation, particularly in the way of auxin antagonists.

INHIBITION OF GROWTH

The extensive studies of D. H. McRae at Caltech have shown that an active auxin is normally bound to the plant receptor entity through its two reactive groups but that, in addition, a substance capable of combining with but one site of the receptor entity and incapable of consummating two-point attachment is thereby an antiauxin—an inhibitor of auxin action. Examples of antiauxins and the way in which they act to block receptor molecules are shown in Fig. 4.

The effect of auxins in promoting plant growth, like the effects of so many biologically active substances, is a twofold one. Although auxins promote plant growth over a wide range of relatively low concentrations (10^{-8}-10^{-5}M), at still higher concentrations the same substances become inhibitory. Thus, if we plot growth rate against concentration of added auxin we find that the hyperbolic relationship of growth rate to auxin concentration obtains up to a concentration of roughly 10^{-5}M. At

95

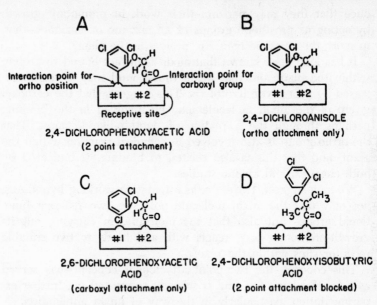

Fig. 4.—Growth substances are activated by consummating two-point attachment. Molecules which can make only single-point attachment are growth inhibitors.

this concentration, growth rate passes through a maximum and dies away too as the concentration is still further increased.

That auxins in high and unphysiological concentrations elicit growth inhibitions of this type has been known for many years. This effect now assumes new interest and importance, since it can be shown that such a dual growth response is a natural and indeed an inescapable consequence of the two-point attachment by which the auxin molecule is bound to the receptor entity within the plant.

Auxin-induced growth inhibition appears to be nothing more than the kinetic expression of two-point attachment. Let us consider the sequence of events which leads to the formation of the active auxin-receptor complex. A molecule of auxin—IAA for example—approaches the receptor entity and combines with it through one of its two functional groups. After a suitable period of twisting it adjusts itself in such a manner as to be able to

96

consummate its second point of attachment through its second functional group.

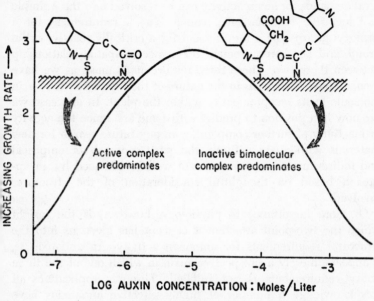

Fig. 5.—The inhibition of plant growth by auxin at high concentrations is due to bimolecular complex formations.

Now let us consider the sequence of events at higher auxin concentrations. At some sufficiently high concentration the probability will become appreciable that two molecules will simultaneously approach the receptor entity and will simultaneously combine with it. In this instance, one auxin molecule will necessarily become attached through its carboxyl group while the other must attach through its reactive ortho position. Each molecule will therefore prevent the other from consummating the two-point attachment which, as we have seen, is essential to the manifestation of auxin activity. The bimolecular auxin-receptor complex is therefore inactive in promoting growth, and to the extent that such bimolecular auxin-receptor complex formation occurs growth rate will be depressed, as is summarized in Fig. 5.

97

CONCLUSION

It is a matter for some intellectual satisfaction that the structural demands for auxin activity can be resolved into three simple and inclusive requirements; namely, (a) a requirement for a carboxyl group, (b) a requirement for a critically reactive ortho group, and (c) a requirement for a specific spatial relationship between these two. These three requirements must, as we have seen, all have their basis in the nature of the binding of the auxin molecule to its receptor entity within the plant. In any case we are now in a position to predict with some assurance the activity or inactivity of further compounds. In any future search for new materials with auxin activity, the past approach of empirical and indiscriminate screening might well be replaced by an approach based on thoughtful consideration of the structures involved.

Of more importance to physiology, however, is the insight which the two-point attachment concept has given us into the structural requirements for antiauxin activity. An antiauxin is, it appears, merely a prospective auxin in which one of the three above requirements is not fulfilled. Through applications of this knowledge a number of highly effective antiauxins have already been made available and it is already apparent that these materials may fill a host of agricultural needs. A hormone is by its very nature normally contained in the living creature, and the kinds of responses which may be elicited in this creature by the application of further hormones are necessarily limited. The antiauxins now offer us the opportunity to practice a chemotherapy of plants which is the obverse of that which we practice with 2,4-D.

Finally, the two-point attachment concept of auxin action has provided us with new insight into the nature of the deleterious effects of high auxin concentrations. This, in turn, has illuminated the question of why it is that a synthetic growth substance such as 2,4-D, which behaves as an auxin at low concentrations, is nevertheless so extremely deleterious as to be herbicidal at higher concentrations.

98

IAA itself cannot ordinarily be used to kill normal green plants, since most such plant tissues are equipped with an enzymatic system for the removal of IAA in excess of a concentration which is well below those which give complete growth suppression. This safety mechanism does not work with such non-native materials as 2,4-D, which are then free to accumulate in plant tissues in concentrations which appropriately reflect those applied. It is characteristic of the 2,4-D concentrations which are used for herbicidal purposes that they are far into the range at which bimolecular complex formation must be expected to predominate. Herbicidal activity of an auxin may therefore be nothing more than an extreme expression and ultimate consequence of the two-point attachment principle.

We have seen that, in the plant, communication of information as between the separate and varied organs and tissues is mediated by a complex system of appropriate chemical materials. Integration, control, and synchronization of the plant's activities are established and maintained by a whole series of hormones, each of which bears from its point of origin to other receptor points an appropriate signal and evokes appropriate responses. Only when we view the plant as a whole can we perceive the wonderful and complete autotrophism of these organisms, their ability to transform such simple materials as carbon dioxide, water, light energy, and a few mineral elements into the complex array of organic substances which constitute living matter. The individual organs and tissues of the plant are appreciably less autotrophic than is the whole and are each dependent upon other organs and tissues for particular and specific chemical substances. Thus, in a sense, the plant makes use of slight variations in its autotrophism to assure the harmonious development of its several parts.

The fact that plant growth and development is so firmly based on hormonal relationships gives us a corresponding opportunity to control and modify the course of plant development by the artificial application of chemical substances which are either identical with, synthetic substitutes for, or antagonists of the native hormones.

SIR CHARLES DARWIN

Forecasting the Future

EVERY DAY THERE ARE EIGHTY THOUSAND MORE PEOPLE ON
THE EARTH. IN ANOTHER FIFTY YEARS THE WORLD POPULATION
WILL BE FOUR BILLION—A HUNGRY FOUR BILLION.
AND IN ONE HUNDRED YEARS?

We none of us can help hoping that when anyone undertakes
to prophesy the future, the facts will prove him wrong. I share
this taste myself, and yet it may appear that I too am starting
to prophesy. In fact I am going to try and do something much
more modest. Forecasting is the word used for the predictions
that the meteorologists make about the probable future weather,
and this is the analogy I am going to follow. Through the
reports he receives the meteorologist knows better than the
rest of us what is happening in other parts of the world, and
though he is very conscious that there are a great many things
he does not know, with the information and experience that
he has, he is in a good position to forecast the *probabilities* of
future weather.

The present director of the British Meteorological Office, Sir
Graham Sutton, wrote an article which describes the situation
admirably. In making his forecast the meteorologist is doing
the same sort of thing that a player does when he bids his
hand at the game of bridge. If he were required to predict
what tricks he would take with absolute certainty, he would
not get very far; for example, if he had the ace and king of a

100

suit he would only be *absolutely* certain of two tricks if that suit were trumps.

In fact, he does not declare that he will get two tricks, but he makes the estimate that he will probably get, say, eight or nine tricks. He reckons that this is the probability; he knows that one or two of his strongest cards may possibly fail to win the tricks he expects, but then he knows that this will most likely be compensated by tricks from some of his other cards he was not so confidently counting on. He estimates probabilities, and if he is an experienced player he is usually not far from right in a general way, even though some of his details may be wrong.

That is the sort of prediction that the meteorologist makes about the weather, and it is the sort of prediction that I am going to try and make about the future prospects of the world.

I want to work out this analogy with meteorology rather further. There are two separate branches of that subject, called respectively weather-forecasting and climatology. In forecasting, the meteorologist uses all the detailed knowledge of conditions in the world at the present moment and applies to them the laws of mechanics and also a good deal of personal experience and personal judgment, and from all this he says what things will be like twenty-four hours hence, and he usually gets it fairly right. He also tries to do forty-eight hours but has a good deal less confidence about that, because as time goes on the things he does not know get proportionately more and more important.

The subject of climatology is quite different. In this there is no forecasting of what things will be like tomorrow, but instead there are general statements such as that this place will be a desert, that place a tropical jungle, while yet another one has a climate which will support good agriculture most of the time. It is much less detailed but a much more general subject, and it is one that must always be in the back of the mind of the forecaster when he makes his predictions.

I am going to try and make a forecast for the fairly close future, say fifty or a hundred years, but before coming to that

I must say something about what I call the climatology of my subject, because that really is a deeper part of it. I will begin this by taking a simplified example. Suppose that somewhere in the ocean there is an island that is completely isolated from contacts with other parts of the world. I am told, in a general way, such things as what its climate is, how hot it is, how much rainfall it has, and what the soil is like. I am also told a little about the inhabitants and their state of culture—say, that they know about the use of metals but have only rather inferior food crops.

With only this information I could say a great deal about the life of the island; for instance, I could make a very fair estimate of the numbers of its population. To do this I should take as my principle that the normal way that any living species survives is by producing too many offspring, of which only a fraction survive. With many lower animals the excess is often enormous, with a million produced of which only one may survive, but the same rule holds for the higher animals, too; the excess production is much less, but it is still there.

The same rule applies to man. The families on the island will mostly each produce several children and the parents will do all they can to keep their children alive and to bring them up. Now, simply to replace the numbers of the two parents, two children would be enough, but most peasant families surely produce more than two children, so that there is a tendency for the population to increase.

What is it that determines the total population then? The whole island will have come under cultivation, and it will be yielding all the food it can. Through the uncertainties of the weather, in some years there will be good harvests and in some years bad, and the peasants will accumulate a certain amount of reserve food against the bad harvests. But sometimes there will be two or three bad years running, and then they will get short of food, and perhaps two or three times in a century there may be four bad years running and then there will be real famine. It will be these occasional famines that will determine the average number of people on the island.

This is not the sort of thing we see now anywhere in the world, but, for example, it was what used to control the population of India until about a hundred years ago. All this may seem rather obvious, but it is worth noting that we can say with some confidence that one of the most important features in the life of the island will be famines at the rate perhaps of three a century and it is these famines that will mainly determine the number of people on it.

Now, suppose that the island has settled down into this state, but that its perfect isolation is broken by a ship which is wrecked on its coast and in which there happens to be a cargo of potatoes or some such crop. The new crop will give a much better yield than any of the previous food crops of the island, and it will be gradually adopted by the inhabitants. Every acre of ground will now yield twice as much food as it did previously.

Man is a rather slow breeder, so that the most conspicuous thing first to be noticed is that there is plenty of food for everyone. The bad old days of famines have disappeared and the population starts to increase. The historians of the island will record that it is a Golden Age, with an easy life very different from that of their parents. They will probably have a very human failing; they will forget about the cargo of potatoes, and they will claim how clever the present inhabitants are in overcoming the difficulties of life that used to afflict their ancestors.

This Golden Age will go on for a century or two, while the population increases to double its previous numbers, but at the end of that time the old troubles will begin all over again, because now again the yield of the crops will only be about enough to provide food for the new numbers of the population. There will be the old trouble over occasional successions of bad harvests which will produce famines again, and this will limit the population in the same old way. Something very like this was what happened in Ireland in the 1840's.

I have developed this imaginary example at some length, because it has a most important application to the present condition of the whole world. The world is just now in a highly abnormal condition, as is shown by the consideration of the increasing numbers of humanity. We are living in a Golden Age, which for man may well be the most wonderful Golden Age of all time. The historians have made fairly reliable estimates of the numbers of world population at different periods of history, and these numbers reveal it rather clearly. At the beginning of the Christian era the population of the world was about 350 million. It fluctuated up and down a bit, and by A.D. 1650 it was still only 470 million. But by 1750 it had risen to 700 million, and now it is 2500 million. That is to say that for 1700 years it was fairly constant, and then in 200 years it has suddenly quadrupled itself.

The increase of world population is still going on at a rate of doubling itself in a century, but it is a most menacing thing to think about. Year in and year out the increase is at a rate of about one percent, and this means that every day there are 80,000 more people on the earth. That is the daily difference between the number of babies born and the number of people dying. Even those who are not conscious of this fact are unconsciously used to it and accept it as natural, but it quite obviously cannot go on forever like this, and the most crucial question for us all is how long it *can* go on.

AN ABNORMAL STATE OF AFFAIRS

This will be the main thing I shall want to discuss, but to see how abnormal the present condition is, I will imagine for a moment that it was the normal condition and I will look at the consequences that would follow. If the population were going to be able to double itself in each century, it would only be two thousand years before it was a million times what it is now, and two thousand years is only a short time in the period of human history. As a matter of simple arithmetic, if the population were a million times what it is now, there would be just about standing room on the land surfaces of the earth, but not room for the people to lie down! This would obviously be a fantastically impossible state of affairs, but it illustrates what an abnormal state the world is in just now with its population increasing at this rate.

It is obvious what has produced this present abnormal state of the world. There have been two chief causes. One of them was the discovery of the New World, much of it barely inhabited, which has provided enormous areas for possible expansion, in particular for the white races. The other is the development of science, through which it has been possible for man to find ways of producing a great deal more food and in particular of transporting it from the places where it is produced to the places where it is needed. The Scientific Revolution, which began about three hundred years ago, must rank as one of the two really great episodes in human history; the only thing comparable with it in importance is the Agricultural Revolution. This happened in about 10,000 B.C., when man learned how to become a food grower instead of merely a food collector.

THE CLIMATOLOGY OF HUMANITY

I want to give more consideration to what I have called by analogy the climatology of humanity. As I have shown, the present time is very abnormal, and so present conditions cannot be of much help in this. Are there any deeper principles that can be used? I think there are sufficient of them for us to be able to say a good deal about it. The first point is that the climate—and here I mean the actual climate—of the earth has been fairly constant for something like a thousand million years at least. It is eminently reasonable, then, to expect that we can count on it for say at least one more million years. Here is one constant datum we can use in our estimates.

A second thing is the finite size of the earth, and the fact that its whole surface is now fairly well known. This knowledge, of course, is quite a new thing; even a century ago there were great areas in Africa and South America that were hardly known, and they might have held something quite unexpected. There may, of course, still be many things to be discovered; there might possibly be other gold fields like the South African one, or perhaps great ore fields of other, more practically valuable metals, but we can now be fairly confident that there is not room on the earth for anything, at present unknown, on a scale that would materially alter the possibilities of our ways of life.

The third principle we can use is much the most important. It is human nature. The characteristics of mankind are conveniently, though only roughly, divided into two parts, which have—as I think, rather clumsily—been called nature and nurture. Nurture signifies the environment in which people grow up and live, and it is, of course, what determines most of their day-to-day behavior. It is thus immensely important in making the short-term forecast, but the conditions of life have varied enormously from century to century, and they will surely continue to do so, and therefore nurture gives little reliable help in estimating what the long-term character of human life will be.

The matter is quite different when we consider nature. Here, as we know from the study of many types of animals, heredity plays a predominating part, and so for as long as any of us can really care about—say a hundred thousand years at least—we must accept that man will be just like what he is now, with all his virtues and all his defects. There is simply no prospect at all of any millennium in which pure virtue triumphs, because that is not in the nature of the species Homo Sapiens. Insofar as heredity determines man's behavior, we can take this as a constant in making our predictions about his destiny.

The most important human characteristics, for my present purpose, are the deepest instincts which human beings have. These are the instincts which are directed towards the perpetuation of the species. One of them is the fear of death, shared by such a vast proportion of humanity that even under the most dreadful catastrophes very few people do actually commit suicide. This instinct serves to help in keeping the individual alive.

Equally important are the instincts serving to reproduce the species. In man and in the higher animals this characteristic falls into two rather separate parts, the sexual instinct and the parental instinct. Among the animals these two instincts suffice to perpetuate the species, and until very recently the same has been true of man. Things have, however, been changed by the developments of methods of birth control, which have revealed a curious gap in our equipment of instincts.

Most people feel the sexual instinct with a force almost as great as the fear of death, and most people, when they have got children, have a very intense instinct to care for them and bring them up, but a good many people lack the desire to have children in advance; or, at any rate, if they have the instinct, it is very much weaker than the other two. The parental instinct seems to be evoked mainly by the presence of the children, and thus it has come about that the sexual instinct can be satisfied without leading to the consequence it ought to have of ensuring the creation of a next generation. This third instinct, coming between the sexual and the parental, may be called the procreative instinct; it is much weaker than the other two and indeed seems to be absent in a good many people.

LONG-RANGE FORECAST

The really important condition essential for human life was first fully described by Thomas Malthus in 1799, in his celebrated book, *An Essay on Population.* In this he drew attention to the necessity of a balance between the numbers of a population and the food it will require. He pointed out, with numerous examples, that there is a tendency for population to increase in geometrical ratio, whereas the area from which they will derive their food cannot possibly increase in this ratio.

Malthus could not be expected to have foreseen the consequences of the Scientific Revolution, which was going for a time entirely to upset the balance between the two sides of his account. During the 19th century it was possible to take the view that the disasters foretold by him had not occurred and that, therefore, his principles had been proved wrong.

This comfortable view overlooked the fact that all through that century population was, in fact, increasing geometrically, just as he had said, but for a time this was being balanced by the opening up for agriculture of barely inhabited regions in the

New World, from which the newly invented railways and steamboats could convey the food to the places where it was needed.

It was the developments of the Scientific Revolution that for a time upset Malthus's balance, but now once again the balance is coming into effect, because we are now very fully conscious of the finiteness of the earth. There are few more regions that can be opened out for agriculture, and once again we have to face the problem of how our rapidly increasing populations are to be fed.

POPULATION AND FOOD PRODUCTION

I have noticed that most people, when for the first time they face the population problem, at once think about the possibilities of producing more food. They first think, perhaps, of the fields we all notice here and there that are not being properly cultivated. Then they may think of improved breeds of plants that will produce two or three crops a year instead of only one. Then there is the possibility of cultivating the ocean. And there is the Chlorella, an alga which might be grown on a sort of moving belt in a factory; it can produce proteins perhaps ten times more efficiently than the garden vegetables do, but unfortunately at a hundred times the cost. Finally, with the rapid progress in our knowledge of chemistry, it is not to be excluded that one day the foodstuffs necessary for life will be synthesized in factories from their original elements, carbon, nitrogen, phosphorus and so on.

All these things are possible, and I do not doubt that some of them will be done, but to accomplish them is no help, because of the central point made by Malthus, that there has to be a balance between food production and population numbers. Until population numbers are controlled, it will always continue to be true that, *no matter what food is produced there will be too many mouths asking for it.* New discoveries in the way of food production may make it possible for many more people to keep alive, but what is the advantage of having twenty billion hungry people instead of only three billion?

108

In the light of these considerations it seems to me that the food problem can be left to look after itself and that all attention must be given to the other side of the balance. Can anything be done about it? Frankly, though perhaps for a short term something might be done, in the long run I doubt it. My reason is this. Nature's control of animal populations is a simple, brutal one. In order to survive, every animal produces too many for the next generation, and the excess is killed off in one way or another. It is a method of control of tremendous efficiency, and during most of his history it has also applied to man. To replace a mechanism of this tremendous efficiency it is no use thinking of anything small; the alternative we must offer, if we want to beat nature, must also be tremendous.

The difficulty is even greater than it appears at first sight, because there would be an instability about any alternative scheme deliberately adopted. Thus, suppose some really good solution was found and was adopted by half the world. For a generation or two this half would prosper. Its numbers would stay constant and the people would not be hungry, but all the time the numbers in the other half of the world would be increasing, so that in the end they would swamp the first half. That is the terrible menace of the matter; there is a strong survival value in being one of those who refuse to limit population.

The most easily imagined solution would be the establishment of some *world-wide* creed prohibiting large families, but when we reflect how many rival religious creeds there already are, all largely subsisting on account of their mutual differences, there seems little hope for any universal creed which would permanently limit population in this way.

It is very much to be hoped that a great deal of thought will be given to this matter on the chance that someone may hit on a solution, but I must repeat that nature's method of limiting population is so brutally tremendous that it can never be replaced by any such triviality as the extension of methods of birth control. It calls for something much more tremendous if there is to be any prospect of success.

SHORT-RANGE FORECAST

I have said all I want to say about what by analogy I called climatology, and I will turn to weather forecasting; that is to say, I will attempt to forecast what will happen in the near future of say 50 or 100 years. I would remind you of the description of forecasting that I gave at the start, that it is like declaring a hand at bridge, where one makes a general estimate on incomplete data and one only expects to be right in general and not in detail. The weather forecaster can only do his work by receiving a great deal of information coming from all over the earth, and I need similar information for my forecasting. I have derived this from a fairly wide variety of sources. One of the most useful sources was a book entitled *The Challenge of Man's Future*, by Prof. Harrison Brown of Caltech. As a geochemist his study of the prospects of shortages in the future supply of various minerals led him on to study other shortages facing the world. A second book, *The Future of Energy*, by P. C. Putnam, deals very usefully with a narrower subject, the rate of exhaustion of our present fuel supplies and the various possible alternatives to them. Another very valuable source of information came from attendance at the UNO Conference on Population which was held in Rome in 1954. I may also refer to a book, *World Population and Resources*, recently composed in England by the organization known as P.E.P.

CAUTIOUS ESTIMATES

As I have already shown, we have been living during the past hundred and fifty years or so in a period of history of quite unique prosperity. Expert demographers estimate that our present two and a half billion population will have become four billion by A.D. 2000 and six billion by A.D. 2050. These estimated increases will be fairly equally distributed among the different races and among the social classes in each. For example, one of the most rapidly increasing groups at present consists of the moderately well-to-do Americans, who are increasing at a rate faster than the peoples of India or Japan. I may say that these estimates should be regarded as cautious ones.

The first thing we may think of which might reduce the numbers is war, but most war is not nearly murderous enough to have any effect. Thus we should count as a really bad war one in which five million people were killed, but this would only set back the population increase for less than three months, and that hardly seems to matter. I doubt if even an atomic war would have any serious influence on the estimate, unless it led to such appalling destruction of both the contestants that the economy of the whole world was entirely ruined and that barbarism and starvation would ensue. There is perhaps some hope that man will be wise enough not to embark on such a war, but anyhow I shall refuse to consider it in my forecast.

Some people may feel that methods of birth control might upset the whole forecast. This is a most important matter, which must be considered. The proponents say a contraceptive may be discovered which would put in our hands the possibility of completely controlling population numbers. It is very possible that such a discovery may be made, and I hope it will, but I do not think it seriously affects the forecast. This is because of the the time-scale in human affairs. Even if we already possessed the full knowledge of what I may call the "contraceptive pill," a good deal of time would be taken in building factories to make it on a scale large enough to provide pills for the whole world population and the worldwide distribution would take some arranging; but there are other more serious troubles which would also have to be overcome.

It is hardly likely that the physiologists could be absolutely confident that such a drastic medicine would have no collateral effect at all and, to verify this, many years of experiment on a smaller scale would be necessary. For example, it would take two or three decades to verify that when the habitual users of the pill did decide to have children, those children would grow up into normal adults. It would be necessary to verify that there were no unforeseen collateral effects, such as a premature aging of the habitual user or perhaps a special liability to some disease —I may quote as a parallel the liability of people exposed to X-rays to develop cancer a good many years later.

Furthermore, there would need to be an enormous educational campaign, and the number of educators would have to be so vast that it would take all of a generation to train them and therefore two generations for them to produce their results.

On all these counts I think it is safe to say that no large-scale effects could possibly be seen under two generations or so, and therefore the contraceptive pill—which in fact we have not got yet—would have little influence in affecting the forecast for fifty years, though it might for a hundred. But things are unlikely to be even as favorable as this; there are religious doctrines that might prohibit the use of the pill and there is a tremendous stock of unreasoning emotion in such intimate matters that would make a lot of unforeseeable difficulties.

A POPULATION OF FOUR BILLION

In the light of these considerations I see no escape from the estimate that by A.D. 2000 the world population will be four billion.

It is time to turn to the other side of the Malthusian account. Malthus only thought of actual food production as the balancing item, but since his day there are a lot of other things to be included which he could not have foreseen—such things as the supply of energy and the metals which are essential for the city life which alone can carry large populations.

First, the agriculturists at the 1954 Rome Conference on Population claimed that a doubling of food production can probably be achieved, but to do so everything has got to be exactly right. There must be no creation of dust bowls by the exhaustion of poor soils, and the stores of artificial fertilizers must not be distributed freely but must be controlled so that they are only used in the places where they will give the most advantage. I am not competent to discuss this matter, but I do wonder how far this strict control will be possible.

In connection with agriculture I may refer to a thing of the recent past which is at least suggestive. Between 1947 and 1953 the world's agriculture made the most tremendous strides; in these seven years it increased by 8 percent, a truly wonderful performance, which we owe largely to the brilliant work of the scientific agriculturists. *But*—during those seven years the world's population increased not by 8 percent, but by 11 percent, so that the world was hungrier at the end than at the beginning. So, as I have said, I forecast there will be four billion people in fifty years from now, but I forecast that they will be hungrier than the two and a half billion we have now.

Now, to turn to other matters, Malthus needed only to think about agriculture, but we have to consider the provision of a lot of other things, because since his day the enormously-increased numbers can only exist by living in large cities, and these demand all sorts of equipment like good roads, railways, water supply, electricity and so on. If some of these things could not be supplied it would be quite impossible to maintain the large numbers we have. So we must add to the right-hand side of Malthus's balance sheet such things as energy and metals and consider whether the supply of these will be adequate to keep us going for the next fifty years.

THE PROSPECTS FOR ENERGY

As to energy, as far as we can see the prospects are not too bad. There are only three sources which can provide power in quantities sufficient to be important. They are the "fossil fuels" coal and oil, nuclear energy, and the direct use of sunlight. Notice that water power is not in the list; this is because the total quantity yielded, if all the rivers of the whole earth were fully exploited, would be only 12 percent or so of even the present energy developed.

At present, of course, practically all the power comes from coal and oil, and it is being used up at an ever-increasing rate. It is not possible to estimate the reserves with any great accuracy because it would be necessary to take some standard of the ease with which the coal can be won; for example, would it ever be worthwhile to mine a seam only a foot thick? But an estimate very definitely on the optimistic side predicts that the coal will all be gone in 500 years. Since it took some 500 million years to make the coal, it may be said—speaking only very loosely, of course—that we are living on our capital at the rate of a million to one. Is it surprising that we can create wonderful prosperity for a short time? Oil is won much more easily than coal, and it is expected it may at most last for a century.

The prospects for nuclear energy are good, but the construction of nuclear power stations will inevitably take a good many years. It has been estimated that at the end of 30 or 40 years something like a quarter of the power developed in Britain will come from uranium instead of coal. Even at the present rates of consumption of power this would still mean a very large demand for coal, and as the demand in fact is growing year by year, there seems little prospect of the coal situation improving. Indeed, I would not be surprised if there was going to be a rather awkward period for us in about 50 years, when the expense of winning the remaining coal has increased a good deal, while there are still not enough nuclear power stations.

These difficulties apply specially in Great Britain. In America the situation is much easier in respect to coal. It is being consumed at an almost fantastic rate here, but there would seem to be enough easily mineable coal to last you a century. I have called the rate fantastic, and this can be justified by the following consideration. In the history of the world man has burnt up a very considerable amount of coal in all, but half of this total has been burned in the United States since 1920.

FAVORABLE PROSPECTS

As far as we can judge in these rather early days there is not likely to be any shortage of uranium for many centuries, and there is always the possibility that the fusion of deuterium into helium may be made to occur slowly instead of, as now, only in the form of a super-bomb. The prospects for the supply of energy are therefore rather favorable, but it must be noticed that it may make very considerable changes in our ways of life. Nuclear power units are likely to have to be very large, and this may mean that there will have to be far fewer small units such as motorcars. This suggests that in the nuclear age the population will be concentrated in the great cities even more than it is now.

The energy arriving at the earth day by day in the form of sunlight is quite enormous, and if it could be turned into mechanical power it would supply many times over the needs of mankind. A square yard facing the sun receives energy at a rate of about a horse power, but this implies that a great area would be required in order to make any reasonable power station. It may well be that improving techniques will solve this problem, but there is certainly a long way to go. Indeed it is rather humiliating to know that at the present time the most efficient way of collecting solar energy is to plant a row of trees, let them grow, cut them down, and burn them.

If the provision of energy is not necessarily going to be a great difficulty, the same cannot be said of many other raw materials, in particular many of the metals, though even the supply of such a common thing as fresh water is going to be a formidable problem. Of course, strictly speaking, the metals, unlike coal, are indestructible; once won they can be used again and again, but in fact there is always some wastage due to wear or to actual loss, and this wastage must be allowed for. There has been the same enormous increase in the extraction of metals as of coal; in fact, of all the metal mined from the earth, half has been dug up in the last 30 years.

The possession of metals in great quantity seems to be essential for industrial development. It would appear likely that there simply is not enough of many of them, such as lead or tin or copper, to permit the underdeveloped countries to become industrialized on a scale at all equivalent to that of the highly developed ones. It is true that substitutes can often be found, but usually they will be inferior; for example, an electric transformer could be made with aluminum wires to replace the copper, but it would be less efficient. The underdeveloped countries which are trying to improve their industrial power are already handicapped in two respects. They lack capital, and they lack engineering experience, and to these difficulties must be added a third, the expected world shortage of constructional materials. So I forecast that at the end of this century industrialization will not have spread very greatly over the less developed parts of the world.

My general conclusion then is that in fifty years the population of the world will be four billion. They will be a rather hungry four billion, busily engaged in straining the resources of the earth to yield enough food, but they will not have succeeded very much in their present ambitions about becoming more industrialized.

I regard the forecast for a century with a great deal more doubt. The demographers forecast six billion for the year 2050, but my own guess is that the world will not have succeeded in yielding enough food for this, and that by then the world will have begun to go back into what I earlier called its normal state, the state in which natural selection operates by producing rather too many people, so that the excess simply cannot survive.

A GLOOMY PICTURE

I fear this is a gloomy picture, and I ought to say that there are many people who forecast quite the opposite. They are the technological enthusiasts. They claim that whenever a shortage has declared itself the technologists have produced a substitute and that things will go on forever like that. To me they do not seem to appreciate the overwhelming importance and difficulty concerning the population numbers, and that is why I must disagree with them. If they are right and I am wrong the world can look forward longer than I expect to a continuance of the present era of prosperity.

I hope that they will prove right, and that I shall be proved wrong, but I must repeat my opinion that the central problem is that of world population. I do not see any happy solution of this, but I earnestly hope that if many people face the difficulties, someone may possibly be inspired to find an acceptable solution.

FRED HOYLE

Forecasting the Future?

A NOTED ASTRONOMER TAKES ISSUE WITH SOME OF THE "DIRE PROGNOSTICATIONS" OF SIR CHARLES DARWIN.

Readers of Sir Charles Darwin's challenging essay, "Forecasting the Future," can scarcely avoid wondering whether any answer can be given to it. Indeed, I suspect Sir Charles of deliberately trying to provoke us all into offering some answer to his dire prognostications. At all events this is the effect his cheerful pessimism had on me, so I resolved to set down what counter-arguments I could think of.

First, a brief repetition of the argument itself. It is convenient to group the ideas under several headings.

1. Animal populations are governed by food supplies, the number of animals of a particular type that are alive at a given time being just the number that can be supported with the food supply available at that time. Let the food supply increase and the number of animals increases. Let the food supply decrease and the number of animals decreases, starvation being the controlling factor.

2. During the last 6000 years or so, and particularly during the last few centuries, human knowledge has developed to an astounding degree. With increasing knowledge have come improved techniques, and with improved techniques has come a sharp increase of food production. Always accompanying the increase of food production there has been an increase of human

117

population. Indeed, the rise of human population has followed the availability of food so consistently and closely that one cannot avoid the unpleasant suspicion that the human animal is responding to biological conditions in a manner not a whit different from that of other animals.

3. The argument that improvements of technique will always keep pace with the rising human population is arrant nonsense. The human population is rising so rapidly today that *if the rate is maintained,* the amount of standing room on the surface of the earth will be reduced in about 1100 years to a ration of one square yard per person; in 5000 years the mass of humanity will exceed the mass of the earth itself; while in about 11,000 years humanity will exceed the mass of the whole universe visible with the 200-inch Hale telescope.

4. The rate of increase of the human population must therefore decline. The word "must" is unqualified. What will cause the decline—starvation or a voluntary decrease of the birth rate?

5. Decline through starvation is a natural process, the natural law whereby animal populations are governed. A decline through a voluntary decision by the human species will require some powerful basis in emotion and logic if it is to compete in strength with natural law. It is to be doubted whether any such strong basis will be found.

6. Even if a voluntary limitation of the birth rate were seriously considered, it is doubtful whether it would be accepted by the whole of humanity. Those who accepted it would limit their numbers, while those who were unwilling to accept it would increase their numbers. The effect would be that those who refused limitation of numbers would automatically swallow up the others, so that in the result there would be no controlled check at all on the human population.

7. The conclusion is that the human being is an animal and that at root he lives like an animal, controlled by exactly the same natural processes as other animals. The rise of food production occasioned by improved techniques cannot continue indefinitely. We live today in an exceptional age, a Golden Age, in which for a little time the inexorable march of natural law

is not immediately apparent. Sooner or later, however, perhaps in a century, perhaps in half a dozen centuries, man will be forced to conform to the self-same conditions that the rest of the animal kingdom conforms to. Eventually he must return to a semi-bestial existence.

This is a powerful argument, but it seems to me that not all of its links are of the same strength. Points (3) and (4) are quite unassailable, point (2) is, I think, correct, point (1) I would accept with some reservation. On the other hand, point (6) seems to me to be a *nonsequitur,* and the last sentence of (5) seems open to serious question. Since the final conclusion turns on the acceptance of (5) and (6), I do not feel that the conclusion is logically compelling. It may, of course, turn out to be correct, nonetheless.

The ideas underlying point (6) would be correct under conditions of primitive technology but do not seem to me to be consistent with modern technology. A community that adjusts its population in a rational manner cannot nowadays be overwhelmed by sheer force of numbers, but only by a superior technology. And this is not likely to be possessed by an overpopulated community. Rather is the situation the other way round; an overpopulated community with large concentrations of humanity would be more vulnerable to modern weapons.

STARVATION IS NOT THE ONLY WAY

The reservation I have about point (1) is that I do not believe starvation to be the *only way* in which populations become adjusted to food supplies. I have read on good biological authority that certain species of songbirds automatically limit their populations without starvation necessarily intervening. The territory available for food is divided not into a number of units equal to the number of contending birds but into the number that can adequately provide enough food for the rearing of a brood of chicks. If the number of contenders exceeds the number of territorial units, then fighting takes place until the birds are separated into two groups, those with territory and those without. The ones with territory breed, whereas those without territory do not. In this way the birth rate is automatically governed to the availability of food, and this is done without the starvation of unsuccessful birds, since enough feeding grounds are left over to support the latter.

I mention this example at length because it comes near the crux of the whole business. It must be granted that a feedback has to exist between food supplies and population, but this feedback need not involve starvation. Starvation is a crude form of control in which the feedback mechanism operates directly on the population. If the population gets too large, individuals die, thereby reducing the population. In the case of the birds, no individuals die. The feedback is a more sensitive system in which the food supplies operate on the birth rate, which then affects the population at one stage removed, as it were. Instead of the excess of individuals dying, they simply are not born.

HUMAN FEEDBACK PROCESSES

Herein lies the root of my disagreement with Sir Charles. I think there is evidence to show that humans are susceptible to even more subtle feedback processes than are the birds. For instance, I think the fact that Sir Charles wrote his article, that I am writing this reply, that Harrison Brown wrote his book, *The Challenge of Man's Future*, are all examples of feedback. Once a man grasps the unassailable qualities of points (3) and (4), some sort of feedback along these lines becomes inevitable. Should this happen to men on a sufficiently large scale, Sir Charles will have the "strong basis" that he requires in point (5).

Of course the feedback may not happen on a large enough scale to produce important effects, but I think there are some considerable indications that it may. An appreciation of the seriousness of (3) and (4) is undoubtedly growing very rapidly; indeed, there is every reason to suspect that the growth has some similarities to a chain reaction. If this is so, then the feedback will almost certainly win out, for the reason that the characteristic multiplication time of the chain reaction (probably one or two years) is far shorter than the characteristic time of the rise of population (about 70 years).

An example of feedback can be given that has controlled the birth rate of a whole nation. During the last 30 years there has been a stability of the birth rate in Britain. This stability is governed not by starvation but by the threat of a lowered standard of living—a far more subtle feedback than is required if points (3) and (4) are to exercise their influence on the world population.

In conclusion I would like to stress that nothing that I have said is intended to minimize the problems raised by Sir Charles Darwin. These problems are in my view far more important, and lie far deeper in the fabric of civilization, than are and do the Communist-Anti-Communist issues we hear so much about in the daily paper. Mankind in its public discussions seems to have a penchant for irrelevancy. Where I do not agree with Sir Charles is in the position that because the problems are severe they are well-nigh incapable of solution.

Harrison Brown:

Probably since he was first endowed with the power of conceptual thought, man has speculated about the past, the present, and the future of his universe. He has asked himself why matter behaves as it does. He has wondered about how the stars, the earth, and the other planets originated and about what might be under the surface of the land and the sea. He has wondered whether the matter which makes up the earth has always existed or whether there was some sort of cosmic "creation." He has wondered about how life originated and whether it might exist outside the earth. He has wondered about the size of the stars and the universe. He has wondered about his destiny.

THE PHYSICAL SCIENCES

Until the physical sciences evolved to their present level, man could do little more than speculate about these problems. But so rapid have been the developments in physics, chemistry, geology, and astronomy during the last few decades that today we have achieved a real understanding of some of these aspects of our universe and at least a glimmering of an understanding of others. Most of the essays that follow have a bearing upon these problems and offer a stimulating sampling of recent work.

These essays represent, too, the wide diversity of knowledge which must be accumulated if we are to understand, even in broad outline, the universe in which we live. All of the physical sciences are involved. If we are to understand the earth, we must understand volcanoes and earthquakes. If we are to understand the solar system, we must understand the earth. Cosmic rays contribute to our knowledge of nuclear physics on the one hand and of the exterior universe on the other. Nuclear physics tells us much about stars, and from the careful study of stars we learn much about stellar evolution. All of the sciences are interrelated. Each contributes something to the others, and all contribute to our knowledge of the whole.

The life span of a human being is but an instant in time. Only about six human life spans, or sixteen generations—a negligible fraction of the duration of human existence—separate Copernicus from Einstein. But in this short interval a cosmology has evolved that dwarfs the world pictures of the ancients. To be sure, many of the cosmologies that were created by the founders of the great religions contain magnificent concepts. Yet most older cosmologies appear drab when compared with the beauty of the universe as it is revealed by modern science.

No scientist can claim to understand all of the workings of our cosmos, and it seems quite possible that scientists may never really achieve an all-embracing comprehension. Such an understanding of the *how* of things may well be like infinity—something that can be approached but never attained. Similarly it seems likely that the philosopher's quest for an understanding of the *why* of our universe may never be ended.

But in spite of our limitations we have learned a great deal during the last sixteen generations concerning the composition, structure, and motions of our solar system, the stars of our own galaxy, and the billions of other galaxies about us in the heavens. We are able to explain many features of stars on the basis of our observations of the behavior of atomic nuclei at high temperatures. We have obtained a precise measurement of the age of the solar system. We even believe that we can now say something about what happened 4600 million years ago, when our solar system, and with it the planet which gave birth to man, was born.

Within the last fifteen years there has been a dramatic change in our outlook concerning the origin of the solar system—a change that has been brought about largely by the merging of the efforts of astronomers, physicists, chemists, and geologists in a concerted attack upon the problem. This change in outlook has had major philosophical implications which markedly affect our attitudes concerning man in relation to his universe. The new philosophy, which is founded upon a reasonable basis of fact, in a sense carries to the limit a trend which was started by Copernicus when he suggested that the earth might not be the center of the universe.

As generation followed generation, we learned that indeed the earth and other planets revolve about the sun, that the sun is vastly larger than the earth, and that, as planets go, even the earth is rather small. We learned that, in relation to other stars, the sun—the new center of the human universe—is not particularly noteworthy. In size and luminosity, it is only an average star. And we learned that our sun is a part of a huge assemblage of stars that we call a galaxy and that our mother star is far from the center of this "island universe." We learned that even our own galaxy, which is separated by millions of light years from other galaxies, is not particularly noteworthy. Others are larger; others shine more brightly. And we learned further that galaxies are frequently associated with one another in "galactic clusters."

Thus our earth became a speck of matter which revolved about a larger speck of matter which was but a part of a still larger speck of matter—which was in turn dwarfed by other agglomerations of other specks of matter. And all of these— earth, sun, galaxy, and galactic cluster—were dwarfed by the seemingly infinite vastness of the universe as a whole.

On the biological side, man for countless centuries conceived of himself as a creature outside the realm of other living things. All living matter was created, he believed, for his use and pleasure. Man believed himself to have been created in the image of God.

Darwin's theory of the origin of biological species and his elucidation of the importance of the forces of natural selection resulted in a further diminution of man's opinion of the importance of man in the universe. The scientist stated that man had emerged naturally within the framework of the biological continuum. Thus man became merely another animal, sharing with other animals a speck of dust which circled another speck of dust and which, in turn, was an infinitesimally small part of the universe.

But the same science that had made man appear small and unimportant then made him appear large and important by making the planet upon which he lived appear unique. The most plausible view concerning the origin of the solar system, and the concept that was held in highest favor by most scientists until a few years ago, was that in some way the planets were born from the sun. And what caused the matter to leave the sun? Proponents of the view argued that the event must have resulted from the tidal action of a passing star.

Astronomers can observe how rapidly stars move relative to one another, and they know the distances which separate the stars. One may use this information to compute the probability of two stars' passing sufficiently close to each other to result in tidal forces of sufficient magnitude to draw matter from one of them. The result of such a calculation is that the formation of the solar system must be a highly improbable event. Indeed, it appeared unlikely that in a time of several billion years the process of disruption resulting from the close encounter of two stars could have happened more than once. It seemed probable that our solar system is unique and it was argued that, if the solar system were unique, life on earth must be unique and man must be unique.

There was something ego-satisfying about this view, and indeed the improbability of solar system formation became a major component of various mathematical "proofs" of the existence of God. But these views were shattered by a rapid succession of developments following World War II.

As a result of the collaborative efforts of chemists, physicists, geologists, and astronomers, we now know that the earth could not have been born from the sun in the simple catastrophic manner visualized by the earlier scientists. Although we by no means completely understand the mechanism of planet formation, we do understand in a general way the processes that must have been involved. In brief, it appears that the planets were formed by the condensation of gaseous matter and by subsequent accretion processes which took place while our own sun was being formed.

The real significance of these developments is that the formation of a planetary system is, in all likelihood, not an unusual event. If our present thinking is correct, there may well be somewhere between 100,000 and 10 million planetary systems within our own galaxy. Correspondingly, within the bounds of our visible universe there may well be somewhere between one million billion and 100 million billion planetary systems!

Thus, once again our own planet is dwarfed by the weight of numbers, a conclusion which obviously has tremendous philosophical implications. But is man himself necessarily dwarfed in the process?

We have already seen, in the section on the biological sciences, that life on earth probably emerged as the end result of a complicated, yet natural, series of chemical processes. If these chemical processes took place on earth, might they not have taken place elsewhere in our universe as well?

It seems likely that life requires for its emergence and perpetuation a certain minimum amount of chemical flexibility. Chemical reactions must take place, and this requires the bringing together of the proper elements in the proper environment. There must be a medium in which compounds can react with one another. The temperature cannot be too high; otherwise complicated chemical compounds will not be stable. Nor can the medium be too cold; otherwise reactions will take place too slowly.

When we examine the planets of our solar system, we find that Mercury probably cannot nurture life because it is too hot. The outer planets, Jupiter, Saturn, Uranus, and Neptune, are probably too cold. The moon has no atmosphere and no water, with the result that there can be no chemical flexibility. Venus apparently has no water, a fact which implies almost equally severe limitations.

Mars, however, has water and carbon dioxide and, as the reader will see from Frank Salisbury's essay "The Inhabitants of Mars" there is evidence that plant life of some sort exists there. If this is true, then its importance to our understanding of man's place in the universe is enormous. If life really exists on Mars, then we must discard thoughts of life's having emerged on earth as the result of an "improbable accident" and accept the proposition that, given the proper conditions, life will inevitably emerge.

Most of the millions of billions of planets in our visible universe probably possess environments that are unfavorable for the emergence of life. Some may have orbits too close to their mother stars; others may have orbits too far away. Some are probably too large and, like Jupiter, are composed mainly of large quantities of hydrogen and helium. Some are probably too small and, like the Moon, possess no medium in which chemical reactions can take place.

But it seems likely that many of these planets have conditions that are favorable—as on Earth and Mars. If only one planet in a hundred possesses favorable conditions, life in our universe must indeed be an abundant commodity. And if life in our universe is abundant—if billions of planets are endowed with it— then intelligent life may likewise be abundant.

Thus we are entering a period in which man and his home are being stripped of their uniqueness. This process may be a disturbing one to many persons, an exciting one to others. Certainly, the possibility that we may not be alone in the universe will, in the years ahead, have profound effect upon our philosophy.

And what of the future? Stars, like people, are born, live, and die. And the life which is supported by an individual star similarly must one day die. Albert G. Wilson, in "Astronomy and Eschatology," has shown that life on earth has a very long span of time ahead of it, that the destruction of life on earth by cosmic forces lies a great distance in the future. If man succeeds in avoiding his own destruction, there is the exciting prospect that many years remain for him to learn in great detail the *how* of his universe, to understand its past, and to predict its future. And perhaps one day in the distant future he may even answer the most difficult and awesome of all of the problems of philosophy—the *why*.

HUGO BENIOFF

Earthquakes

WHERE THEY COME FROM—WHY THEY OCCUR—
AND WHAT THEIR EFFECTS ARE.

California is situated within an active earthquake zone. Ever
since white man his lived here it has been subjected frequently
to large shocks. Moreover, from geological evidence we know
that this activity has been going on for millions of years and is
likely to continue for a very long time. Consequently, we who
live here must learn to get along with earthquakes. To do so
we must have knowledge about them—where they occur, what
produces them, and what their effects on human habitations are.

Earthquakes do not occur throughout the whole body of the
earth. They are absent in the core, which we believe to be
composed of liquid iron and nickel. They are also absent
throughout most of the mantle surrounding the core. All the
earthquakes which have been observed since seismographic instruments were developed have originated within the outermost
400-mile layer of the earth.

Some of the earthquakes which occur at the maximum depth
of 400 miles are quite large, but since they are at least 400
miles from the nearest man-made structure, they produce little
or no damage. The most destructive shocks are shallow, originating within a thin surface layer, not more than 27 miles in
thickness. California has only the shallow-type earthquakes.

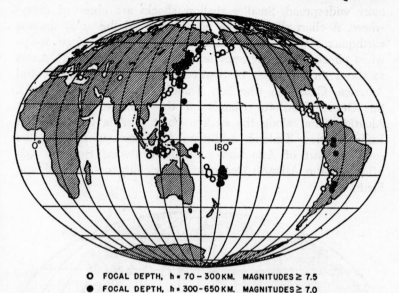

○ FOCAL DEPTH, h = 70 – 300 KM. MAGNITUDES ≥ 7.5
● FOCAL DEPTH, h = 300 – 650 KM. MAGNITUDES ≥ 7.0

Fig. 1.—World distribution of great earthquakes having focal depths from 150 to 400 miles—1904 to 1950.

The very deep earthquakes, 150 to 400 miles, are not distributed uniformly over the globe but are confined to the circumpacific arc (Fig. 1) with the exception of a single one which occurred recently in Spain. Thus, in the western hemisphere, they occur along the Pacific coasts of South America, Mexico, and Central America. There have been none on our California coast, and none along the Canadian coast. Beginning with the Aleutians, the very deep active arc continues through Kamchatka, Japan, Manchuria, the East Indies, and terminates in the southern end of the Tonga Islands near New Zealand. Earthquakes of intermediate depth (27-150 miles) occur over the same regions as the very deep ones and, in addition, along a belt extending from Southern Asia through Asia Minor and the Mediterranean region.

The distribution of the great shallow earthquakes is, in general, about the same as that of the deeper ones, but somewhat

131

more widespread. Smaller shallow shocks are observed everywhere. A chart showing the positions of all the great shallow earthquakes which have occurred on the earth since 1904—when effective seismographs became available—(Fig. 2) shows locations on the coast of South America, in Mexico, Central America, California (the San Francisco earthquake of 1906), the Queen Charlotte Islands off the coast of Canada, the Aleutians, and along the eastern coast of Asia and the East Indies to New Zealand. Additional locations appear along the southern part of Asia and continue westward through Asia Minor to the Atlantic Ocean in the vicinity of Portugal and Spain.

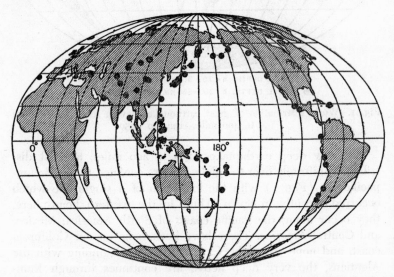

Fig. 2.—World distribution of great shallow earthquakes, magnitudes ≧8.0, from 1904 to 1950.

These great earthquakes do not occur uniformly in time but rather in alternate periods of activity and quiesence (Fig. 3). Beginning before 1904 there was a period of great activity which lasted until 1908. This was followed by a rest period of 10 years with only two earthquakes. Following this rest period an active period began, and so on up to the present date.

Peculiarly, these alternate periods of activity have decreased regularly in amplitude and duration with time. We do not know the full meaning of this behavior. It does indicate, however, that the great shallow earthquakes of the earth are related in a single global stress-strain system.

The chart shows that at the present time the active periods have become so short that the great earthquakes are occurring about as fast as the strain builds up—one great earthquake per year, approximately.

A map of all western North American earthquakes of magni-

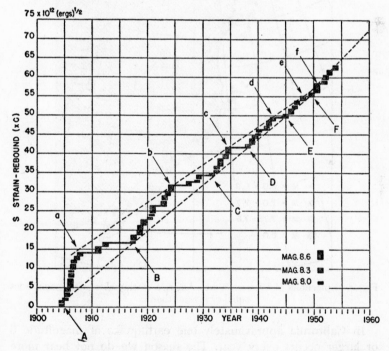

Fig. 3.—Accumulated strain release for all great shallow earthquakes, magnitude ≧8.0, 1904 to date.

tude 6 (the size of the Long Beach earthquake of 1933 and the Santa Barbara earthquake of 1925) or larger which have been instrumentally located is shown in Fig. 4. It will be noted that the epicenters are concentrated along the Pacific Coast. Actually, California and Nevada account for 95 percent of all the earthquakes in the United States.

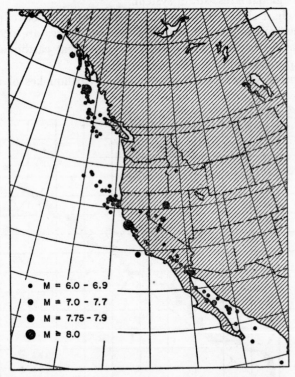

M = 6.0 - 6.9
M = 7.0 - 7.7
M = 7.75 - 7.9
M ≥ 8.0

Fig. 4.—Epicenters of Western North America earthquakes with magnitudes equal or greater than 6.

In California approximately one earthquake of magnitude 6 or larger occurs every year. The reason we do not hear more about these frequent occurrences is that the state is large and most shocks thus occur in areas of low population density.

134

Earthquakes can be produced by volcanic activity, by blasts, even by the fall of meteorites, but the large destructive quakes are believed to be produced by slipping on faults. A fault is a fracture in the crust of the earth. The forces which presumably originally produce this fracture may continue to operate for long periods of time afterward and so produce many additional slips along the original break.

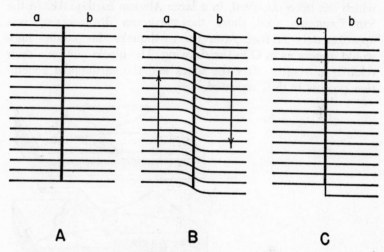

Fig. 5.—Diagram representing fault earthquake generating mechanism.

The manner in which the fault mechanism operates is shown in Fig. 5. Following an earthquake such as that of San Francisco, in 1906, a series of parallel lines drawn across the fault (as at A) will be distorted at some later date, as shown at B of the figure, indicating that the block on one side of the fault has moved relative to the one on the other side. As a result of the high pressures which exist within the earth's crust, the friction of the fault surfaces prevents slippage until the adjacent region is severely distorted.

There comes a time, however, when the stress at some point along the fault becomes greater than the friction holding the blocks together and they slip. Slip at one point increases the stress at neighboring points, and consequently the slip is propagated along the fault up to distances of several hundred miles in great earthquakes. In the San Francisco 1906 earthquake the segment of the fault along which the slip occurred was approximately 180 miles in length, extending from some position under the ocean off Point Arena in the north to San Juan Bautista in the south. The amount of slip at any point may vary from a few inches in a small earthquake to some 47 feet—the maximum which has been observed, in a large Alaskan earthquake. In the San Francisco 1906 shock the maximum displacement was approximately 21 feet. After the earthquake the parallel lines would appear as in C in the drawing. The blocks continue their relative movement after the shock and the earthquake generation process is thus repeated.

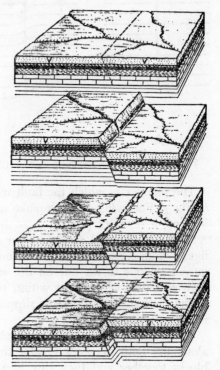

Fig. 6.—Diagram representing three principal types of faults.

The three principal types of faults are illustrated in Fig. 6. The upper drawing shows the fracture just before slip has occurred. The second from the top represents the type known as a normal fault (for reasons unknown to the writer). The fault plane is inclined to the vertical and the overlying block moves downward relative to the underlying block. The 1954 Fairview Peak, Nevada, earthquake occurred on a fault of this type. In a reverse fault, represented by the third diagram from the top in Fig. 6, the overlying block moves up relative to the other one.

In the third type of fault, shown in the drawing at the bottom, the blocks slip horizontally. This type is characteristic of California's great San Andreas fault, which generated the San Francisco earthquake of 1906 and a similar one in the southern part of the state in 1857. It is the principal fault of California. With its branches it extends from a point off the coast of Oregon (Fig. 7) through the California coast in the region of Point Arena, passing very near the city of San Francisco, and continues on through Gorman, Palmdale, Cajon Pass, San Gorgonio Pass, and the eastern edge of the Coachella Valley. It ends near the southern tip of the Gulf of California.

The 1857 shock was probably the first great California earthquake which occurred since white man has lived here. The active segment extended from a point north of Gorman to some point near the Mexican border. In 1857 this region was thinly populated, and the evidence we have for the size of the earthquake is not very extensive. However, in the vicinity of Gorman a rancher reported that his circular corral became S-shaped after the earthquake. This indicates that the slip was of the same order of magnitude as that which produced the San Francisco earthquake of 1906. In fact, we feel rather confident from this and other evidence that the 1857 shock produced violent shaking throughout the whole southern section of the state.

Another fault north of Mojave, known as the Garlock fault, takes off from the San Andreas fault in the vicinity of Tejon Pass and extends at least 150 miles eastward. This fault has not

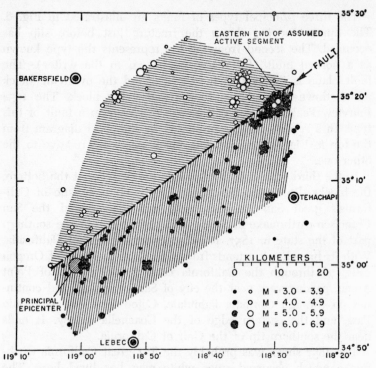

Fig. 7.—Map showing principal faults of California.

been active in recent years, but the geological evidence indicates that it is very much alive. The San Jacinto fault, which is actually a branch of the San Andreas, has produced destructive earthquakes in the last 50 years. The small Inglewood fault was responsible for the 1933 earthquake in Long Beach. The White Wolf fault produced the Kern County earthquakes of July, 1952.

In 1872 there was a great earthquake on the Owens Valley fault in the vicinity of Lone Pine and Bishop. This earthquake shook down nearly all of the buildings at Lone Pine and killed a number of people.

The motion of the San Andreas fault is such that the oceanic side is moving north relative to the continental side. Measure-

138

ments by the U. S. Coast and Geodetic Survey indicate that the rate of this movement is roughly two inches per year. If this movement continues at a uniform rate, Los Angeles will be opposite San Francisco in ten million years. If the two inches a year is approximately correct, we may expect the stress in this fault to build up at such a rate as to repeat the slip along a given segment about once per century and a quarter. A slip of the southern segment similar to that which produced the 1857 shock may thus be expected to occur any time within the next 25 or 50 years.

The San Francisco earthquake of 1906 liberated a thousand times as much energy as the Long Beach earthquake in 1933,

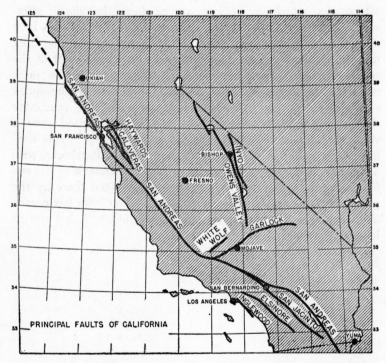

Fig. 8.—Map showing epicenters of principal earthquake and aftershocks of Kern County earthquake of 1952.

but it was liberated over a much larger area, so that the intensity in the regions of maximum shaking was not very much greater. We do not know definitely the total off-set on the San Andreas fault which has accumulated since it first started slipping, but a recent paper by Hill and Dibblee indicates that it may be as much as 350 miles.

In the 1952 earthquakes in Kern County faulting began at a point near Wheeler Ridge at a depth of about 12 miles (Fig. 8). The slipping reached the surface in something like three seconds and moved northeastward along the fault for a distance of approximately 36 miles to the vicinity of Caliente in a matter of about 16 seconds.

Every earthquake of any size is followed by a number of aftershocks, which we believe are produced by elastic after-working in the rock. If a straight piece of wood or metal is bent and held fast for an instant and then released, it will fling back most of the way quickly, but there will be a small part of the recovery which takes place slowly. Rocks behave in this same manner. The principal shock is thus produced by the quick elastic recovery and the aftershocks represent the remaining slow creep recovery. Aftershocks may be distributed over a wide area adjacent to the fault (as shown in Fig. 7) as they have been in Kern County. It was one of these aftershocks, with a magnitude of only 5½, which occurred close enough to Bakersfield to cause greater damage than was produced there by the principal shock. In some instances aftershock activity has ceased in a matter of two or three days, and in others it has run as long as three years.

FRANK PRESS

Volcanoes, Ice, and Destructive Waves

RESEARCHERS ARE STILL INVESTIGATING THE EFFECTS OF A
NATURAL EXPLOSION THAT OUTDID THE HYDROGEN BOMB.

The newspapers in recent months carried dispatches about the
detonation of a hydrogen bomb in the megaton range. This was
the largest man-made, or artificial, explosion ever achieved.
Impressive as this was, however, one of nature's explosions still
transcends all of man's attempts in this field to date—the explosion of the volcano Krakatoa which took place in the Sunda
Strait on August 27, 1883. Not all of the phenomena associated
with this explosion are understood even today, nearly 75 years
later. Fortunately for modern students of Krakatoa phenomena,
the data are readily available in the form of a detailed report
prepared by a committee of the Royal Society appointed soon
after the explosion.

Krakatoa lies almost in the middle of the Sunda Strait, a
narrow, shallow body of water, with an average depth of about
200 feet, which ties the Indian Ocean to the China Sea. The
volcano was in a period of relative inactivity prior to May, 1883.
Gas and steam issued from a few scattered vents, but in May
a new series of violent eruptions began. Typical of these eruptions, as the old books describe them, was a flaming region
where the boiling lava poured down the sides, and a tremendous
cloud of steam and volcanic ash that went high into the atmos-

phere, producing rain and severe electric storms in the vicinity of the volcano. Pumice and ash filled the Sunda Strait, and ships had difficulty cruising there. As the eruptions became more and more severe the strait was cloaked in darkness even in midday as clouds formed by a combination of steam, mud and water blotted out the sun. There was a rainfall of hot mud and soot which fell on the decks of nearby ships, until the crews had to use their sea pumps to play water on sails and decks to remove the hot sulphurous materials that came down from the sky.

It is only a matter of conjecture at this time as to why Krakatoa exploded the way it did. Volcanoes erupt in different ways. They erupt through fissures that occur in the earth, through which lava flows freely and forms plateaus such as we have in the Pacific Northwest. At the opposite extreme are the eruptions which result in cones with very steep sides, formed by falling cinders. Severe explosions are rarely associated with a volcano; in fact, Krakatoa represents the only known occurrence of a cataclysmic explosion in which a tremendous amount of energy was released almost instantaneously.

THE REASON WHY

Why this occurred at Krakatoa is not known. Conjecture has it that the ready access of sea water surrounding the island was responsible—not so much in forming superheated steam as it floated into vents and tissues, but in entering the crater and forming a cap by chilling and solidifying the lava. This did not stop the volcanic activity below, of course, which continued with the generation of steam and gas. Pressure was gradually built up, while the cap prevented its release. Then, at one stroke, the cap was impulsively blown out. The explosion was so tremendous that it almost entirely eviscerated the volcano, and it profoundly altered the surface and submarine topography in the surrounding region. A vast quantity of solid material was blown into the atmosphere, the coarse components falling locally, creating new banks and shoals in the Sunda Strait. The lighter material went into the atmosphere and formed clouds. These clouds were so extensive that at Batavia, more than 100 miles away, there was almost complete darkness at noon. The rain which fell was essentially a rain of mud—the drops consisting of 90 percent mud and 10 percent water. Associated with the mud-fall were severe electric storms. It was quite a frightening spectacle.

The fine dust went high into the atmosphere—so high as to reach air currents which disseminated the particles throughout the world. Unusual atmospheric optical effects appeared. Brilliant sunsets with unexpected hues, blue-colored moons, and rings and halos around the sun and moon were observed throughout the world.

The main loss of life which was connected with the eruption of Krakatoa resulted from destructive sea waves which were excited by the final explosion. Some 36,000 inhabitants of the adjacent coastal areas lost their lives in 100-foot waves that came without warning. (But, strangely enough, ships in the Sunda Strait close to the volcano were not harmed.)

As is the case with most tidal disturbances, it was the local effect of the coast line which funneled the destructive waves into certain areas. The Krakatoa tidal wave was not unlike the earthquake-generated sea waves which occasionally visit the coasts of South America and Japan. One theory has it that the earthquake initiates a submarine avalanche which runs down the continental slopes into the deep ocean, providing enough push to set the big tidal wave into motion.

CALIFORNIA TIDAL WAVE

California is fortunate in not having tidal waves associated with its earthquakes—though this is not entirely true because, in 1812, one of our big earthquakes was accompanied by a tidal wave that may have reached a height of 50 feet at Ventura and at Gaviota, and about 30 to 35 feet at Santa Barbara. There was not much habitation in that area then, and the reports that we have are quite meager, but if it happened today, of course, tremendous destruction would occur.

Once excited, a tidal wave crosses the ocean at a very definite

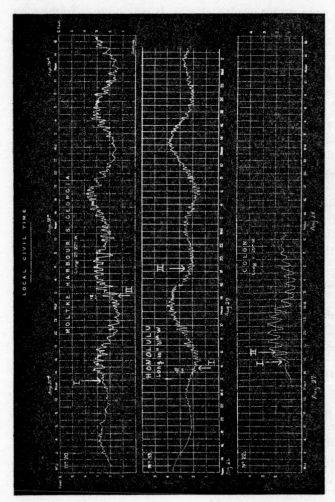

Fig. 1.—Tide gauge records from South Georgia, Honolulu, and Colon showing Krakatoa sea waves superimposed on the normal tides. Arrows indicate arrival of first and second atmospheric waves.

144

speed (given by the square root of gh, where g is the acceleration of gravity and h is the depth of the water). Tidal waves sometimes traverse the ocean many times. Earthquakes have been known to send them across the Pacific to another continent, where they are reflected and returned to the continent from which they started. These are by far the most destructive tidal waves.

Another variety is that associated with a storm. This is the kind of wave that did such damage on the East Coast in 1955, along with the Edna and Hazel hurricanes. This wave is associated with the low pressure area and the winds of the hurricane moving on the shore. When these arrive at a time of normal high tide, the excess above high tide produces an inundation on the coast line. This is not so much a wave coming in and going out as it is a general rise of the sea level that lasts from 6 to 24 hours.

The Krakatoa tidal wave was different. The explosion, the debris coming down, and its impact on the water—all of these together produced the tidal wave.

One of the most important features, scientifically, of the Krakatoa explosion was the sea wave which reached remote places throughout the world. These waves were only one or two feet high—too small to cause any damage—but of great significance because of their mechanism of propagation. Our knowledge of these comes from records made by tide gauges which were operating in important harbors. It is very important for shipping to measure the tides precisely so that ships can know the best time to come into harbor, the best time to tie up, and to sail. It was especially important, of course, in those days when so much depended on wind. Fortunately, the tide gauges of 1883 were sufficiently well designed to provide fairly good records of the Krakatoa waves. Thus we have instrumental data for the Krakatoa sea waves from such widely separated places as Honolulu, San Francisco, Colon, South Georgia, and English Channel ports.

Another significant phenomenon associated with the explosion of Krakatoa was the atmospheric waves. We would expect an explosion of this sort to make a big sound—and it did; in fact, it was probably the biggest sound that was ever created, that we know of. It was as if there was an explosion in New York and the sound was heard in Los Angeles. Audible sounds, not unlike distant cannonading, were reported from as far as central Australia and India. The sub-audible atmospheric pressure pulse was detected by barographs on each of four passages around the earth. The fact that these early instruments were able to detect the wave after it had travelled some 75,000 miles testifies to the strength of the explosion.

One feature of the Krakatoa sea wave remained unexplained until very recently. The wave that reached the English Channel had to go around Africa and travel up the Atlantic Ocean. The wave that reached Colon had, further, to cross an effective bar-

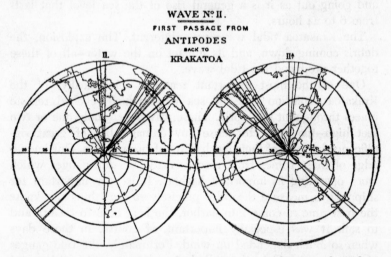

WAVE Nº II.

FIRST PASSAGE FROM

ANTIPODES

BACK TO

KRAKATOA

Fig. 2.—Atmospheric waves sent out by Krakatoa explosion made at least four passages around the earth. Diagram shows wave front of aerial disturbance after first passage through Antipodes. Times noted are in hours after zero hours, GCT, August 27, 1883.

rier formed by the Antilles. The wave that came to San Francisco could not have gone by a direct route because of the barrier formed by the East Indies; in order to explain its arrival it was necessary to postulate a path involving a detour below Australia.

Even if these unlikely paths are accepted, the observed travel times of the waves correspond to velocities that are inconsistent with the known depths of the ocean. Thus, the Krakatoa sea waves that reached widely separated parts of the world presented such a problem that most investigators came to doubt their connection with the explosion. The only explanation that could be offered was the unlikely one that local earthquakes, occurring coincidentally, produced the local sea waves. This basically untenable explanation of the Krakatoa sea waves remained with us until very recently.

ICE PROVIDES A CLUE

Oddly enough, it was work on ice that finally gave us a clue to the mechanism of propagation of the Krakatoa sea waves. Several years ago, together with colleagues at Columbia University and the Air Force Cambridge Research Center, I worked on ice—in the form of floating sheets, as it occurs in northern lakes or in the Arctic Ocean. Our interest in floating ice was stimulated by an Air Force problem—that of finding a method by which planes can determine the ice thickness in order to know whether it is safe to land or not. We thought of all sorts of fancy electronic schemes to use in the solution of the ice-landing problem, and in the very early days of this project we had some weirdly complicated contraptions—all of which were in sharp contrast to the simple solution found by a few Arctic pilots. They just bounce their planes off the ice without losing flying speed, then circle around and examine it. If the ice has a hole or a crack in it, they know it isn't thick enough. With the modern trend towards electronic methods, however, such a simple scheme never had a chance for wide adoption.

Our first serious approach to this problem involved the use of elastic waves transmitted through the ice. We conceived the idea of parachuting a small telemetering seismograph to the ice so that elastic waves excited by a small bomb could be detected in the airplane. We started experimenting directly

147

on floating ice by exploding small charges and detecting the resultant elastic waves with small microphones—geophones—placed on the ice surface at distances of several thousand feet from the explosion. Explosions in the ice, or below it, gave the expected results of flexural vibrations which are characterized by a gradual variation of frequency and phase velocity with travel time.

To avoid the trouble of digging shot-holes in the ice, several tests were made in which the charges were detonated on the surface. Much to our surprise, the character of the resultant vibrations was profoundly altered. The geophones detected a train of constant-frequency vibrations in which the phase velocity was equal to the speed of sound in air. In other words, we inadvertently demonstrated in this experiment that an explosion in the air can produce significant elastic waves in the ground of a special kind—in that the phase velocity of these waves in the ground is the speed of sound in the air.

AIR WAVE AND SEA WAVE

So the tidal waves from the Krakatoa explosion were not tidal waves in the usual sense, but were excited by the great air wave as it swept across the ocean adjacent to the tide gauge stations. Indeed, a check on the arrival time of the Krakatoa air and sea waves at a number of widely separated locations shows that this is the only plausible mechanism.

Thus the ice work, completely unrelated, and performed for an entirely different purpose, provided the key to the unexplained sea wave from Krakatoa. Another clue was provided by an equally unrelated research project.

This part of our work began when the New York *Times* published a news dispatch concerning a disturbance which occurred on Lake Michigan on the morning of June 26, 1954. About a dozen people were fishing from docks in the vicinity of Chicago. The weather was clear at the time. Suddenly a wave appeared out of nowhere and swept seven people to their death.

This unique event was all the more peculiar since Lake Michigan is located in a non-seismic area and the weather was clear.

148

Why should a destructive sea wave, with an amplitude of 10 feet, suddenly appear and wash all of these people into the lake?

A COUPLING MECHANISM

It occurred to us that this might be another example of the coupling mechanism we found in our ice studies, which so well explained the Krakatoa wave. We surmised that an atmospheric pressure disturbance swept across the lake with just the right velocity to excite a destructive sea wave, and an examination of the meteorological records showed this to be the case. A pressure pulse did indeed occur an hour before the accident, and its velocity was the critical one for this part of Lake Michigan— 65 miles an hour. Fortunately, though atmospheric pressure disturbances occur frequently, very few travel with this high velocity.

We have seen how three apparently unrelated phenomena are tied together by a common mechanism. In one sense we have here an argument for broadness in science, for had we not known about the Krakatoa problem, our ice work could have been simply an interesting experiment, performed for a very special purpose. As it turned out—not only could the special purpose be satisfied, but a fundamental geophysical mechanism could be demonstrated.

JAMES M. KENDALL

Hypersonic Research at Caltech

STUDIES OF HOW AIR FLOWS AROUND A BODY AT SPEEDS
"FASTER THAN SUPERSONIC" KEEP RESEARCH AHEAD OF
THE EVER-GROWING NEEDS FOR KNOWLEDGE.

Pioneering work in one of the newest phases of aerodynamics is being carried forward at Caltech's Guggenheim Aeronautical Laboratory by a research group under the direction of Dr. Clark B. Millikan and Prof. Lester Lees. The group is investigating, both experimentally and theoretically, how air flows around a body in the hypersonic speed regime. Literally, this means "faster than supersonic" and is arbitrarily taken to be Mach 5 and higher. The group is currently operating two hypersonic wind tunnels, one of which has achieved flow at Mach 11, or 11 times the speed of sound.

The reason for the extensive research program is the rapidly growing need for fundamental knowledge about hypersonic flow to be used in the design of high-speed vehicles. The United States now has many types of guided missiles which are capable of high Mach-number flight. As early as the spring of 1949, a two-stage rocket consisting of a V-2 and a Bumper WAC attained a Mach number of about 7.5 during tests at White Sands. As newer missiles are designed, aerodynamic data at ever higher Mach numbers are needed. For example, a long-range ballistic

150

rocket of 4000 miles range would require a speed corresponding to Mach 13 at the end of burning, and a rocket designed to escape from the earth would require about Mach 35 at the end of burning. But the hypersonic program at Caltech is definitely not concerned with the design of missiles or space stations. The models tested are not futuristic shapes; they are simple cones, spheres and wedges, because the information obtained from these is more basic.

Hypersonic flow differs from low-speed flow in several ways, many of which can only be regarded as disadvantageous to high-speed flight. One of these is extreme aerodynamic heating. Transfer of heat to a body surface is brought about on the region near the forward parts of the surface by rapid compression of the air as the body pierces the atmosphere. The after parts of the surface are heated by friction as the air flows over the surface, even though air is only slightly viscous. It so happens that these two processes produce nearly identical final temperatures, but the rate of heat transfer is in general widely different at different parts of the surface. The final temperature depends mostly on the Mach number of the flow.

By way of illustration, two missiles sustaining flight at Mach 5 and 10 respectively, on a day when the air temperature is 70°F, are heated to 2650° F and 10,600°F. Because steel melts at about 2600°F, it is quite evident that high-speed missiles can withstand flights of only short duration so that time does not permit heating to the equilibrium temperature. Flight time decreases, however, as speed goes up, and a missile traveling vertically upward from sea level at Mach 5 would remain in the earth's atmosphere less than 10 seconds.

PRESSURE DISTRIBUTION

A second unfortunate effect is that the pressure distribution about a body in high-speed flight is highly unsymmetrical fore and aft, so that a large drag results. High pressures occur on the nose of the body as it pushes aside the air in much the same fashion as a nail penetrates wood, while parts of the surface behind the thickest section of the body experience virtual vacuum, because it is difficult for the air to accelerate sidewards fast enough to follow the surface contour.

The power used to drive the body forward against the drag force due to the pressure is converted to heat by the dissipative action of the shock waves produced—as shown in Fig. 1.

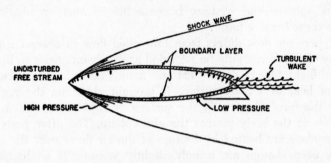

Fig. 1.—Shock wave patterns and growth of boundary layer on a body in hypersonic flow. The drag results from the pressures and from the boundary layers.

The shock waves are the interface of the lower pressures of the undisturbed free stream and the high pressures produced by the motion. These waves extend with decreasing strength to great distances from the body, and their action is to deflect the air outward as the body contour passes by. It is of importance that the higher the Mach number, the closer the shock waves lie to the surface, and correspondingly the stronger they become. These changes produce subtle effects which are peculiar to hypersonic speeds.

For hypersonic studies, as with most other phases of aerodynamics, the basic instrument of experimental research is the wind tunnel. In 1885, Horatio Phillips used the first aerodynamic tunnel for experiments, and since that time tunnels have become ever more extensively used. The justification for wind-tunnel testing is usually a matter of economy in the form of reduction of design costs. At the present time, the development of a new aircraft requires a vast amount of research, the cost of which may well run into millions of dollars and take many months.

The wind tunnel, wherein scale models are tested, offers a means of reducing time and costs and offers to hypersonic research, in particular, certain ease of gathering data.

SIMILARITY PARAMETERS

The comparison between data obtained in a tunnel and that needed for full-scale application is made on the basis of so-called similarity parameters. These are dimensionless numbers which depend on various important physical quantities, such as the density, viscosity, and speed of the air. The two most important of these parameters are the Mach number and the Reynolds number. The Mach number is the ratio of the air speed to the speed of sound. The Reynolds number depends on the viscosity, density, and speed of the air and on the length of the body. This number, in a sense, provides a certain measure of all processes which depend on viscous effects, such as heat transfer rate and surface or skin friction.

This notion of similarity parameters is expressed by saying that the coefficient of drag of a body, for example, is a function of Mach number and Reynolds number, and if these two are adjusted to be the same in the tunnel as in the desired free-stream conditions, then the value of coefficient of drag measured is the correct one. It is on the basis of this similarity that one is able to use wind-tunnel measurements to predict full-scale performance.

The experimental facilities of the Caltech hypersonic group center around two tunnels referred to as Legs 1 and 2, both with 5-by-5-inch test sections. The principal part of a hypersonic tunnel is the set of contoured blocks of steel which comprise the nozzle. High pressure air enters the nozzle at a low Mach number, and when it gets to the narrowest part, which is known as the throat, it has attained Mach 1.

When air moves at supersonic speeds the familiar principle of "the larger the area, the slower the flow speed" is reversed. Thus the air is accelerated by a difference in pressure until it reaches a final high Mach number and a low pressure at the widest part of the nozzle, the test section.

153

As the air expands in going from the high to the low pressure, the temperature drops very sharply; for example, by a factor of 6 for Mach 5 and by a factor of 21 for Mach 10. Also, the speed of sound, which depends on temperature, goes down correspondingly, so that high Mach numbers may be produced with somewhat lower air speeds than might seem necessary at first thought. The actual air speed in Leg 2 operating at Mach 11 is about 3000 miles per hour.

HEAT AND HIGH MACH NUMBERS

To prevent its temperature from dropping below the liquefaction point, the air must first be heated. It is this heating that places the limitation on producing higher Mach numbers in wind tunnels. A steam heat exchanger raises the temperature of the air supply of Leg 1 to 300°F, and a 300-kilowatt electrical heater raises the temperature of the Leg 2 air supply to 1100°F, so that the temperature at the test section of either tunnel is not lower than −385°F, which is approximately the temperature of liquefaction. After the air passes the test section, a series of shock waves slows the air to low speeds, and simultaneously the temperature returns to that to which it was initially heated. The air must then be cooled by a water heat-absorber before it can be returned to the compressors.

When either tunnel is run without heating the supply air, the air becomes so cold that it condenses into tiny droplets of liquid air, which look like fog if illuminated by an intense beam of light passed into the tunnel through a window. No satisfactory comparison between data of condensed air flows and single-phase air flows has been obtained; most experiments, therefore, require the use of the air heaters.

FLOW CONDITIONS

The contours of the nozzle blocks are of an exact shape which depends on the desired Mach number. The specific shape produces uniform flow conditions across the height of the tunnel at the test sections for only the one Mach number the nozzle was designed for. However, because the Mach number

154

produced by a nozzle depends only on the height ratio of the throat and the test section, one may vary the Mach number by changing the throat height. The flow conditions across the test section height will still remain acceptably uniform for a fairly wide range of Mach numbers. The throat height for Leg 1, which normally operates at Mach 5.8, is .080 inches; for Leg 2, operating at Mach 8, it is .020 inches. Because the nozzle throat is so narrow for hypersonic flow, the rate of flow of air through it is correspondingly low, and consequently the power required to drive the compressors is not excessive. The 16 compressors, comprising 7 stages of compression, are driven by electric motors of about 1000 horsepower total.

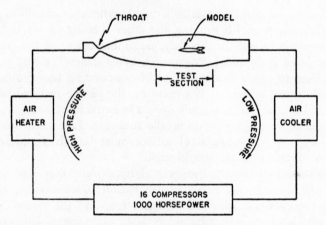

Fig. 2.—Components of a hypersonic wind tunnel system. The wind tunnel, in which scale models are tested, offers a means of reducing time and costs in the development of a new aircraft.

As previously mentioned, the Mach number produced by a hypersonic tunnel depends only on the area ratio of throat to test section, and not on the pressure available. However, to keep the test section pressure at a realistic value in comparison with conditions a missile might meet, the supply air pressure is elevated. The supply pressure of both Legs 1 and 2 may be raised to 1000 pounds per square inch. In spite of this compression, the pressure falls to a hundredth of atmospheric pressure or less at the test section.

Observation of the flow over the model being tested, and the shock-wave configuration, is made possible by the use of a Schlieren apparatus. The Schlieren employs a beam of parallel rays of light from a mercury vapor arc which is passed through the test section of the tunnel, illuminating the model. The variations of air density in the regions of the model and of the shock waves refract the light, thus causing an increase or decrease of illumination in the image formed on the ground glass or photographic plate used for observation.

OPERATING SCHEDULES

Tunnel running time is scheduled, whenever possible, so that while one tunnel is running, the other is being instrumented and prepared to run. In this way, maximum usage of the compressor plant is obtained. Preparation takes somewhat longer in Leg 2 than in Leg 1, because the higher operating temperatures pose additional problems. For example, the plastic medical tubing used for connecting pressure probes in Leg 1 must be replaced by stainless steel hypodermic needle tubing in Leg 2. All joints made with this stainless steel tubing must be silver-soldered, because ordinary solder would melt.

There are two principal aspects of hypersonic flow that one may wish to study: the pressure distribution about a body, with its corresponding shock-wave configuration; and the viscous effects, which are known as boundary layer phenomena. However, the pressure distribution is already well understood as a result of the more classical compressible-flow theory. In fact, the shock-wave equations were deduced as early as 1870. Consequently, most hypersonic research is currently directed toward an understanding of boundary layer phenomena, which are of very great interest.

BOUNDARY LAYER

The boundary layer is a layer of air that clings to a surface because of the viscosity of the air. It is responsible for both

156

the viscous drag and the aerodynamic heating and may take two forms: laminar or turbulent. In the laminar form the air within it flows smoothly over the surface, and the speed varies in an orderly fashion between the surface and the outer edge of the boundary layer. On models in the tunnel, the laminar boundary layers get as thick as an eighth of an inch. In the turbulent form the flow in the boundary layer is highly irregular. It is not difficult to imagine that this chaotic flow produces more drag and heating than the streamlined laminar flow.

It is observed that as a surface moves through the air, a laminar layer forms at the front and extends to a rearward position which depends upon, among other things, the Reynolds number and the surface roughness. At this position, the flow in the boundary layer begins to be turbulent, and after another length, called the transition region, it is fully developed as a turbulent layer.

TURBULENCE, DRAG AND HEATING

Among various problems recently investigated in the hypersonic tunnels is that of how much the occurrence of turbulence changes the drag and heating, and what influences affect transition. Using a flat plate model which had a small element of its surface connected to a force balance, direct measurements of skin friction were made. The boundary layer at the measuring element was normally laminar, but could be made turbulent by injecting air through a series of small holes in the plate surface located across the width of the plate near its leading edge. It was found that when transition occurred, the skin friction increased 4 or 5 times. However, it was noted that the laminar boundary layer showed much less tendency to become turbulent at hypersonic Mach numbers than at lower speeds. The result of this behavior is that a missile would have a larger laminar boundary layer region at high speeds than at low, and hence not so high a viscous drag as predicted by lower speed measurements.

Another investigation has been concerned with the effect of the closeness of the shock wave to the boundary layer at the leading edge of a flat plate. It has been found that for a short distance rearward of the leading edge, the high pressure behind the shock wave influences the manner in which the boundary layer builds up, and produces an accompanying increase of skin friction and heat transfer. While this may sound like a matter of only academic interest, it is of importance to an understanding of the high heat-transfer conditions near the nose of a missile.

An investigation currently being made is concerned with a method of cooling a surface exposed to hypersonic flows in an attempt to overcome the adverse effects of aerodynamic heating. The surface to be cooled is made of a porous material, so that a coolant gas may be ejected outward through the surface by pressure. It acts, in a sense, as a heat-insulator. To be studied are the effectiveness of the method and its influence on transition.

The group is using two other means for producing high Mach-number flows: a shock tube, and a helium tunnel. The shock tube (as shown in the diagram, Fig. 3) essentially consists of

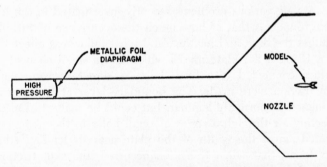

Fig. 3.—The shock tube is also a means for producing high Mach-number flows. It is a steel tube, closed at one end and leading into a nozzle at the other. A diaphragm closes off one end of the tube, and high pressure air is pumped into this chamber. When the diaphragm is broken by puncturing, the nozzle produces high temperature flows at about Mach 6.

a steel tube several feet long, closed at one end and leading into a nozzle at the other. A length of the tube near the closed end is made into a compartment by closing off with a diaphragm of metallic foil, and high pressure air is pumped into this chamber.

When the diaphragm is burst by puncturing, a shock wave followed by a supersonic flow rushes down the tube until it reaches the nozzle. There it expands, just as in the wind tunnel, and produces flows of about Mach 6. The flow lasts only a few thousandths of a second, so that as it arrives at the model located in the nozzle, it must be observed by high-speed photography. The shock tube has as its advantage temperatures more nearly like those encountered in free flight conditions, rather than the temperatures of about $-385°F$ in the wind tunnels.

HELIUM TUNNEL

The helium tunnel now undergoing testing is designed to produce flows of Mach 20. The helium tunnel, like the wind tunnel, produces high Mach numbers by expanding the gas in a nozzle. The advantage of helium over air is that its liquefaction temperature is so low that condensation does not occur, even without heating. The helium comes in steel cylinders from a commercial supplier, and although the tunnel exhausts three such cylinders in a matter of minutes, much valuable information about the shock-wave pattern and the pressure distribution on a model will be obtained.

While the projects that have been discussed are of an experimental nature, it should be realized that theoretical research receives equal emphasis. Because there is strong coordination of the two types of work, experiments are frequently suggested by analytical studies, and theory always modifies experiment when possible. Conversely, theoretical work many times depends upon experiment to guide it in the formulation of the problem.

The hypersonic program at Caltech's Guggenheim Aeronautical Laboratory, sponsored by Army Ordnance and the Air Force, is part of a long-range program designed to put research ahead of the ever-growing needs for knowledge imposed by the high-speed flight of the future.

LYMAN FRETWELL

Cosmic Rays at the North Pole

COSMIC RAYS HAVE BEEN STUDIED AT THE EARTH'S SURFACE,
AT THE BOTTOMS OF LAKES AND MINES, AND HIGH IN THE
ATMOSPHERE. NOW CALTECH RESEARCHERS ARE STUDYING
THEM AT THE NORTH GEOMAGNETIC POLE.

Cosmic rays are invisible but powerful charged particles that
constantly bombard the earth's surface. They are so numerous
that at sea level about 10 particles will pass through a person
each second. Their energy is so great that they are found even
at the bottom of the deepest mines, having penetrated hundreds of feet of rock.

The most powerful of these rays has a thousand billion times
as much energy as is released from a single uranium atom in an
atom bomb explosion. Our biggest accelerators today produce
particles of about five billion electron volts, but cosmic rays
have energies as high as a billion billion electron volts. In fact,
the energy reaching the earth in the form of cosmic rays is
roughly equal to that reaching the earth as starlight (excluding
our own sun, of course). Geological evidence indicates that cosmic rays have continued their bombardment of the earth for at
least 35,000 years, and studies of meteorites indicate that they
have been bombarded by cosmic rays for hundreds of millions
of years.

Cosmic rays have been studied, however, only for about the
last 50 years, and Millikan, Anderson, Pickering, and Neher

at Caltech have figured prominently in much of this work. Cosmic rays have been studied at the earth's surface, at the bottoms of lakes and mines, and high in the atmosphere by means of airplanes, balloons, and rockets. In recent years Dr. H. V. Neher, Caltech professor of physics, has been studying them at the north geomagnetic pole.

The particles originally entering the earth's atmosphere from outer space are known as primary cosmic rays. But very few of these primaries ever reach the earth's surface; they interact with the atoms in the earth's atmosphere, producing other particles known as secondaries. The primaries are known to consist of about 88 percent protons (hydrogen nuclei), 10 percent alpha-particles (helium nuclei), and the remaining 2 percent heavier nuclei such as oxygen, nitrogen, carbon, and on up to at least iron, following roughly the abundance of the elements in the stars as determined by astronomers. This might lead one to wonder if cosmic rays originate in the stars. Some cosmic rays are in fact known to come from rare solar flares, but the majority do not seem to originate in the sun. Just where they do come from and how nature accelerates them to such high energies remains a problem to be solved.

Studies of individual cosmic ray particles in Wilson cloud chambers have resulted in the discovery of the positron, of mesons, and of many other particles believed to relate to the nucleus and what holds it together. Studies of this type have established cosmic rays as a source of particles of extremely high energy, through the use of which fundamental nuclear processes can be examined—just as they are with a high energy particle accelerator.

No less important for our knowledge of nature is our understanding of the cosmic ray particles themselves, and their effects upon our atmosphere and upon us. Much is to be learned from studying large groups of particles rather than individual particles; this is usually done by means of ionization chambers and Geiger or scintillation counters.

One of the properties of cosmic radiation is the so-called latitude effect, which describes the variation in the energy and intensity of cosmic rays with geomagnetic latitude. The earth's magnetic field interacts with cosmic rays approaching the earth just as a magnet will act on any charged particle passing near it. This makes the particle move in a curved path, the radius of the curve being smaller as the energy is less. Thus a particle coming toward the earth will be deflected and may even be sent back into space if it does not have sufficient energy to penetrate to the earth's surface. This bending effect is least at the geomagnetic poles and greatest at the equator (in fact, at the equator a particle must have an energy of at least 10 to 12 billion electron volts in order to reach the earth's surface). Thus, studying cosmic rays in different places seems to be such a good way to locate the geomagnetic poles and equator that a plane is now being equipped to do just this.

Only at the geomagnetic poles can cosmic rays of low energy come near reaching the earth—and even there, only to the top of the earth's atmosphere. It is to study these low-energy cosmic rays at high altitudes that Dr. Neher has been making trips during the past few years to the region of the north geomagnetic pole. In the summers of 1951, 1954, and 1955 he made trips to northern Greenland, where his main base of operations was Thule, a small spot in the northwest corner of Greenland only a few hundred miles from the north geomagnetic pole. In 1955 Neher made all his cosmic ray observations at Thule itself, since previous observations had indicated that cosmic rays behave essentially the same there as at the pole.

LIFE ON AN ICEBREAKER

On his 1955 trip, Neher was taken to Thule on the *East Wind*, a U.S. Coast Guard icebreaker. Since Thule is well above the Arctic Circle, one must get used to a land where the sun never sets, but the ever-present light, of course, did not keep the Coast Guard from maintaining a strict schedule aboard ship; breakfast was served between 7:00 and 8:00, lunch at 12:00 or 12:30, and dinner at 5:30. Then a movie was usually shown in the "evening."

The food and living accommodations aboard ship were quite

good; it was not too difficult getting used to the continuous sunlight and the roll of the ship, and a good night's sleep was just
as easy to obtain aboard the *East Wind* as at home—except when
the ship was plowing through ice.

The charging, the grinding halt as the ship rose up on the
ice, the slow return to the sea, then the backing up to start over
—this was something Neher never did learn to sleep through.

Icebreakers are a sturdy lot, with rounded bottoms and carefully braced sloping hulls to withstand the terrific impacts with
the ice. This special construction is necessary because of the
way an icebreaker makes its attack; it backs off, gets a running
start, and slides up on the ice. The weight of the ship then
breaks the ice, and the ship settles back into the water. Because
this method of icebreaking puts a terrific stress on the hull, the
ship is divided into water-tight compartments. In fact, the ice
struck back at the *East Wind* in 1954 and punched a large hole
in her, so that the expedition was forced to turn back to Thule
a good deal sooner than it had planned.

THE PERILS OF RESEARCH

Neher was glad that the *East Wind* had a rounded hull
when, during the trip north of Thule in 1954, ice began to jam
together around the ship. The force of the wind-driven ice would
crush the hull of a normal ship, but the icebreaker's rounded
bottom merely caused it to be lifted high and dry. The *East
Wind* was trapped this way for three days. All aboard calmly
got off the ship and proceeded to explore the ice sheet mashed
together around them; it was easily solid enough to walk on,
being eight to ten feet thick. They knew that there was nothing
they could do but wait for the wind to change, as it inevitably
must. And surely enough, on the third morning they awoke to
find no trace of the ice that had held them captive the two
previous days; it had blown away and out of sight during the
night.

(A rounded bottom has its evils, too; Neher vividly recalls
the time the ship was rolling 30 degrees each way from the vertical. But this was nothing to the crew, who had experienced a

60-degree roll—and even less to the ship's builders, who had designed the ship to take an 87-degree roll without capsizing.)

To measure the cosmic ray intensity at high altitudes Neher uses an ionization chamber. In this type of instrument the gas ions produced by the cosmic rays discharge a gold-plated quartz fiber, just as a familiar gold-leaf electroscope can be discharged by X-rays. In its discharge this fiber eventually makes contact with a second plated quartz fiber connected to the grid of a vacuum tube. This causes a radio pulse to be sent back to the recording device and at the same time deposits a new charge of electricity on the movable quartz fiber. Thus the frequency of pulses sent back is a measure of the rate of discharge of the electroscope and therefore of cosmic ray intensity. Neher's equipment can measure the intensity to an accuracy of a few tenths of a percent. In addition to this information, other signals are sent out, giving the temperature and the atmospheric pressure around the device. The whole unit—transmitter, ionization chamber, and power supply—is attached to a helium-filled balloon and is sent aloft. Some of these balloons have reached a height of almost 24 miles before bursting.

In 1954 Dr. Edward Stern, then a Caltech graduate student, went along with Dr. Neher to Greenland. At the same time that Neher was making his flights, two other graduate students, Alan Johnston and Robert Morris, sent up similar flights at Bismarck, North Dakota, for purposes of comparison.

Some of the results of Dr. Neher's trips are shown in the accompanying diagrams. Fig. 1 shows that there was not much difference in the cosmic rays at Bismarck (55°N.) between 1951 and 1954, but there was quite a difference near Thule (88°N.). Since the weaker cosmic rays could not reach the earth at Bismarck because of the earth's magnetic field, but could reach the earth near Thule, this curve seems to indicate that much more low energy cosmic radiation was present in 1954 than in 1951.

Weaker cosmic rays would also be more strongly absorbed in the upper atmosphere than their more powerful relatives. Fig. 2 shows that the ionization (and hence the number of cosmic rays) was greater in 1954, and the upward swing of the 1954 curve toward the left indicates the presence of relatively more low energy rays in 1954 than in 1951. Hence it appears that low energy radiation reached the earth in considerably greater quantities in 1954 than in 1951.

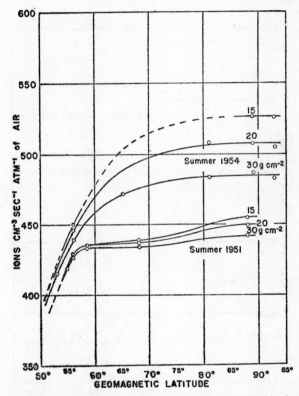

Fig. 1.—Recordings at Bismarck (55°N.) and Thule (88°N.) show more low energy cosmic radiation in 1954 than in 1951.

Why should this be so? According to Neher, the explanation that seems most plausible at the moment is one that has been blamed for everything from the weather to politics—the sunspot cycle. In 1951 there was a fair amount of sunspot activity; 1954, on the other hand, was the quietest year for sunspots in 24 years. It is known that when sunspots occur, large amounts of matter may be shot out from the sun. These clouds of ionized gas could possess fairly strong electric and magnetic fields, and thus prevent some of the weaker cosmic rays passing near them from reaching the earth.

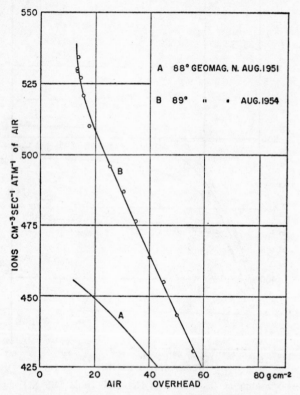

A   88° GEOMAG. N. AUG.1951

B   89°   "   .   AUG.1954

Fig. 2.—Diagram shows that the ionization (and hence the number of cosmic rays) was greater in 1954 than in 1951.

If this is the correct explanation, we might have expected to find more variation in the day-by-day cosmic ray intensity in 1951 than in 1954, due to the random nature of the sunspots and the matter they emit. Just such a difference in the variation was actually observed to exist.

Return trips to Thule by Dr. Neher in the summers of 1956 and 1957 confirmed the solar-cycle hypothesis. It has been shown quite conclusively now that the cosmic ray curves tie in with solar activity. However, it must still be ascertained that there are not other factors contributing to this change in low energy cosmic radiation (for instance, contrary to supposition, cosmic radiation from outer space may not be constant). But it does seem that low energy cosmic rays may provide a valuable tool for studying the regions of space in the planetary system, and they may provide some clue as to the origin of cosmic rays. Only time can tell just how important they may be to interplanetary studies.

FRANK SALISBURY

The Inhabitants of Mars

A BIOLOGIST EXAMINES THE DIRECT EVIDENCE THAT LIFE DOES
EXIST ON MARS—AND COMES TO AN INTRIGUING CONCLUSION.

Are there Martians? Are there entities on the planet Mars which,
according to our standards, possess life? Certainly, of all the
objects which an astronomer may directly observe with his
telescope, Mars is the only one with an environment even re-
motely enough related to our own to possess life at all as we
know it. Mercury is as hot as a furnace on one side and as cold
as space on the other. Venus has no water, and its surface is
probably subjected to constant sand blasting. The planets beyond
Mars are frozen wastes with atmospheres containing large
amounts of astringent gases such as ammonia and methane. Most
of the satellites of the solar system planets have no atmospheres
(nor does Mercury), and beyond the solar system the suns
the astronomer sees appear only as points of light, and planets
which might support life can only be inferred.

If there are Martians, what are they like? Are they extremely
small and simple, comparable to earthly bacteria, algae, or
lichens? Or do they possess reflective intelligence, comparable
to that of man? Certainly, the only way to obtain answers to
such questions would be to build a rocket ship and fly to Mars.
Since this isn't being done at present, everyone is left to his
own speculations.

Speculation can be lots of fun, both to read and to indulge in. As a framework for logical speculation about the possibilities and characteristics of Martian life, one should have all the known facts regarding the Martian environment. But first, to see whether or not any speculation at all is warranted, let us examine the direct evidence that life *does* exist on Mars.

The direct evidence for life on Mars is easily seen even with a small telescope. When it is winter in the southern hemisphere of Mars, the planet appears as a reddish disc with a brilliant white polar cap covering the south pole (the top pole, as the inverted image appears in the telescope). Some rather faint brownish markings extend irregularly from the polar cap to, and slightly beyond, the Martian equator. As spring arrives in the Martian southern hemisphere, the polar cap begins to recede, and the brownish areas begin to become bluish-green, and finally, in summer, after the polar cap has completely disappeared, these areas are quite green. In the fall the areas become brown again, and the cap begins to appear. The colors involved in these changes are strongly reminiscent of the changes seen in earthly vegetation as the seasons succeed one another. The colored areas are not static from year to year, but change in both size and shape. Observation in the summer of 1954 revealed a fairly large area which had not previously been seen.

In the spring the markings first become green in the area nearest to the polar cap, and the greening then progresses away from the pole and toward the equator, rather than from the equator toward the pole as on earth. This striking fact implies that the melting of the polar cap is a direct cause of the change of color in the markings rather than merely coincident with it, both phenomena being the result of the general increase in temperature.

All of the above features have been photographed, and their reality is accepted by everyone. Of a more controversial nature, however, are the so-called Martian canals. Since 1877, when the Italian observer, Giovanni Schiaparelli, published a map of Mars showing the planet covered by a network of fine lines (which he called *canali*, probably for want of a better term), many observers have confirmed his observation and many others, equally well trained, have denied that such markings exist.

Professor Percival Lowell has been, perhaps, the greatest champion of the canals. To detect the canals, it is said that the "seeing" must be exactly right; that is, that the air above the observatory must be perfectly clear and still. To obtain these conditions, Lowell established the Lowell Observatory in Arizona, around the turn of the century. After many years of patient observation by him and his co-workers, a map was published showing 700 canals on the surface of Mars. Many of the canals were double lines, and often at the intersection of two such sets of canals there would be a small green area, which Lowell called an oasis.

Lowell gradually developed an extensive hypothesis relating the canals to intelligent life. The oases were said to be Martian cities, surrounded by farms, and the canals, which varied in width from a few to many miles, were actually farms located along Martian waterways extending from the polar cap to the equator and beyond. Lowell reported that the canals, as well as the other areas, became green in the spring, starting at the pole and working toward the equator.

THE PROBLEM OF THE CANALS

Few people nowadays agree with the theories of Lowell. Although the canals have been seen by many people and some of the major ones seem to be present on some of the best photographs of the planet, no one claims to have seen all 700 described by Lowell. Fairly plausible explanations have been advanced to account for them on some basis other than that of intelligent life. Some consider them to be optical illusions. Others suggest that they mark boundaries between unlike areas. Certainly the problem of the canals is far from solved. Perhaps the strongest evidence against the sort of civilization proposed by Lowell is found in the description of the Martian environment given below.

Whatever the significance of the canals, the facts concerning the green areas are well established and are very difficult to interpret under any other hypothesis except that they represent life—probably vegetation. No one has been able to think of a chemical which would change color, as do the green areas, with slight increases in relative humidity. Dean B. McLaughlin, astronomy professor at the University of Michigan, suggests that the areas consist of volcanic dust, which is green because of the lack of oxygen, and are blown around and made more visible each spring as the Martian winds increase. (Shades of the March winds!)

This would account for the changes in size and shape, and windrows of volcanic dust might account for the canals; but why should the areas turn brown in the fall, and why should the greening progress from the poles towards the equator in the spring? Furthermore, astronomers often see clouds of yellow dust from the red and yellow deserts blowing across the face of the planet. If the green areas consist of green volcanic dust, why isn't it seen blowing across the planet and why hasn't the yellow dust covered the green areas? The best hypothesis still seems to be that the green areas consist of Martian vegetation, able to "grow through" the yellow dust which is often deposited upon it.

LIFE LIKE OURS?

Could the Martian environment support a type of life akin to our own? The Martian soil probably would be suitable. Dr. Gerald P. Kuiper of the University of Chicago concludes from spectral studies that the red deserts consist of igneous rock, possibly felsitic rhyolite, or something similar. (The red color was long thought to be due to large amounts of iron oxide, but Kuiper's studies failed to bear this out.) The weathered products of this rock, as well as most other related materials, would be a perfectly suitable substrate for plant growth.

The atmosphere, however, is much more critical than the soil for life as we know it. The polar caps are almost certainly ice (rather than frozen carbon dioxide—dry ice—as has been suggested), although they may be only a few millimeters thick.

Clouds are occasionally seen in the atmosphere, and they have the spectral characteristics of earthly clouds consisting of minute particles of ice. Indeed, the thin haze which covers the planet almost all of the time may consist of fine ice crystals, which would give the Martian sky a brilliant white appearance—making the sun almost invisible. As the morning twilight zone crosses the planet, a narrow white line can be observed which disappears as soon as it is in the direct rays of the sun. This is probably frost on the surface of the planet.

All of these facts indicate that water must be present, but, so far, no vapor has been detected in the Martian atmosphere. Because of the large amounts of water in our own atmosphere, the problem of observing water in the atmosphere of Mars is very difficult. None the less, our methods are sensitive enough to show clearly that the atmosphere of Mars, by our standards, is very dry. So dry indeed, that liquid water must exist, if at all, only in areas immediately adjacent to melting ice crystals.

Carbon dioxide does occur in the atmosphere of Mars. There is probably about twice as much above the surface of Mars as there is above the surface of the earth at sea level. Oxygen, on the other hand, has never been detected in the Martian atmosphere. Once more, we are limited by the methods available, but the most optimistic upper limit set by astronomers for the amount of oxygen present is still far too low to support animal life as we know it on earth. This one fact throws into very serious doubt all the inferences of Lowell about intelligent animal life.

The total amount of atmosphere on Mars can be roughly estimated, and carbon dioxide, the only gas so far detected, is not present in nearly large enough quantities to account for the total amount of gas. Argon must be present, as it is produced in fairly large amounts from the radioactive decay of an isotope of potassium. The principal gas is thought to be nitrogen, but no method is known by which this assumption could be directly tested. A fair estimate of the composition of the Martian atmosphere would be: 0.3 percent CO_2, 4.0 percent A, and about

96 percent N_2. The atmospheric pressure is probably equal to about .10 to .20 atmospheres as measured on earth.

The average maximum temperature on Mars seems to be from 0° C. to about 16° C. In the green areas, near the equator and in the Martian summer, the temperature may reach 30° C. in the middle of the day. The night temperature may drop as low as −100° C., and is always very much below freezing.

A factor of great importance in consideration of life on Mars is the ultra-violet radiation which strikes the surface of the planet. The ice-crystal haze and the carbon dioxide and nitrogen of the atmosphere allow most of the ultra-violet light from the sun to reach the surface. On earth the ozone layer of the upper atmosphere is the primary agent which filters out this ultra-violet radiation, but ozone has not been found on Mars.

THE MARTIAN ENVIRONMENT

Thus the Martian environment can be summed up as follows: The atmosphere contains considerable carbon dioxide (0.3 percent compared to 0.03 percent in our atmosphere) and nitrogen, but very little water or oxygen. The temperature has a great daily variation from far below zero to somewhat above freezing. Because of low atmospheric pressure, a dry atmosphere, and a normally frigid temperature, water does not commonly exist as a liquid, but only as a solid or a gas. Ultra-violet radiation strikes the surface almost with undiminished intensity. There are seasonal variations in climate and rather frequent storms of yellow dust. Mars is an extremely cold, extremely dry desert.

Nothing exactly comparable to this environment occurs on earth. Of course our atmosphere differs greatly in composition from that of Mars, and only small amounts of ultra-violet radiation strike the earth. Even temperature and moisture conditions are not duplicated on earth. On earth, where it is very dry, it is also very hot, and where it is very cold, it is also very wet, at least for part of the year. Yet in spite of the striking differences between the environments of the two planets, conditions on Mars more nearly approach conditions on earth than do the conditions found on any of the other planets.

Could earthly vegetation survive in an environment like that of Mars? On Mars most of the familiar plants would perish immediately. Astronomers, however, have considered the possibility that lichens might survive the Martian climate. Lichens are a sort of symbiotic "double plant," consisting of an alga (which photosynthesizes) and a fungus (which seems to help in water storage) with their cells in intimate contact. They are the little green, brown, or reddish patches seen on rocks. They are found in the coldest, driest, and highest places on earth. Assuming that Martian plants contain less than half as much water as plants on earth, and taking into account the total amount of water on Mars, it has been estimated that Martian plants, from their area on the planet and their water content alone, could be at most a fraction of a millimeter high. The patches of lichens seen on rocks are often less than a millimeter thick. The infra-red reflection spectrum of the green areas on Mars is nearly the same as the infra-red reflection spectrum of earthly lichens. The spectrum, however, is lacking in detail in both cases, probably because of lack of water, and certainly no definite conclusions can be drawn from such data.

MARTIAN PLANTS

In the opinion of this author, there are two striking differences between lichens as we know them on earth and the green areas of Mars. First, the completeness of cover of the green areas is hard to reconcile with the lichen growth habit. For an area to appear green, the cover must be very nearly complete, as in our forests. In our deserts, a distant hill may appear barren, although a fair percentage (perhaps 30 percent) of its area may be covered by plants. There are lichens in the desert, but their detection requires careful examination; they are never a conspicuous part of the landscape. In the far north they do form a complete cover, but during at least a part of the year they have a super-abundant supply of liquid water, a circumstance far different from conditions on Mars.

Second, the rate of change of size, shape, and color of the Martian green areas is many times greater than would be expected if these areas consisted of lichens like those found on earth. The thin, flat type of earthly lichens (those which fit the calculated size range of Martian plants) is extremely slow-growing. Erosion can be estimated from the line of lichens on a rock above the soil level, for the lichens may extend their area only a fraction of an inch in a century. Of course some earthly lichens grow more rapidly than this, but they occur only in moist places, as on the trees of a rain forest or on the soggy tundra of the north. Lichens do change color as their moisture content changes (becoming brown in summer as they dry), but it would seem unlikely that the slight change in relative humidity which seems to cause the color changes on Mars would be sufficient to bring about such a color change in earthly lichens.

On earth, the continuance of life is absolutely dependent upon oxygen. There are organisms that are able to live in the absence of oxygen, but if all life on earth consisted of such organisms, the processes of decay could never be complete. Dead organisms would pile up until essential nutrients such as carbon were no longer available but were all contained in these dead remains, and then life would stop. Decay is an oxidation reaction, and although various stages of it take place in the absence of oxygen, oxygen must ultimately be present or the process will come to a halt. Thus it is highly short-sighted to suggest that Martian plants live by an anaerobic metabolism. Most plants on earth, including lichens, require oxygen, as do virtually all animals.

Dr. Hubertus Strughold, head of the department of Space Medicine at Randolph Field, Texas, in a recent book, *The Green and Red Planet*, suggests that the key to this problem is the "internal atmosphere" found within the plant body. Oxygen produced in photosynthesis would be trapped in the inner spaces and used in respiration. It is, however, rather difficult to imagine how an internal atmosphere could contain one gas (oxygen) without allowing its escape and yet allow another gas to enter (carbon dioxide). Certainly the plants on earth from which this model was taken have no such mechanism. Nor does the "internal atmosphere hypothesis" explain how the decay organisms might obtain oxygen.

Perhaps the most serious problem of all concerns the ultraviolet light striking the surface of Mars. This type of radiation, at such high intensity, would probably be fatal to most things living on earth, at least after an extended period of time.

Lichens could be subjected to an artificial Martian environment in the laboratory to see if they could survive the rigors of Mars. It would seem, however, to the present author, that even in the absence of such tests, we might be quite certain that earthly lichens transplanted to Mars could not produce the effects described above. Indeed, they would probably not survive for long.

A NEW TYPE OF LIFE?

The conclusion of this discussion, then, is that earthly vegetation—even lichens—could not survive the Martian climate, let alone flourish and expand in the manner described by many careful observers such as Lowell. Certainly the oft-painted picture of Martian lichens struggling for existence on a dying planet does not seem to convey a true representation of the Martian green areas.

Hence, since speculation is free, we may be justified in postulating an entirely new type of life. We might assume, in our Martian biochemistry, that nitrogen instead of oxygen plays the active role in energy transfer. Various soil bacteria on earth oxidize nitrogen from ammonia to nitrite and then to nitrate, and derive energy from so doing. Martian biochemistry would certainly involve the many compounds of carbon, as does our biochemistry, for there is ample carbon in the atmosphere (CO_2). Martian photosynthesis might use red and blue absorbing pigments (which appear green, as does chlorophyll), but it might involve the formation of carbon-nitrogen bonds as well as carbon-carbon bonds. The medium of reaction might be water, as it is on earth, or it might be some other compound which remains liquid at much lower temperatures (a sort of protoplasmic anti-freeze—synthesized by the "plants" themselves).

The fact that the areas become green in the Martian spring nearest to the melting polar cap indicates that water is of distinct importance to the Martian vegetation, but it may act in a limiting way as a growth regulator rather than as a primary solvent. In our oceans, when some disturbance in the current brings water from depths, the concentration of critical elements such as phosphorus and nitrogen may be increased, and the result is a rapid growth of the sea flora and fauna. Perhaps, in an analogous manner, the slight increase in relative humidity of the Martian atmosphere, caused by melting (or subliming) of the polar cap, provides the few molecules of water required by the Martian vegetation to flourish in the Martian spring.

Perhaps the compounds involved in Martian biochemistry are relatively stable to ultra-violet radiation, or they are protected by screening pigments on the surface of the organisms. Indeed, important reactions may occur through absorption of ultra-violet radiation, such as the production on earth of vitamin D from certain sterols.

NO PRECEDENTS

Our knowledge of biochemistry rests upon the study of earthly enzymes produced under earthly conditions, and hence there are no real precedents known to us for a synthesis of a new biochemistry. One might consider a biochemistry with the oxidation and reduction of sulfur as its basis, or perhaps manganese is responsible for certain phases of energy transfer in Martian protoplasm. On earth this element is lethal in doses larger than trace amounts, but such trace amounts are essential for life!

The idea of water as a growth regulator rather than a primary solvent has some rather interesting implications. The calculation of the size of Martian plants based on their water content would no longer be valid. Plants much larger than one millimeter might be found, and animal-like organisms having locomotion would not be out of the question. They might obtain "vitamin

H_2O" from the plants! Even intelligence is conceivable, and Lowell's canals could have some of the significance which he tried to attach to them.

Whatever sort of life exists on Mars, it must have an ecology. There must be numerous like and unlike individuals, struggling for existence with each other and with their environment. The complete cover would certainly seem to indicate this. Probably all ecological niches are filled and natural selection operates in full force.

Seasonal and secular cycles in the Martian vegetation may be observed from earth. A biochemist studying the inhabitants of Mars would also study their life cycles, and a bio-geochemist would study elemental cycles. If carbon and nitrogen are fixed in photosynthesis, some other processes must ultimately free them to the atmosphere. Again it is tempting to think of animal-like forms occupying a position between the autotrophic "plants" which are able to live on minerals from soil and atmosphere and the organisms of decay which finally release these minerals from the Martian biosphere. On earth food chains become very complex. How complex are they on Mars?

Plant succession must be a Martian phenomenon as well as an earthly one. Some forms must be more adept at surviving on the undisturbed Martian red deserts than others. Indeed, the deserts may be sparsely covered with vegetation, as our own deserts are. Some of these forms may, by their reaction upon the environment, modify conditions so that other species are able to move in. The invaders then probably crowd out the pioneers, as they do on earth. Eventually a climax is reached in which no other Martian species is able to compete with the existing ones, and the resulting environment is quite different from the original bare red desert. The color and insulating quality of the climax vegetation result in significantly higher temperatures. A soil has formed in equilibrium with the climate of the region. When disasters such as severe yellow dust storms wipe out a climax population, a secondary succession must take place.

Species distribution is probably correlated with latitude,

topography, etc. Plant (or animal) communities probably result from the control of certain dominants and the association of species having common environmental requirements.

And what effect would intelligence have upon all this?

It is intriguing to a biologist to think of life on Mars. Would the ecological and physiological principles worked out on earth today apply there? An earthly biologist likes to think of things such as plant succession, photosynthesis, and natural selection as fundamental principles of life. Yet they have only been studied under one general set of conditions, those of earth, and their universal nature can only be inferred. It would be a most striking evidence that they are indeed of a fundamental nature if such principles were found to apply to the inhabitants of Mars as well as to the inhabitants of earth. Astronomer, geologist, chemist, and physicist would all like to test their theories on another world, but what could surpass the enthusiasm of the biologist if he were given a chance to examine the inhabitants of the red planet in their native habitat?

MARGARET BURBIDGE
AND
GEOFFREY BURBIDGE

Cosmical Alchemy

COMBINED RESEARCH FROM FOUR FIELDS OF SCIENCE—
PHYSICS, ASTROPHYSICS, ASTRONOMY, AND GEOCHEMISTRY—
LEADS TO A NEW THEORY OF THE SYNTHESIS OF
ELEMENTS IN STARS.

For many years physicists and astronomers have speculated on
the origin of the chemical elements. In every case they have
tried to understand the conditions under which all of the elements could be built up out of the fundamental building blocks,
which are protons, neutrons, and electromagnetic radiation. In
the last three or four years many ideas have come from staff
members or visitors at Caltech. These suggest that the element-
building processes have gone on, and are continuously going
on, in the interiors of stars.

It has been known since the classical work of Hans Bethe in
1938 that the energy radiated by stars is released in the stellar
core by the conversion of hydrogen into helium through the
carbon cycle or the proton-proton cycle. From 1950 to 1952 R. N.
Hall, E. J. Woodbury, and A. W. Schardt, working as graduate
students in Caltech's Kellogg Radiation Laboratory under Drs.
W. A. Fowler and C. C. Lauritsen, made measurements on the
carbon cycle reaction probabilities at low energies and experimentally confirmed Bethe's ideas.

Until recently, reactions producing elements heavier than

helium were not considered to be possible in stars. However, in 1949 Dr. Alvin Tollestrup, now assistant professor of physics in Caltech's Synchrotron Laboratory, investigated, with Fowler and Lauritsen, the properties of beryllium 8, an isotope of beryllium of mass approximately eight times that of the proton or neutron, which does not exist in nature and is therefore presumably unstable but which can be produced momentarily in the laboratory. He showed that the beryllium 8 was indeed unstable but broke up into two helium 4 nuclei (alpha-particles) with the release of only 100 kilo-electron volts of energy.

This result laid the groundwork for Dr. E. E. Salpeter of Cornell University, on a visit to Caltech in the summer of 1951, to show theoretically that if sufficiently high temperatures (about 100 million degrees) could be reached in the helium cores of stars, a small but not negligible amount of beryllium 8 would be formed in equilibrium with the helium. Before breaking up, the beryllium 8 has a chance to capture another alpha-particle to produce a stable carbon 12 nucleus. Then further alpha-particles would be captured by the carbon to produce, successively, oxygen, neon, magnesium, and silicon.

Since beryllium 8 exists only for a very short time it cannot be bombarded in the laboratory as can stable nuclei. However, at the present time an experiment is under way in the Kellogg Radiation Laboratory in which the break-up of an excited carbon 12 into beryllium 8 and an alpha-particle and thus eventually into three alpha-particles is observed. This indicates, by the general laws concerning the reversibility of physical reactions, that the process by which alpha-particles form carbon 12 will take place in stars under appropriate conditions. It appears, therefore, that some of the lightest and most abundant elements can be produced by helium reactions.

To build the rest of the light elements, such as fluorine, sodium, and aluminum, we need to suppose that the carbon, oxygen and other light elements will interact with protons and alpha-particles. The consequences of such activity have been worked out by Fred Hoyle, Fellow of St. John's College, Cambridge—when he was visiting professor at Caltech in 1953—and by W. A. Fowler—when he was visiting Cambridge as Fulbright professor in 1954-55—with Margaret and Geoffrey Burbidge at the Cavendish Laboratory, University of Cambridge.

It may be asked at this stage whether there is any observational evidence that there are stars which have central temperatures hot enough for such reactions to take place. Recent work on the evolution of the stars suggests that the red giant stars, which are colossal nuclear furnaces, and which have diameters many times larger than that of the sun, but whose surface temperatures are cooler than the sun's, do have conditions near their centers which are suitable.

Now, in order to build elements heavier than those already mentioned, more complicated processes have to be introduced. Hoyle has suggested that the elements from silicon right up to titanium may be built by the interactions of charged nuclei, such as helium and carbon. However, it is almost certain that this is not the whole story.

In this connection, a very important step forward was made by Dr. A. G. W. Cameron of the Chalk River Atomic Energy Establishment in Canada, who suggested that if a carbon 13 nucleus captures an alpha-particle, the end product would be an oxygen nucleus together with a neutron. Thus, if this process goes on inside red giant stars, a source of neutrons will be produced.

These neutrons will very rapidly reach equilibrium with the hot gas in the star's interior and then they will be captured by the other elements. If a number of successive capture processes take place on the same nucleus, we can easily see that we shall build heavier and heavier elements. There are some measurements of the probabilities of capture of neutrons by different nuclei, and it is possible to calculate what will be the relative numbers of nuclei of different kinds which are produced by such a process.

Such a calculation suggests that maybe not enough neutrons are produced by Cameron's process to build the elements to the required levels, and Fowler and the Burbidges have therefore suggested, as an alternative, a similar process in which a neon 21 nucleus interacts with a helium nucleus, giving a magnesium 24 nucleus and a neutron.

Under suitable conditions this process will provide more neutrons than that described by Cameron. So neutron sources of this sort may arise inside either stars which have already built the light elements up to neon or silicon or in stars which already contain iron and the elements near to it in the periodic table. If the stars have only got the light elements, these then will capture all of the neutrons, and the intermediate elements between neon and titanium will be built.

Calculations by Fowler and the Burbidges suggest that a large proportion of the elements in this region of the periodic table will be built by this process, though some may also be built by the charged particle reactions described by Hoyle. If on the other hand, the star already contains the metals in its core, these will capture all of the neutrons and the very heavy elements from nickel to lead will be built up.

When the cosmical abundances of all of the elements are collected together and plotted on a curve of relative numbers of atoms against their atomic weight, as has been done, for example, by Dr. Harrison Brown, Caltech professor of geochemistry, this curve shows a large peak for the atoms in the metallic group, with the maximum at iron.

This peak cannot be explained by any of the processes described so far. To explain it, Fred Hoyle has suggested that the star contracts again and so its temperature and density rapidly increase. When a temperature of about five billion degrees is attained, the nuclei reach equilibrium, one with another, and calculations made by Hoyle suggest that most of the matter in the core of the star will be transmuted into atoms of iron and other elements close to it, so that in fact the central region of the star is simply an iron ball.

More detailed calculations along these lines are now being made at Caltech. In Fig. 1, the various reactions which have been described by Fowler and the Burbidges are shown schematically.

Thus the various steps of this argument suggest that the

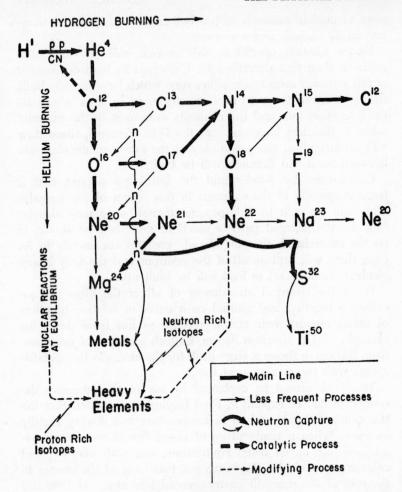

Fig. 1.—Synthesis of the elements in stars.

majority of the elements between hydrogen and lead can be processed over very long times in the interiors of stars. Observational evidence in support of this type of theory has been found by astronomers who have analyzed the spectra of stars of different brightnesses, masses, and ages, and they find evi-

dence in them of differences in chemical composition. Much
of the work along these lines has been carried out by Dr. and
Mrs. Martin Schwarzschild of Princeton and Dr. L. H. Aller
of the University of Michigan—when they were visiting the Mt.
Wilson Observatory—by Dr. Jesse L. Greenstein and Dr. Paul
Merrill of Mt. Wilson and Palomar and Caltech, by the Burbidges and Dr. W. P. Bidelman—when they were working at
the McDonald Observatory, and the Universities of Chicago
and Texas—and by others.

Some stars show large amounts of carbon, and the ratio of
the numbers of carbon 12 and carbon 13 atoms in them is different from the ratio in normal stars, suggesting that the processes involving the building of carbon have been going on in
there. Greenstein has made contributions on this subject, and
also on the abundance of lithium and beryllium in the sun,
which are of importance in considering the depth to which the
surface material of the sun is stirred up and mixed inward by
convection currents.

Other stars in the red giant stage show apparently large
abundances of the very heavy elements, suggesting that in them
the neutron capture processes are going on. The discovery of
technetium in some of these stars by Merrill is an extremely
good pointer in this direction. This element is unstable and has
a half-life against decay of about 200,000 years. It has been
produced in the laboratory by bombarding molybdenum with
neutrons from a nuclear pile. Thus when it is found in stars
this is a good indication that it is being produced in their interiors by neutron bombardment and that it is traveling to the
surface in a time which will be less than 200,000 years. Also,
some of the older stars appear to have proportionately less of
the metals and heavy elements than younger stars.

No adequate theory has yet been proposed to account for the
production of the elements heavier than lead and up to uranium.
The difficulty here arises through the decay properties and short
decay times of some of these nuclei, but it remains a challenging
problem for the future. The very light elements, deuterium
(which is the heavy isotope of hydrogen), lithium, beryllium,

and boron cannot be built in the interiors of stars, as they are unstable at temperatures of only a few million degrees and will frequently tend to be broken up.

To overcome this difficulty Fowler and the Burbidges have proposed that these elements are built on the surfaces of stars, where in some cases peculiar conditions of magnetic fields, etc., exist which allow ions to be accelerated by giant betatron effects, so that they can gain enough energy to interact with the other material which is only at a few thousand degrees, and in the resulting collisions produce these elements.

To conclude, we can indicate schematically what conditions are demanded for this kind of cosmical alchemy. Fig. 2 shows how the interchange of material between stars and the interstellar medium may take place.

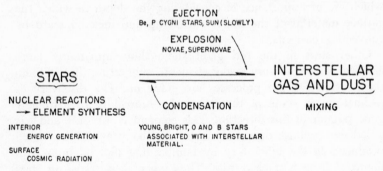

Fig. 2.—How elements are produced in stars and distributed in space.

We believe that our galaxy was, about five billion years ago, a large turbulent whirling sphere of hydrogen gas. Within this sphere stars began to condense out of hydrogen, and the sphere began to flatten, forming the disk which we see today. Probably a number of very large stars formed, and, because they were so massive, they had a comparatively short lifetime during which a proportion of them built some of the elements by the processes described above. Then, possibly through gigantic supernova explosions, the material was blown out from them, and it formed part of the gas out of which the second generation stars were formed.

These stars may now be those which we observe to have low abundances of the metals. However, some of these stars also may have become unstable and blown off some of their material. Thus third generation stars may have formed. The majority of the stars which we can study are comparatively near to the sun. These stars are considered to have the normal "cosmical abundances" of the elements and thus may be third generation stars. However, on the basis of a theory of this sort, we would expect that the chemical composition of the stars would be related to their age and to their evolutionary tracks in time.

ALLAN SANDAGE

The Birth and Death of a Star

ASTRONOMICAL STUDIES OF THE LIFE HISTORIES OF
THE STARS LEAD TO SOME INTERESTING SPECULATIONS
ABOUT OUR OWN FUTURE.

The master problem in the field of stellar evolution is to describe, explain, and understand the life histories of the stars, from the time they were created and began to shine, until the time they exhaust their fuel supply and become dark clinkers on the stellar ash heap.

It was not so many years ago that the topic of stellar evolution was considered to be nothing but speculation—a fit subject of conversation on those dark and stormy nights when observational astronomers have leisure. But today, stellar evolution is a rapidly developing field of astronomical research, touching almost every branch of astrophysics. The genesis of this change occurred in 1938 when the physicist Hans Bethe found that the source of stellar energy is atomic. Reasoning from general principles of nuclear physics, Bethe outlined the now famous set of catalytic nuclear reactions called the carbon cycle, which operates in the stars and which converts four hydrogen atoms into one helium nucleus with a subsequent release of energy. This discovery opened the door to detailed studies, both by the theoretical astrophysicists and the observational astronomers, of the way in which the structures of the stars change as they age.

The problem of tracing the life history of a single star like the sun is most difficult because the time scale for stellar evolution is enormous. Put in familiar terms, the astronomical problem is similar to the dilemma of a biologist if he were required to describe the aging process in human beings by observing the human scene for half a minute. We shall later see that the lifespan of the sun is about 12 billion years. Because the human span is short, any particular astronomer can observe the sun for less than one part in a hundred million of the total solar lifetime.

Now, obviously, the biologist cannot direct his attention to a single individual and expect to find evidence of aging in 30 seconds. He must rather devise some indirect method to solve his problem, such as surveying a large sample of the human population and noting age parameters among this sample. Variations in the size of individuals could be one difference which depends upon age. The degree of wrinkling of the face or the baldness of the human head would be others. A careful study of such differences would permit our biologist to construct a reasonable picture of human development. This snapshot method of solution is the only one available to the astronomer, and by its use a theory of stellar development has emerged.

Inspection of the stars in our immediate neighborhood gives evidence of a large diversity of age. Unmistakable signs of extreme youth are found side by side with extreme old age. The oldest stars date to nearly the beginning of the universe, while the youngest are less than a million years old. Astronomers determine stellar ages the same way that a heat engineer finds the burning time of a coal furnace, when he knows the amount of coal contained within his furnace and knows the rate at which his fuel is being consumed.

As we have seen, the source of stellar energy is atomic, obtained from the conversion of hydrogen into helium. We know from nuclear physics how much energy is released per nuclear conversion. We also know how many hydrogen atoms are available in a given star (that is to say, we know the star's mass). We therefore know the total potential energy content of the stars. For any particular star, observational astronomy gives the *rate* at which this available energy is being used up and radiated into space. Ipso facto, the age of that star is determined.

Direct measurements of stellar distances and light intensities show that some stars are spendthrift of their fuel supply. They release into space over one-millionth of their energy store every year. At this rate, their entire available energy supply will be exhausted in a million years and they will die of fuel starvation. Because such stars are visible in our skies today we know they must have been created less than a million years ago.

A million years is an extremely short time in terms of the total age of the universe. It is about equal to the time that has elapsed since some rudimentary form of man first emerged upon earth. We therefore have good evidence for the creation of stars within very recent geological times. It is indirect evidence to be sure, because a star has never actually been seen in the process of creation, but something almost as convincing is observed.

It is a remarkable fact that these very young and highly luminous stars are found in and *only* in regions of our galaxy containing large amounts of free cosmic gas and dust. This strongly suggests that the birthplace of new stars is in the dust clouds between the older stars, and that this dust is the material out of which stars condense.

These observations are so suggestive that astronomers now believe (perhaps somewhat optimistically) that they know what physical processes must take place in the creation of new stars. Presumably, when the density of a cloud of gas and dust becomes large enough, a sizable segment of the cloud becomes gravitationally unstable and begins to collapse under its own weight. The packing of matter into a smaller and smaller space due to slow collapse releases energy from the gravitational field and the gas and dust becomes hot. And as this pre-star condenses more and more, the central temperature within the globule goes higher and higher until, at the stage where the volume has shrunk a billion, billion times, the temperature and density are large enough for collisions between the hydrogen atoms to begin. These collisions lead to nuclear reactions of the same type as in a hydrogen bomb. At this stage an explosion does *not* occur, however, because a new star has the unfailing ability to adjust itself to release this energy gradually, contrary to the conditions inside a bomb. When nuclear reactions begin, the contraction of our protostar stops and a stable star is born.

STABLE STARS

A stable star is one of nature's most magnificent inventions. The large amount of matter within a star is in equilibrium at every point; that is to say, it neither collapses nor expands. This means that a star arranges itself so that the forces acting on every small element of volume in the interior just balance. These forces are the gravitational force tending to pull the material toward the center, and the pressure of the gas tending to push the material outward. From the laws of physics we know that the pressure of the gas is determined by the temperature, and the gravitational pull by the total mass. The higher the mass of the star, the higher the central temperature must be to overcome the increased gravitational force.

But this is not the whole story, because the rate of nuclear reactions also depends critically on temperature. At high temperatures the hydrogen atoms are speeding about at breakneck speeds and collisions are frequent. High temperature therefore means high energy production and a very luminous star is the result. From similar arguments it can be shown that the final radius of our stable star depends upon the distribution of pressure, which is also given once the mass is known. Hence all the conditions of a stable star—i.e., its radius, its luminosity, and, as a direct consequence, its surface temperature—are determined by the total mass.

This means that there is a unique relation between surface temperature and the luminosity of the stars, and these are quantities which can be found directly by observation. The astronomer summarizes this information in the so-called color magnitude diagram (Fig. 1), where the observed data are plotted for all stars. New stars which are just at the beginning of their evolutionary life lie on a line in this diagram which is called the main sequence.

It is now of interest to follow the history of a star as time goes on. By fairly easy calculation it can be shown from the theory of stable gas masses that the internal conditions of an aging star must change with time because of the presence of the

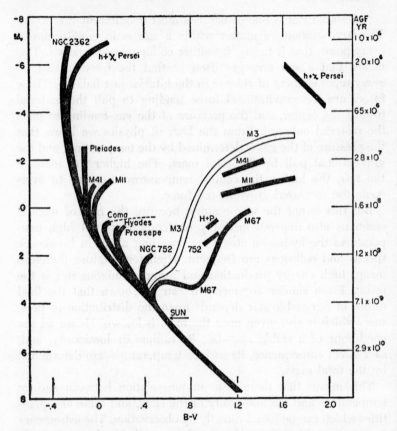

Fig. 1.—Color-magnitude diagram for stars in the individual clusters named above. The horizontal scale (B-V) is a measure of color or surface temperature. Blue stars are to the left, red stars to the right. The vertical scale is a logarithmic measure of the energy output.

waste products of the nuclear burning—namely the created helium atoms. These helium atoms are the ashes of the nuclear flame and remain deep in the stellar interior, close to their place of formation.

At first glance it would seem that helium atoms replacing the original hydrogen would not make much difference to the balance of forces within the star but this is not correct. Atom for atom, helium weighs four times as much as hydrogen and this weight difference per particle means that, for the same temperature, there is a difference in pressure of hydrogen and helium gas.

Detailed consideration of the relevant physical processes shows that the star compensates for the change in its internal chemical composition by increasing in radius and luminosity. It must brighten and expand to remain stable as the helium content increases. This change occurs quite gradually until 12 percent of the original hydrogen supply has been transferred into helium. During this period of gradual change, the star remains close to the main sequence. The sun is now in this stage of its evolution, because it has converted only 6 percent of its available hydrogen supply into helium.

Theory tells us that when 12 percent of the fuel has been exhausted, the star can no longer compensate for its increased helium content by small changes, but must drastically increase in radius and move rapidly from the main sequence. At this point the star is near the end of its life, because it swiftly increases in luminosity, consumes its remaining fuel at a tremendous rate, and finally sinks into obscurity and death as its fuel is depleted.

These predictions from the theory of stellar structure are *not* idle speculation. First, they follow from very basic principles of physics, and second, *they are observed to occur* in clusters of stars. We cannot, of course, follow the evolution of a single star for reasons of time scale already explained. However, individual stars in a group are all the same age but have an initial range of mass. They evolve at different rates because the rate of hydrogen consumption increases rapidly with the mass. Hence, in a cluster, we find stars at all different stages in their evolutionary history. We follow the evolution by the snapshot method.

The observational data are shown in Fig. 2. The data for a number of different clusters are superimposed on the same diagram. Some stars in this diagram are still near the main sequence, while others have reached the 12 percent limit and have increased rapidly in radius and moved to the right.

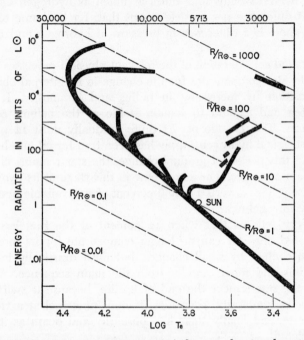

Fig. 2.—Temperature (Te)-luminosity (L) diagram showing the position of stars in certain clusters that were shown in Fig. 1. The main sequence is the straight line running from the upper left to lower right. New, unevolved stars lie on this sequence; evolved stars lie to the right. The radii of the stars in different parts of the diagram are shown by dotted lines. The unit R⊙ is the present radius of the sun; L⊙ is the luminosity of the present sun.

From the data in these diagrams we date the stars in the various clusters by the coal furnace method already described. In particular, we can determine the age of the oldest cluster,

M 67, to be about 5 billion years. Notice the position of the sun. It has moved slightly from the sequence because it has already consumed part of its fuel and is contaminated with helium. It is still below the 12 percent limit and is comfortably close to the main sequence. The sun has lived perhaps half of its total life span. It is now approaching middle age.

If the theory outlined above is correct, and observation confirms it at every point, we can predict the evolutionary track of the sun for future time and, in particular, determine the effect of such evolution on the conditions of the earth.

There is good reason to believe that the sun's evolutionary track in the color magnitude diagram should be quite similar to the tracks in M 67. From this similarity transformation we construct the predicted track of the sun, which is shown in Fig. 3.

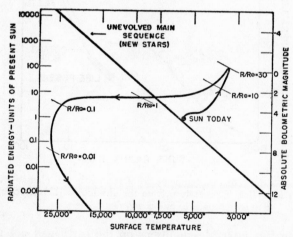

Fig. 3.—Temperature-luminosity diagram showing the evolutionary track of the sun. The radius of the sun, in terms of its present value, is shown along the track.

In another 6 billion years the sun will have reached the 12 percent limit and will then begin to expand rapidly in radius, moving to the right in the color magnitude diagram. At its maximum size the aging sun will grow to 30 times its present radius, and will appear in the sky as a dull red globe 15 degrees in diameter, instead of its present ¼ degree. In this stage, our sun is burning its fuel at a tremendous rate and will soon after exhaust its hydrogen supply. Now begins the slow decline in brightness along the nearly horizontal track shown in the diagram, until finally the sun must die and most likely will become a white dwarf.

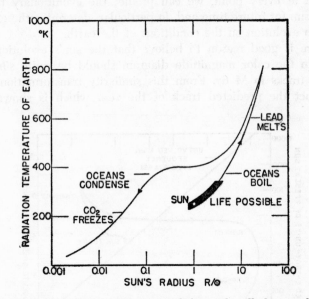

Fig. 4.—How the radiation temperature of the earth will change when the sun alters its radius. Temperature is on the absolute or Kelvin scale, where zero corresponds to minus 273 degrees centigrade.

During this interval, conditions on the earth will not remain as they are today but the temperature at the surface must go up. Our state of knowledge of stellar evolution is now advanced to a point where fairly definite predictions of these temperature changes can be made. Fig. 4 shows the calculated values of the radiation temperature of the earth plotted against the radius of the sun. There will be a catastrophe to most forms of life when the sun reaches four times its present radius. At this point the earth's temperature will be about 70 degrees centigrade. As the sun continues to expand it will brighten and will drive the temperature first above the boiling point of water and then to the melting point of lead, until finally, at the sun's greatest brightness, the earth's temperature reaches more than 800 degrees centigrade. Life will have ceased, the oceans will have boiled away, and conditions will be miserable.

Under these conditions it would be interesting to compute what the atmosphere of the earth would be like. For one thing the oxygen-carbon equilibrium, which is now in operation due to plant life, will probably be destroyed. For another, the water originally in the oceans will exist as dense clouds high about the earth's surface. These clouds will reflect a large fraction of the sun's rays and the temperatures may be somewhat lower than those shown in the diagram, but not much lower.

From the high of 800 degrees centigrade, the temperature of the earth will decrease as the sun declines in brightness. It will eventually cool until the oceans rain down over the scorched land. This will be a brief period followed by continued cooling until the oceans freeze. And as the sun becomes dimmer and dimmer, the coldness on the earth will be profound.

It is of great interest to compute the time scale of these future temperature changes. Fig. 5 shows the variation of the earth's temperature with time. The present age of the sun is taken to be 6 billion years. We see that the rise in the temperature of our planet has been gradual over the past 6 billion years—amounting to less than 20 degrees centigrade. The rise will continue in a gradual way for 6 billion years more and then the catastrophic rise begins which dooms civilization to the final heat death. The end comes rapidly when the temperature goes up 500 degrees in only 500 million years.

In the 6 billion years remaining it is conceivable that biological evolution by adaptive processes can change the human species sufficiently rapidly to compensate for the remaining gradual temperature rise of the earth. Presumably a biologist could in principle predict the course which evolution of the human species must take to meet the changing conditions.

The picture which has just been painted may be one of great terror to sensitive people. From these facts of astrophysics it appears quite likely that human life is doomed by natural processes, if not by man's folly. It is as if the Lord were playing a mad game with things of his creation. After 12 billion years of trial and error, chance mutations and evolution of living matter, the Lord tires of this play and puts his toys away with fire.

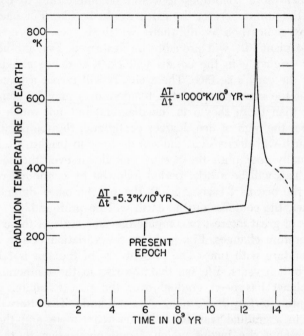

Fig. 5.—How the radiation temperature of the earth will change as time goes on. Average change of temperature per unit time is shown here.

But let us not despair of *our* plight. Our sun is only one among millions in our galaxy and our galaxy is but one among millions in the universe. Most astronomers now believe that solar systems like our own are common. If this view holds, then there may be other places much like our own where life exists. We on this planet are lucky. The rate of aging of our sun is slow. We have another 6 billion years to live. Many stars more massive than the sun exist and here the rate of aging is more rapid. Planets circling these stars go through the same temperature cycles as ours but at a more rapid rate. It follows that there may be people in the universe *this very day* facing the dilemma of the heat death. God made the sun of such a mass that we yet have time ahead. A 10 percent increase of the original solar mass would put us today at the end of life. Is it chance, or does it have some purpose that our sun was not so massive?

EDWARD HUTCHINGS, JR.

The Size of the Universe

RESEARCH REVEALS THAT THE RANGE OF THE 200-INCH
PALOMAR TELESCOPE IS ABOUT TWICE AS GREAT
AS WE HAD THOUGHT.

In recent years, it has become increasingly apparent that there were discrepancies between the different methods astronomers used for measuring distances. Research done with the 200-inch Palomar telescope has now resolved these discrepancies—and revealed that the observable universe is more than twice as large as we had supposed it was before.

This discovery was made by Dr. Walter Baade, staff member of the Mount Wilson and Palomar Observatories, as a consequence of a remeasurement of the distance to the great spiral nebula in the constellation of Andromeda. This distance is a yardstick used in measuring the distances of all more remote objects.

Dr. Baade's findings indicate that the astronomical distance scale was in error by a factor of more than two, and further research is expected to refine this figure. These corrections would mean that:

1. The limit of the *observable* universe—as expressed by the range of the 200-inch telescope—has doubled. That range is now well over one billion light years. Distance of the Andromeda galaxy, one of the nearest to us, has increased to about 2 million light years.

2. All the inhabitants of outer space—everything beyond our own galaxy, the Milky Way—are more than twice as far from us and more than twice as large as hitherto believed. However, the dimensions of the Milky Way are not affected. These facts remove a discrepancy of long standing—namely, that our galaxy formerly appeared to be larger than the biggest galaxy which was found in the universe. With the new data, our galaxy is still among the giants, but it is no longer larger than any other.

3. The volume of the *observable* universe—that sphere of space which can be scanned with the 200-inch telescope—has increased over eightfold because its calculated radius has more than doubled.

4. The expanding universe—outgrowth of the generally accepted interpretation of red-shifts in the light from distant galaxies as velocity shifts—is expanding at less than half the previously accepted rate. The rule of thumb must now be that for every million light years of distance, the speed of expansion is increased 35 miles per second instead of 100.

5. Estimated age of the universe—based on the expansion interpretation of red-shifts—is over twice as great. This age represents the span of time since all the great objects in space hurtled away from a common origin, some of them at great speed and some at lesser. The figure now stands at nearly 6 billion years instead of the previously estimated 2 billion years. This revision eliminates a disturbing disagreement with physicists' estimates —based on the rate of radioactive decay of uranium and thorium —that the earth itself (not the universe as a whole) was created 2 to 3.5 billion years ago.

The beacons astronomers use to find the distances of far-off stellar systems are Cepheid variables. These are pulsating stars which periodically brighten and dim. Their periods of pulsation range from less than a day to about 50 days and correspond to their inherent brightness ("absolute magnitude"). Astronomers use these absolute magnitudes to calculate distances.

It is now clear that the errors in the astronomical yardstick crept in with the assumption that *all* Cepheids with the same period of pulsation were equally bright. Dr. Baade has shown that they are not. Rather, there are actually two types of Cepheids, one fainter than the other, even though both pulsate identically. Distances calculated on the basis of the old period-luminosity relationship are therefore wrong.

These errors were not apparent until Dr. Baade recognized that there are two kinds of stellar populations in galaxies, each with its own distance indicators.

"We know now," he said, "that Cepheids of one type were used for the distances and dimensions of our own galaxy, while Cepheids of an entirely different type were used for distances outside our galaxy.

"The second group of distance indicators had been wrongly calibrated. This we learned from observations of the Andromeda galaxy, its satellites, and globular clusters in the Milky Way. We found all extragalactic distances were in error."

Dr. Baade has been assisted in his research by Allan R. Sandage, staff member of the Mount Wilson and Palomar Observatories.

Their present work grew out of Dr. Baade's discovery of the two stellar populations during the second world war. Astronomers have hailed that discovery as one of the greatest contributions to our understanding of the universe in recent years.

Using red-sensitive plates, Dr. Baade was able to resolve the central portion of the great Andromeda galaxy into stars with the 100-inch telescope on Mount Wilson. This feat had never before been accomplished. This and associated work pursued in great detail by Dr. Baade led him to the discovery of two stellar populations, which he dubbed Populations I and II.

The brightest members of Population I are very hot blue stars, more than 100,000 times brighter than our sun. In contrast, the brightest members of Population II are red stars, only 1000 times brighter than our sun. If they were side by side, at the

---

Plate I. 48-inch Schmidt telescope photograph of the Andromeda galaxy. Remeasurement of the distance to this nebula led to corrections in the astronomical distance scale.

Plate III. 200-inch photograph of Andromeda satellite shown at upper right of Plate I. Work with this telescope proved all previous extragalactic distances wrong.

Plate II. 100-inch telescope photograph of the lower area of the Andromeda galaxy. Baade's work with this telescope led to his discovery that there are two stellar populations.

same distance from us, the brightest Population I stars would be 100 times more luminous than the brightest of Population II.

Ever since the two stellar populations were recognized, there have been strong reasons to suspect that the pulsating Cepheid variables, although present in both populations, really represented two different species and hence each group of Cepheids had to be calibrated independently.

Dr. Baade has found that the two types do indeed differ. Type I Cepheids (of Population I) steadily brighten and dim. Type II Cepheids (of Population II) brighten, dim a bit, level off and then dim a great deal more before they repeat the process. Although both types include stars whose repeated periods of brightening and dimming range from about two days to fifty, there is another important difference:

Cepheids with periods shorter than one day exist only in Population II, and are exceedingly abundant. These are the cluster-type variables, named for the globular star clusters of our galaxy in which they were first found in quantity. They also are found outside our galaxy.

The two stellar populations exist side by side in the great Andromeda galaxy. Population I stars are in the spiral arms and Population II in the central region and between the spiral arms. (See Plates I, II, and III.)

The first definite experimental indication of error in the distance indicators came more than two years ago when Dr. Baade tried to find the short-period, cluster-type variables of Population II in the Andromeda galaxy.

They should have been visible on 200-inch plates because their median absolute magnitude placed them at apparent magnitude 22.4—one-half magnitude brighter than the faintest object the 200-inch can photograph.

They were not visible, however. In fact, only the brightest stars of Population II—which are 1½ magnitudes (or four times) brighter than its cluster-type variables—were visible, and barely so. Either the cluster-type variables were fainter than had hitherto been supposed—or else the Andromeda galaxy was farther away than we thought.

To settle the question, the 200-inch telescope was used to check the luminosities of cluster-type variables in the globular cluster Messier 3 by comparing them directly with stars of solar brightness. This check showed that the accepted luminosity for these Type II variables was correct within about one-quarter magnitude.

This meant, Dr. Baade said, that the calibration of Cepheids of Population II was essentially correct and that the 1½ magnitude error which appeared in the Andromeda work had to be attributed essentially to Type I Cepheids.

These latter had formed the basis for distance determinations on the Andromeda galaxy and other galaxies, so that when their luminosities are increased by 1½ magnitudes, all the distances and dimensions of galaxies have to be increased by a factor of two.

Dr. A. D. Thackeray at the Radcliffe Observatory in Pretoria, South Africa, has found the same discrepancy in the calibration of cluster-type variables in the Small Magellanic Cloud, a galaxy visible only in the Southern Hemisphere. The cluster-type variables were expected at apparent magnitude 17.5, but he actually found them at magnitude 19.0—again a difference of 1½ magnitudes. This was the first striking confirmation of the Palomar findings.

Corroboration also came from Dr. Henri Mineur, director of the French Institute of Astrophysics in a recent note to the Paris Academy. The once-puzzling calibration which he reported in 1944, he pointed out, is now understandable in view of the Palomar findings. That calibration agrees with Dr. Baade's, said Mineur, when he allows for the fact that it involves two different distance indicators which correspond to the two sorts of stellar population.

ALBERT G. WILSON

Astronomy and Eschatology

WHAT THE ASTRONOMER FINDS WHEN HE STUDIES
THE COSMIC DISASTERS WHICH COULD END
THE EXISTENCE OF MANKIND.

After passing several centuries in a state of neglect, the ancient
art of prophesying is again becoming quite fashionable. This is
easily verified by going into any bookstore and looking over
the drove of books currently appearing on such subjects as
human destiny, the next million years, the end of the world, etc.,
etc. The men behind these books, the modern Jeremiahs and
Daniels, do not get their source material from handwriting on
walls, but from the data science has accumulated concerning
the evolutionary processes of stars, rocks, and living organisms.
And unlike their ancient predecessors, modern prophets generally avoid forecasting the time and place at which a specific event will occur; they prefer to confine their prophesying
to the delineation of rough bounds within which future events
must lie.

But in spite of this dilution, prophecy is still as popular as
ever. For example, an informal sampling of the thousands who
every year visit Palomar to view the world's largest telescope
reveals that most of these people look on Palomar as a sort of
20th century Delphi, and are primarily interested in those phases
of astronomy which are relevant to the old questions of the purpose, significance, and destiny of man in the universe.

Traditionally, such questions have been the monopoly of theologians, who have gone into these matters in great detail, even giving a name to the subject—eschatology, the study of the ultimate destiny of man and the world. But with the great progress which science has made during the past few decades in disentangling evolutionary processes, it was inevitable that scientists should invade this field.

Though science has accumulated enough facts to enable certain types of long-range predictions to be made, the picture is still extremely fragmentary and fraught with uncertainties. The largest uncertainties in the predictions do not arise from the incompleteness of science's picture of nature and its evolutionary processes, but from the fact that intelligent life, through its increasing control over nature, can alter the course of future development to conform with its own purpose. If man's control of his environment were complete, and if his goals were well established and intelligently pursued, then a prophet could simply say that the future is circumscribed by these goals and he would be close to being right.

But this is not the case. The present situation is somewhat between that of the past, in which the laws of organic and inorganic evolution alone determined the course of events, and the case described above in which an intelligent organism possessing complete control of itself and its environment determines the future.

This uncertainty factor imposed upon evolutionary development by the impact of intelligence is negligible in those areas of the natural order which lie beyond the control of men. In such areas science may predict the future from natural laws with confidence.

The extraterrestrial universe stands as a region wherein man's influence will in all likelihood forever remain of minute importance. When the limited extent of man's domain is compared to the background of the vast distances of space, it is quite evident that the cosmic stage is almost completely unaffected by what man does on this planet. Even if he should choose to blow the earth to bits, the effects would be of no cosmic consequence.

The cosmic order remains indifferent to the aspirations and efforts of man. And though man may eventually completely subdue nature on this planet, his ultimate destiny on earth is circumscribed by the earth's destiny in the cosmic order. And the earth's destiny, in turn, is circumscribed by the evolutionary processes of the universe.

THE ROLE OF ASTRONOMY

It is then the role of astronomy, in science's prophecy of the future for man, to ascertain the earth's probable future as determined by the action of cosmic forces. Specifically, astronomy must seek to discover what the prospects are for the earth's continuing as a suitable abode for life, and study those events which could end the existence of mankind.

It is difficult to imagine life being obliterated by purely terrestrial forces. Cataclysmic earthquakes or meteorological changes which would terminate all human life could occur only as a result of a change in our cosmic environment.

What, then, are the cosmic events whose occurrence would either directly by their own action, or indirectly through the triggering of terrestrial forces, effect a termination of the delicate conditions necessary for life? Two types of such cosmic disasters are conceivable: first, a collision or a close encounter between the earth and another celestial body which could disrupt the earth, or cause gigantic earthquakes, tides, and/or loss of the earth's atmosphere, or perhaps even cause the earth to assume a new orbit which would alter its mean temperature; second, a change in the intensity or nature of radiation received by the earth from the sun, as for example would occur if the sun's luminosity or temperature were to change.

This array of Sunday supplement materal has been carefully considered by astronomers and it is now possible to make some evaluations and predictions.

First, the likelihood of collisions and encounters: Every day the earth's mass is increased by several thousand tons through its collisions with meteoritic material. For the most part, this accreted material consists of fine dust or small grains which, striking the earth's atmosphere with velocities of the order of 30 miles per second, are immediately consumed by friction. Larger particles, weighing up to about 200 pounds, may strike the earth with frequencies of perhaps five or six times each day. But this material poses no threat to human life, although a meteorite about the size of a fist struck a garage in Illinois a few years ago and, passing through the top of a car, came to rest in the car seat.

But larger masses frequently strike the earth. Twice during the present century two large meteorite falls have occurred, both fortunately in relatively uninhabited regions. In 1908 a group of large meteorites, estimated as having a mass of a few hundred tons, struck in the Tunguska River region in Siberia. The resulting hot air blast devastated an area of some 3000 square miles. And again in 1947 a fall of comparable size occurred in eastern Siberia. It has been estimated that meteorite falls of this size occur once every 50 to 100 years.

But what is the chance of the earth's colliding with a really large body? Within the past few years about a dozen new asteroids have been found whose orbits cross that of the earth. In October of 1937 one of these objects passed at a distance only three times that of the moon, a near miss on the celestial scale. If the number of these asteroids whose orbits bring them closer to the earth is no greater than the number observed up to the present time, E. J. Opik (of the Armagh Observatory in North Ireland) then estimates that a direct hit would occur about once every 30 million years. If, as is more likely, there exist several hundred such asteroids, the estimate is every 2 million years.

But even a collision with one of these asteroids whose mass is comparable to that of a mountain would not be a total disaster. One recently discovered at Palomar is the smallest yet observed, having an estimated diameter of only a quarter of a mile. A collision with such a body would create a crater perhaps 25 miles across and devastate an area about the size of Texas. This is about the worst that could happen. The orbits of all objects significantly larger are known, and none come near the earth.

STRANGERS FROM OUTER SPACE

This survey takes care of visitors from within the solar system, but what of strangers from interstellar space?

A subject very popular with writers of science fiction is the destruction of the solar system by an encounter with a passing star. This idea used to be popular with astronomers too, not for the destruction of the solar system, but for its creation. A once highly regarded theory would have the planets formed from pieces of the sun torn out by the tidal action of a passing star. But when the probability of such encounters was computed it was found that even among the hundreds of billions of stars in the galaxy, only one or two encounters would have occurred in the 3 billion years believed to be the galaxy's age.

A remaining possibility in this field of Sunday supplement disasters is the disintegration of the moon, resulting in huge pieces raining down from the sky, leaving the earth dead and pock-marked like its late satellite. Actually, this event could happen. Sir George Darwin and Harold Jeffreys have worked out the effects of tidal friction on the stability of the earth-moon system. If the loss of energy through tidal friction continues at the present rate, the month and the mean lunar distance will increase. The maximum will occur when the earth's sidereal day and the month are equal to 47 of our present days. After this time the effect of tidal friction will be to shorten the month and bring the moon closer. When the moon comes within a distance of about 2.4 times the earth's radius it will be torn apart by gravitational attraction, parts falling to the earth and parts going into the formation of rings like Saturn's. If this theory is correct, the date at which the disaster will occur is January first, 100,000,000,000 A.D.

The second type of cosmic event which could affect the existence of life on earth is a change in the sun's integral properties, such as its size, luminosity, or temperature. It is estimated that the atomic furnaces in the sun's interior have been operating for roughly three billion years, helping to maintain the earth's surface at a nearly constant temperature. How much longer the sun's thermonuclear reactions will continue to operate and what will happen when the fuel supply is exhausted are problems studied by a branch of theoretical astronomy called "stellar interiors."

The present theories of the structure of the sun do not pretend to be definitive and revisions are constantly being made. However, some zero order ideas concerning the sun's future can be derived from these present models.

One idea is to represent the sun by a model consisting of two zones: a core, whose temperature is sufficiently high to enable thermonuclear energy generation processes, such as the carbon cycle, to be operative; and a cooler surrounding envelope in which no energy generation occurs. Initially, a star is composed almost entirely of hydrogen. Within the core the hydrogen is being converted into helium, accompanied by convective currents which keep the substances thoroughly mixed. The envelope, cooler and less disturbed, remains hydrogen-rich. As long as there exists an adequate supply of hydrogen in the convective core, there is little change in the star's integral properties. Eventually, however, the hydrogen in the convective core becomes exhausted and within the core there no longer exists nuclear energy production. The central core becomes an extremely hot isothermal core, and at the interface between the core and the hydrogen-rich envelope, nuclear energy generation occurs in a thin shell. The isothermal core grows in mass and radius as the thermonuclear shell eats its way out through the hydrogen envelope. Chandrasekhar and Schönberg have shown that this process cannot continue until the shell traverses the entire envelope, but must terminate when the isothermal core acquires a mass about 12 percent that of the entire star. During the time of growth of the isothermal core, the star increases somewhat in luminosity, but remains constant in temperature. Schwarzschild and Sandage have developed an evolutionary sequence which comes into operation after the 12 percent limit has been reached. According to their theory, after the isothermal core reaches the critical mass it begins to contract, and through contraction gravitational energy is released. During this phase the total luminosity of the star remains nearly constant, but the envelope becomes greatly extended. Later, when the contracting helium core reaches a much higher temperature, a thermonuclear reaction in which helium nuclei form carbon becomes operative. Then the star becomes more luminous. After this stage, the star may collapse and become what is known as a white dwarf star. These are stars whose matter is in a degenerative form. The nuclei of the atoms, devoid of their electronic shell, are pressed together, giving densities of the order of tons per cubic inch.

THEORIES AND OBSERVATIONAL DATA

These are theories. But some very remarkable agreements have obtained between the consequences of these theories and the observational data. The rate at which a star consumes its hydrogen depends on its mass. The most massive stars burn their fuel at the highest rates and are therefore the most luminous. It follows that massive stars reach the Chandrasekhar-Schönberg limit earlier than less massive ones and start out earlier on an evolutionary track such as that proposed by Schwarzschild and Sandage. In a large aggregate of stars, such as a globular cluster, containing stars of all masses, there should be some which are still consuming the hydrogen in their cores and some which have reached the post-12 percent evolutionary stages. Sandage, at Mount Wilson and Palomar, has studied the luminosities and temperatures of several hundred stars in the globular cluster M3, and finds that all the stars heavier than 1.2 solar masses have taken off on an evolutionary track resembling that predicted by the theory.

If the universe is in the neighborhood of 3 billion years old, as is derived from several independent observations, and stars down to 1.2 solar masses have consumed the hydrogen available to them, how much time remains before stars of mass 1.0 reach this critical evolutionary stage? Assuming that our sun is of the same age as the stars in M3 and is subject to the same interior processes, then it should continue to radiate more or less as in the past for another four or five billion years.

We may now relax. Based on what has been observed of the cosmic order, it appears that man will not be exterminated by nature before he can perfect the means of doing the job for himself.

Our prophecy may well end here, but it is usual for the prophet to tell first what the future will be and then tell how this future can be avoided by following his advice. In the present discussion, the future described can be avoided by simply constructing a different sort of stellar model.

Further, according to the best traditions of prophecy, the predictions must be supplemented by exhortations and admonitions. Whereas the predictions themselves are usually well received, the sermons which prophets insist on giving with their forecasts have always made them unpopular. (First-rate prophets have never measured their success by the success of their predictions, but by how unpopular they can become.) Therefore, both in order not to disappoint anyone and to help crystallize reader opinion, I shall conclude with some brief admonitions and exhortations.

A DIFFICULT PROBLEM OF CHOICE

Mankind today is in the position of the child who has spent his life thus far under rigid parental guidance, but, now coming of age, suddenly acquires freedom and means. The laws of evolution which developed intelligence on this planet are now at the disposal of that intelligence. The knowledge of the processes of nature and the ability to utilize these processes for his own ends have come to man at the same time. But like the child with newly acquired freedom and means, man is faced with a difficult problem of choice: What shall he do with his control of nature? What ends shall he seek? What destiny should he wish?

Perhaps no better advice can be given than that the child should continue to pursue those ideals and principles laid down by its parents, at least until it acquires sufficient maturity to evaluate all the courses open to it. Man can set no better goal for himself than to emulate the goal of nature: To develop a

212

species with the maximum possible survival potential. In the past, survival potential has depended on adaptability to environment; in the future it will also depend on control of environment. So man must use the understanding and control which his science affords him to increase further his control and to establish those conditions which enhance the long-range survival of his own or derivative species.

The astronomer can only assure man that cosmic forces give him a green light for whatever he plans. To others he gives the task which is the most important of all—to derive from the above general goals and principles the specific rules and patterns for action.

Hunter Mead:

This section might have been titled "The Philosophy of Science" if we had chosen to use this phrase in a lay sense. Most laymen would probably define the philosophy of science as the investigation of the relations between science and society, science and religion, science and systematic philosophy, science and morality, science and government, and—particularly in 1958—science and education. However, the men who consider themselves (and one another) philosophers of science would find such a definition unacceptable. To the professionals, the philosophy of science deals directly with none of these relations—and indirectly with only one, systematic philosophy.

SCIENCE AND SOCIETY

A well-known definition of the field is that of a prominent American philosopher of science, A. C. Benjamin.

> Philosophy of Science: That philosophic discipline which is the systematic study of the nature of science, especially of its methods, its concepts and presuppositions, and its place in the general scheme of intellectual disciplines.
>
> (D. D. Runes, *Dictionary of Philosophy*, 1955.)

There is a striking absence here of any mention of the relations of science to society, to religion, or to business. Although the last phrase does acknowledge that science has relations to something outside itself—namely, the other intellectual disciplines—it is obvious from the definition as a whole that the contemporary philosopher of science regards science as an essentially autonomous kingdom. And certainly he assumes that his job should be a thorough analysis of the intellectual foundations and methodologies of this autonomous realm, both for purposes of making clear these foundations (concepts, assumptions, presuppositions) and for codifying the intellectual laws under which this realm operates.

Benjamin extends his definition by dividing this analytical activity into three sub-areas, and I, for one, cannot improve on his suggested divisions. First, we have "A critical study of the method or methods of the sciences, of the nature of scientific symbols, and of the logical structure of scientific symbolic systems." It is apparent that this study tries to make explicit the *rationale* of science—that is, its logical structure and the logical processes it employs. Having laid these bare, it proceeds to analyze them and usually to criticize them in the sense of seeking and examining the justifications offered by scientists for their employment.

It is here that the philosophy of science joins the vast body of literature making up such subdivisions of systematic philosophy as *logic* and *epistemology* (theory of knowledge). Both of these philosophic disciplines are very old, antedating by centuries the philosophy of science as defined above. Consequently, they have attained a notable degree of intellectual sophistication and analytical refinement. They thus provide the contemporary philosopher of science with a vast tool-crib, so to speak, from which he can check out intellectual tools of great precision. The development of epistemology, which is concerned with the origins, the tests, and the limitations of human knowledge, has been a significant part of the intellectual life of the Western world during the past three centuries. In the last fifty years it has become the core of systematic philosophy, and most of the problems with which contemporary philosophers wrest are epistemological problems. It is not surprising, therefore, that philosophers in general and philosophers of science in particular should regard science as a vast mountain into which they can sink epistemological shafts in increasing numbers, always sure of finding pay dirt.

The development of modern semantics (or, more properly, of semiotics or theory of signs, of which semantics is a subdivision) has again contributed much to the expanding toolcrib of today's philosophers of science. Since science is a symbolic system, the general theory of signs must inevitably be an important part of any theoretical study of science. And since analysis of the language of science is one of the central tasks of the philosopher of science, it is obvious that semiotics, or semantics, is one of his basic tools.

The second major subdivision of the philosophy of science is (again quoting Benjamin), "The attempted clarification of the basic *concepts, presuppositions* and *postulates* of the sciences, and the revelation of the empirical, rational or pragmatic grounds upon which they are presumed to rest." In short, the task here is to make explicit what is usually mostly implicit, and then inquire as to the validity of the conscious or unconscious assumptions.

Men have known for centuries that every field and every discipline has many assumptions and presuppositions as its intellectual basis, and they have also known for centuries that many of these are held unconsciously or uncritically. In fact, any well-educated person knows that the avowed postulates upon which men base their thinking and reasoning are usually far outnumbered by the concepts they take for granted. One is tempted to use the well-worn iceberg simile: no matter how large the body of acknowledged assumptions and axioms, the mass of those unacknowledged is sure to be even larger.

Now, along with this awareness that men assume far more than they say or think they do goes a strange belief that it always is the other man, or workers in another field, who are most guilty in this regard. And scientists, for all their intelligence and intellectual caution and exactitude, are still human enough to hold this almost universal belief. In other words, scientists as a group have also frequently had to rely on outside critics to point out the assumptions and presuppositions implied in their thinking. For several centuries it has been the philosophers who have performed this usually friendly service, and today the philosophers of science have secured the monopoly in this critical area.

Once these presuppositions have been revealed or acknowledged, how are they to be justified? Scientists as a class have generally been satisfied with a pragmatic justification: "The assumption in question works—that is, gets results—so what further justification is needed? When a new assumption or set of assumptions shows itself capable of getting better results, we will shift to these."

For the most part, assumptions that have continued to work well over long periods of time are eventually incorporated into the growing rational structure of science. The justification has by then proved to be not only pragmatically valid but also logical or rational in that it is consistent with the rest of the established knowledge ("laws") of that field. It is only after scientific assumptions have become rational in this sense that the philosopher of science begins to find material to work on.

When the philosophy of science attempts to analyze and clarify the basic concepts and presuppositions of science, it begins to draw from another large storehouse of established ideas, those subsumed under the heading of "metaphysics." Metaphysics is usually defined as the intellectual discipline (or branch of philosophy) dedicated to discovering the nature of ultimate reality. The rise of positivism in the nineteenth century, and the great influence of its contemporary offspring, logical empiricism, has cast much doubt upon the validity of seeking "reality," particularly by intellectual means. However, even scientists appear unable to formulate concepts or make assumptions which do not imply a belief that certain things are more "real" than certain other things. I have always been amused at the spectacle of science students using the adjective "real" freely, while showing either irritation or bewilderment when they hear the noun "reality." And I have recently been bemused to see one of the major aircraft companies, in advertisements announcing its participation in space research, state that it is interested in metaphysics. These advertisements defined the term in its original sense, as indicating the field that lies beyond physics. This would suggest that not only contemporary scientists but even contemporary engineers find it hard to escape metaphysical issues entirely, so it is not surprising that philosophers of science still need to employ metaphysical categories from time to time.

❋   ❋   ❋   ❋

Benjamin's definition of what he considers the third subdivision of the philosophy of science is necessarily less enlightening than his two previous definitions, since the material discussed is more ambiguous and more speculative. This third area he describes as "A highly composite and diverse study which attempts to ascertain the limits of the special sciences, to disclose their interrelations one with another, and to examine their implications so far as these contribute to a theory either of the universe as a whole or of some pervasive aspect of it." Here indeed is an area in which speculation is inevitable.

The most systematic part of this subdivision has been the numerous attempts to classify the sciences. These interesting—sometimes amusing—efforts to lay out the geography of the sciences made up a good part of the philosophy of science during the nineteenth century. However, the facile charms of pigeonholing have become tarnished during the twentieth century; in part because these classifying activities have proved to be largely sterile, in greater part because science will not hold still long enough to permit a stable classification of its parts. As science has proliferated during the past hundred years, the would-be classifier has had to tack on so many new subclasses and subsubclasses that the resulting system became hopelessly unsystematic.

Today the classification of the special sciences is a minimal part of the work of the philosopher of science. The other main task in this area—to discern the implications that science, both as a body of knowledge and as a methodology, offers for a general world-view or theory of the universe—still remains important. There is little general agreement about the degree of this importance. Again, those who are much influenced by logical empiricism seek to avoid metaphysical thought as futile and meaningless because unverifiable, and therefore they tend to minimize this area. In fact, many of them prefer to divide the philosophy of science only into subdivisions one and two, as defined above. However most philosophers (as distinguished from philosophers of science) consider this third area the most interesting of the philosophy of science. Certainly, much of the philosophical, as well as theological, argument of the last two centuries has raged around this issue. What does science as a whole suggest as regards idealism, materialism, mechanism, teleology, monism, dualism, pluralism? Although most contemporary scientists dislike being considered purveyors of, or even implicators of, a metaphysical view, inevitably their work has been interpreted as supporting one world-view against possible rival world-views.

Thus, we see that the professional considers the philosophy of science to be a well-organized and thorough study of the logic or methodology of science, including its presuppositions and its implications. Such a study is inevitably technical, relatively abstract, and treats science as an autonomous realm with its own laws and logic. And in terms of efficiency, the philosopher of science is probably wise to restrict himself to these logical aspects of his field.

However, as far as society or civilization as a whole is concerned, this is not enough. Science has become too important for society to permit either its practitioners or its philosophers to claim diplomatic immunity, free from contact with the rest of contemporary civilization. Thus it is inevitable that the narrow, strictly technical view of the philosophy of science will be broadened, or else a new field will come into existence (perhaps called "Science and Society," or "The Sociology of Science"). However important the logical and strictly intellectual implications of science may be, its broad social implications can now certainly claim equal importance.

SCIENCE AND SOCIETY

The essays that follow are pioneering trips into this new field, for they are genuine efforts to think about science in the modern world—or, if you prefer, science in its broadest implications. L. A. DuBridge's contributions are concerned with the nature of the scientist, his aims, purposes, duties, and responsibilities, his role in the world today. Both Dr. DuBridge and Linus Pauling discuss the general value of science, as do Richard P. Feynman and Fred Hoyle. Both DuBridge and Pauling are much concerned with the necessity of a greater understanding between scientist and layman; Feynman has some interesting ideas on the relations between science and religion—a very old topic that is still vital; and Ira S. Bowen discusses both the value of astronomy to the average man and some of the philosophical implications of astronomical discoveries. J. Robert Oppenheimer and Elting E. Morison present some stimulating ideas on change, both scientific and social. Thus, these discussions all relate to that enormously vital subject: science in the modern world. The reader will recognize their challenge if he approaches them with the realization that as a contemporary man, he is directly involved in the issues the writers pose.

L. A. DuBRIDGE

The Inquiring Mind

HOW ARE WE DOING IN THE FIELDS OF SCIENCE AND
TECHNOLOGY TODAY? HAVE WE PROPERLY VISUALIZED
OUR TASK AND OUR GOALS? ARE WE PUTTING FIRST THINGS
FIRST? DO WE EVEN KNOW WHICH THINGS ARE FIRST?

In 1798 a monk by the name of Thomas Robert Malthus published a paper with a long and complex title which attempted to analyze man's future on this planet. Examining past experience and bringing to bear on this experience the brilliant logic of an analytical mind, he came to some rather dire conclusions about the future. It was quite obvious to him that men had to eat; that the only major source of food was the arable land; that the area of such land was limited. Therefore, there was a limit to the potential food supply, and hence to the population that could exist on the earth.

On the other hand, he noted that the human population tended to grow at an ever-increasing rate. Any sort of voluntary birth control, it seemed to him, would be either unnatural or immoral. Therefore, the only possible future was one in which the population eventually outgrew the food supply, and thereafter death by starvation, disease and war would take over to balance a birth rate which knew no control.

Clearly, a world in which most of the people would assuredly die of one of these causes was not a very pleasant one to contemplate.

However, here we are 156 years after the Malthusian prediction, and the portion of the world that we live in does not face the Malthusian death sentence. Our population is expanding at a rate never dreamed of in Malthus' time. There are four times as many people on the earth now as then. At the same time, here in the United States at least, we have far more trouble with food surplus than with shortage. We buy potatoes and dye them blue, butter and let it spoil, wheat and give it away, in our desperate effort to avoid the economic consequences of growing more food than we can eat.

Surely Malthus was the most mistaken man in history. Or was he?

Actually, as Harrison Brown points out in his book (from which I shall now borrow heavily) *The Challenge of Man's Future,* Malthus' reasoning and logic were entirely correct. His only misfortune was that his observations and assumptions were later rendered obsolete by unforeseeable new developments. What were these new developments? They were of two kinds— technological and social. On the technological side men learned how to raise more pounds of food to the acre, learned to get more nutritive value to the pound, and learned how to transport food quickly from areas of surplus to areas of shortage. On the social side, great segments of the human race came to regard voluntary birth control not as a sin but as a virtue.

Now I think it is quite evident that without this latter factor —voluntary population control—the Malthusian disaster can be only postponed, and not finally prevented, by any advances in technology. We must admit that the supply of land is limited, that the productivity of land can *not* be expanded beyond all limit. But population, if not controlled, does expand without limit, and sooner or later—in 50, 250, 500 or 5000 years—a population which is doubling every 75 years or so is bound to outrun any given food supply.

This makes it clear that the primary need of the world is to insure that in all parts of it the population recognizes the need for growth that is controlled by voluntary action rather than through starvation. Clearly, this is not primarily a job for science and technology, but rather for education.

But science and technology do have some terribly important tasks to perform in this field. First, there is the task of improving the technology of producing, processing and preserving food so that the food supply will keep pace with population for the 25, 50 or 100 years required to complete the educational job. Second, there is the task of improving standards of living over a larger part of the world—for increased education goes only with increased living standards and increased disposable wealth. Finally, science and technology have the task of providing the necessary tools so that any segment of the population that has overcome the starvation limit can then proceed to help men and women lead happier and richer lives.

Now I claim that these constitute quite substantial and immensely challenging tasks. Another way of expressing them is to say simply that if men are to attain those social, moral and spiritual goals which we of the Christian nations believe desirable, then science and technology must provide the physical tools to make their attainment feasible.

This being about as important a goal as I can think of, it behooves those of us who are working in the fields of science and technology to ask ourselves how we are doing. Have we properly visualized our task and our goals? Have we properly analyzed and evaluated the steps which need to be taken, the prerequisites for progress? Are we putting first things first and do we know which things *are* first? Are we creating within science and technology itself, and within the community at large, the conditions most likely to nurture progress and success?

Now it would be presumptuous of me to attempt to answer these questions or to try to solve the problems they suggest. But I can presume to raise the questions and ask you to think about them, in the hope that if enough people think about them, we may some day get them answered.

THE GOALS WE SEEK

It seems to me obvious from the way in which I have

stated the problem that it is important that we keep in mind the goals we seek. As I have suggested, these goals are not merely more food, more products, more gadgets. Our goal in the last analysis is a moral goal—more happiness for individual human beings, expressed in whatever terms their own philosophy of life dictates.

I emphasize and repeat this matter of ultimate goals precisely because it is so obvious to us that it is often forgotten. We become so absorbed in our gadgets, our machines, our new foods, new medicines, our new weapons, that only too often we think of them as ends in themselves—forgetting what they are *for*.

Now if we ourselves—if we scientists—forget the ends in our absorption with the means, that is bad enough; for then our work loses its meaning. But it is even more dangerous if we let the public believe that our machines and our mechanisms are ends in themselves. For then our work, which in the end depends upon public support, will surely be destroyed. And it will be destroyed by the public even though the public itself, rather than the scientists, would be the principal losers.

Let us bring this closer home. It is a paradoxical fact that, in these days of the mid-20th century, science and technology are being simultaneously praised to the skies and damned with religious fervor; they are being handsomely supported and heartily kicked. Scientists are publicly acclaimed as a group and privately slugged as individuals.

Why is this?

Clearly, we have not told our story adequately. Our physical achievements are evident. But, because they are physical, we are accused of being materialists. Because the tools of science are powerful, their power is feared and those with the power are suspected of evil motives. Because weapons have been produced to help men fight in their own defense, it is assumed that they also make men *want* to fight. So we see that as we brag about our knowledge but are silent about our aims, then the public will come to ignore our knowledge and denounce our aims.

WHAT SCIENTISTS WORK FOR

So my first plea is that scientists shall throw off their reticence in speaking of their feelings and come out boldly and unashamedly to say, "We are working for the betterment and happiness of human beings—nothing less and nothing more."

But, in spite of the romanticism of the poet, we know full well that for most human beings *happiness* is not attained solely by sitting under a tree with a loaf of bread and a jug of wine. And even if it were, someone has to bake the bread and bottle the wine. The poet was right in suggesting that the essential elements of happiness consist of food, shelter, companionship and leisure. He only forgot to mention that these must be achieved by effort, and that the effort itself may bring happiness, too.

In any case, we are forced at once to consider how human effort can be most effectively employed to provide the physical elements for happiness and also the leisure to enjoy them. Nor are we content—as were those of medieval and ancient times —to have *many* people exert the effort and a few people enjoy the leisure. We have proved that *all* may work and *all* may play.

Now what is it that has made it possible for us today to think of a modest amount of happiness coupled with a reasonable amount of work as a possible goal for *all* people, rather than just a few? The answer is, clearly, that a series of *intellectual achievements* have enabled men to enlarge, to expand, and to dream of achieving a moral goal.

What are the intellectual achievements?

I think it is fair to say that the essential cause of the difference in the physical and the moral outlook of the western world in the 20th century as compared to the 10th is simply that, along some time between those dates, men invented a new process of thinking.

Men had, of course, always thought, always observed, always speculated, always wondered, always asked questions, always explored. But along about 1700 men began to do these things in a new way. Men began to realize that by making observations carefully and analyzing them quantitatively, it could be shown that nature behaved in a regular manner and that these regularities could be discovered, reduced to mathematical form and used to predict future events.

This was an astonishing discovery. And as this new concept, outlined by Francis Bacon, was pursued—first by Galileo, then by Newton, then many others—a new world of understanding was opened to men's minds. Nature was partly comprehensible, not wholly mysterious and capricious. The falling stone and the moving planets became suddenly not only understandable but miraculously and simply related. Men couldn't *affect* the motion of the planets, but they *could* control the motion of the stone and of other objects.

And so, machines were invented, the concept of energy emerged, steam was put to work—and suddenly, after thousands of years of doing work only with the muscles of men and animals, men found that a piece of burning wood or coal could take the place of many slaves or horses or oxen.

From that time on, happiness and leisure for all men became a possible goal, not a crazy dream.

A LIMITLESS QUEST

But that was only the beginning. The scientific method led from physics to astronomy to chemistry to biology. A beachhead on the shores of ignorance became a vast area of knowledge and understanding. Yet, as the frontiers of knowledge advanced, the area of ignorance also seemed to enlarge. Nature was not simple after all. A literal eternity of new frontier was opened up. The quest for understanding, we now see, will, for finite man, be limitless.

I need not recount the way in which this new understanding has spread—often slowly, often with startling rapidity—from one field to another.

But I would like to direct your attention to the conditions that are required for knowledge and understanding to grow and to spread. Intellectual advancement does not come about auto-

227

matically and without attention. There have been throughout human history only a few places and a few periods in which there have been great advances in knowledge. Only under certain special conditions does the inquiring mind develop and function effectively. Can we identify these conditions? Certainly we must try.

The first condition, of course, is that at least a few people must recognize the value of the inquiring mind. Here we all take for granted that new advances in understanding come only from the acts of creative thinking on the part of individual human beings. We know that, and we respect and admire the men who have shown the ability to think creatively. But we musn't get the idea that our admiration for original thought is shared by all people.

Even in this country, the man who thinks differently is more often despised than admired. If he confines his new thoughts to the realms of abstruse theoretical physics or astronomy, he may not be molested. For then he will be speaking only to those who understand him. But if he wanders into biology or medicine, into psychology or sociology or politics, then he should beware.

Now in recognizing the virtues of thinking differently, we do not mean that we must encourage the idiot, the criminal or the traitor. Honest, truly intellectual inquiry is perfectly easily recognizable by those who have some training in the field. But just here we run into difficulty. Those who are incompetent to judge may nevertheless render judgment and pass sentence on those with whom they disagree, or whom they fear.

One of the great unsolved problems of a democracy is how to insure that, in intellectual matters, judgments are left to those who are competent, and the people will respect that competence. But when uneducated fanatics presume to choose and to censor textbooks, when government officials impose tests of political conformity on the scholars that may leave or enter a country, and when the editors of a popular magazine set themselves up to judge who had the proper opinions of nuclear physics, then the inquiring mind finds itself in an atmosphere not exactly conducive to maximum productivity.

Fortunately, for the past 100 years in Western Europe and in the United States the impediments to creative scholarship have been less important than the great encouragements. In the past 10 years the physical conditions necessary for research in the sciences have enormously improved. More opportunities have been created to study, to travel, to carry on research, than ever before existed.

THE NEEDS OF THE INQUIRING MIND

But physical conditions are not enough. Big, beautiful laboratories do not themselves produce research—only the men in them can think. And if conditions are such as not to attract men who think or such as to impede their thinking, then the laboratory is sterile. Such laboratories, as you well know, do exist. There is no use storming and raging at the perverseness of scientists who refuse to work when conditions are not just to their liking. We don't call a rose bush perverse if it fails to bloom when deprived of proper water and soil. A community or a nation which wishes to enjoy the benefits that flow from active inquiring minds needs to recognize that the inquiring mind is a delicate flower, and if we want it to flourish we are only wasting our time if we do not create those conditions most conducive to flowering. The cost of doing so will be well repaid.

The inquiring mind then needs, first of all, some degree of understanding and sympathy within the community. And if there are those who cannot understand, then at least they must be insulated by those who do, so that they do the least harm. As someone has said, we can stand having a few idiots in each community—as long as we don't put them on the school board.

As I have already suggested, it is not enough for the scholar or the scientist to wring his hands and wish that there were fewer idiots or that they had less influence. He must also, to the extent of his ability, explain to those who can understand what he is doing and why. We now see that an intelligent and informed segment of public understanding is essential to the progress of scholarly endeavor.

This leads me to another subject which has become timely to the scientist and to the citizen in recent years; that is, the relation of the scientist and the government. This is obviously a very large subject which I cannot attempt to explore here. But as the scholar needs an informed community to support him, so he owes an obligation to that community.

The prime obligation of the scholar, of course, is to pursue scholarship. That is, he must seek answers to important questions, observe carefully, analyze accurately, test rigidly, explain imaginatively, and test and test again. Then he must publish his results, fully, fearlessly, objectively, and defend them enthusiastically unless or until the facts prove him wrong. Through such intellectual struggle does the truth emerge.

But in these days the results of science impinge so heavily on public affairs that the public—in particular the government—needs the scientist's help in so many ways. Obviously, the government needs the direct services of thousands of scientists and engineers to carry on work in public health, standards of measurement, agriculture, conservation of resources and in military weapons, to name a few.

But when there is developed a new weapon, a new treatment for a disease, a new way of using public resources, does the scientist's responsibility end there? I think not. There are so many ways in which important matters of public policy are affected by these new scientific achievements that scientists must stand by as advisers at least to interpret, explain, criticize and suggest on policy matters.

SCIENTIFIC ADVICE

We would not think, of course, of allowing a new law affecting public health to be passed without asking a physician's advice on whether it is wisely conceived. Yet I am sure state and federal legislatures *have* thought of it—in the various antivivisection bills, for example. Fortunately, (for this purpose at least) the medical profession has great influence and can make its opinions heard. And most of the public respects its doctors.

But when national security matters are being discussed which involve the nation's strength in atomic weapons, it is clear that those in charge of forming policy will need to have much help on questions of what atomic weapons really are, what they do individually, and what would be the effects of setting off the whole stockpile. I am not saying that such scientific advice is not sought (though I think it is not always adequately used). But I do say that scientists need to be ready to help. Yes, they may need to be ready to intrude with their advice even if it is not asked for.

This problem has, of course, caused much recent trouble and misunderstanding. Many prominent citizens, including many politicians and editors, apparently feel that scientists should stick to the laboratory and let public policy matters be handled by others. Now no one argues that *decisions* on public matters must not be made by the properly constituted responsible officials. But *advice* and *information* on scientific aspects of the problem is often essential and must come from scientists.

It is often true that the scientific aspects of a problem are so important that they overshadow all else—and the scientist's advice becomes adopted as a decision. But in other cases, other factors may appear important and the scientist's advice may be wrong, or may not be taken. Even the scientist, being human and being a citizen, will take nonscientific matters into account in rendering his advice. He may be just as competent to do this as anyone else. Being a scientist does not disqualify a person from being an intelligent citizen. But the possibilities of disagreement and misunderstanding are very great.

A RISKY COURSE

A very great and admittedly loyal scientist was just recently persecuted partly because, though he gave advice of surpassing value on many, many occasions, he gave on one occasion advice which some (but by no means all, then or now) believe was wrong. The sad part of this case is not so much the harm to the individual, as the harm to the country that will result if scientists cannot give honest advice to their government officials, or will be no longer asked for advice, or listened to. Dire disaster could indeed follow from such a course pursued in the thermonuclear age.

I fervently believe that the world has been remade the past century—remade physically, socially, and spiritually—by the work of the inquiring scholars. These scholars have sought new knowledge and new understanding; they have sought to use this understanding to produce those things that men needed—or thought they needed—to improve their health, their comfort, their happiness, their security.

Scholars will continue these activities and the world will continue to change. Their efforts must be aided; for though what they do may yield dangers, the dangers are far greater if they do less. And since what they do affects the world, affects you and me and our community and our country, we should have these inquiring and active minds around all the time to direct their attention to the most difficult of all problems—how to help men make better use, in their relations with each other, of the great new areas of knowledge which can yield so much to make men happier and better.

L. A. DuBRIDGE

Science, the Endless Adventure

SOME EXCITING DEVELOPMENTS IN TODAY'S SCIENCE—AND
SOME ILLUSIONS ABOUT IT THAT MUST BE ELIMINATED.

Much has been written in recent years about science as the
hope of man's future and also about science as the instrument
of man's destruction. You have read of the possible glories of
tomorrow's world of technology when people won't have to
work—but only push buttons—and can spend endless hours
of leisure speeding across the country in radar-guided, air-
conditioned, pink Cadillacs at 120 miles an hour or more. And
you have also read of the utter ruin which civilization would
face in case of an all-out war using all the modern techniques
of destruction.

You have heard of many such things which are probably true.
Advancing technology is going to bring about great changes
in our methods of living—changes in the next 50 years as great
as those in the last 50. But it is also perfectly possible that an
all-out nuclear catastrophe will intervene.

You have also read other things that are untrue or improbable.
I think the imminence and practicality of space travel by
humans (not to mention its desirability) have been grossly exaggerated. Cheap and abundant atomic energy is still a long
way off—though in some parts of the world (not in America)
it will soon be cheaper than other sources that are available.

Still other promises you have heard violate basic laws of physics, or else they would be fantastically expensive.

Yes, the comic-strip artists, the science-fiction writers, as well as good solid scientists and engineers, can paint exciting pictures of the new devices, gadgets and machines that we will all have in 25 years. But these are not things I am going to discuss now.

Nor am I concerned with whether these extraordinary things that technology is going to bring us are good or bad. In fact, no one can say—for *anything* can be *either* good or bad, depending on how it is used, whether it's a stick of wood or a stick of dynamite. *Things* aren't bad; only *people* are bad. And as to whether people are going to be bad or not there is no argument; some of them certainly will be. But whether they are or not, these new *things* are going to come anyway—*for no force on earth can stop men from thinking,* from inventing, from exploring.

But I am not going to discuss the things men will invent. I am going to talk about the things men are going to *think*; the ideas they are going to explore.

The things men invent will arise from new things they learn, from new understanding they acquire about the world. On the foundation of new ideas, men create great new technologies, new industries, new machines, new ways of doing things.

I propose to examine not the superstructure that men have erected on the foundation of knowledge, but the foundation itself. I am not going to explore the glittering upper rooms and towering pinnacles of technology—I propose to go to the basement and examine the foundations of science on which all technology is based.

And I propose to talk first about science not in the light of the new technology to which it may lead, but to talk about science for its own sake—science as a method of thinking, science as a method of acquiring new knowledge, science as the key to understanding, the road to comprehension of the physical world. I am going to speak of science, the endless adventure.

From the day that man first acquired consciousness he began

to observe the things about him—the nature of fire, of water, of the winds, the sea, the stars. And as he observed, he remembered and reflected. He noted the regularities of nature. Fire could nearly always be produced in a certain way and extinguished in certain ways. The sun marched regularly across the sky— though more careful observation showed that its path changed almost imperceptibly from day to day, from week to week, and at the same time the weather became warmer, then cooler, then warmer again. When these invariable regularities of nature are reduced to their simplest form, we call them the "laws of nature."

At a very early time man must have been conscious of numbers—the number of his children, the number of his wives, how many animals he killed, how many enemies he had. Primitive men had words for only three numbers—one, two and *many*. Gradually the "many" became sorted out—3, 4, 5, 10. Curiously enough, it was a very long time before men discovered the number "zero" and learned to use it.

THE IMPORTANCE OF NUMBERS

At this juncture I should like to pause a moment and reflect upon the importance of numbers—and upon the science of mathematics which has been built upon them. How many of us realize how utterly impossible our modern way of living would be without a number system and without our science of mathematics. Suppose we had not yet invented numbers above 10. Suppose even we had to add and multiply with Roman numerals. For example, how do you multiply XVI by MCMXL?

Suppose we were unable to deal with numbers higher than a million, or even a billion. That might have a salutary effect on government budgets, of course, but there are quite a few large corporations whose gross incomes are above one billion dollars too.

But, if we come to think of it, how many people *do* know what a billion really means—or even a million? Counting as fast as you can—say 3 per second—it would take you 3 days, 24 hours a day, to count to a million—over 8 years to count to a billion.

As an illustration, let me ask you how big a house would be if it were a million times as big as your house—assuming you occupy an average size dwelling. Would it be as big as the Empire State Building? As big as an Egyptian pyramid? As big as the Pacific Ocean? As the whole earth? As the solar system? You might amuse yourself by proving that a house with a million times the dimensions of yours would have a volume some 10 to 50 times the volume of the *earth*.

My point is that very few people really know what a factor of a million really means. Especially when we deal with a million *cubed* as we do in computing a volume.

Is it any wonder that we find it difficult to realize what it means when we say that a modern hydrogen bomb has an explosive energy 20 million times as great as a 1-ton TNT bomb? But we should not be misled the other way either. For the radius of destruction of a bomb depends on about the cube root of its explosive energy. And that means a 20-megaton bomb has a radius of damage only the cube root of 20 million—or 270 times as big as for a 1-ton bomb. That's still a damage radius of 10 miles or more. But a Los Angeles paper recently published a letter expressing fear that Los Angeles people might be hurt by the blast of the Bikini tests—5000 miles away! To do that would take the power of 125 million 20-megaton bombs.

DEALING IN BILLIONS

Now I am not trying to confuse you or scare you. I am only giving some spectacular illustrations of the importance of numbers in the modern world—the importance of being able to think in quantitative terms. Why do we still teach arithmetic as though numbers bigger than 100 or 1000 were too complicated to grasp? A million is 10^6, a billion is 10^9, a million squared is 10^{12}, and $10^6 \times 10^5$ is 10^{11}. It's very simple! Even a little experience with exponents would give youngsters a lot of fun—and would make it possible for them, out of their own experience, to deal with millions and billions in a more meaningful way.

I noted the other day a curious example of this inability to deal with numbers larger than a billion. A science story in a weekly news magazine contained the statement that in a certain volume of air there were "billions of molecules." Now, of course, that is perfectly true but it is about as significant a statement as though we said that on the earth there live dozens of people. There are, of course, many dozens of people on the earth; in fact, there are about a quarter of a billion dozen. Similarly, there are many billions of molecules in a cubic centimeter of air; in fact, there are 30 billion *billion* molecules. We feel sorry for primitive men who were unable to distinguish numbers higher than 3 and referred to everything else as "many." Some day in the future, people will think of us 20th century humans as being rather primitive because we were unable to think in terms larger than a billion.

Our whole modern civilization is built on mathematics! Not a street can be laid, a foundation dug, or a building constructed, without the use of algebra, geometry and trigonometry. Not a machine can be designed, an engine's performance predicted, an electric power plant constructed without mathematics through calculus. The design of an airplane, a ship, a guided missile or an electronic computer requires a profound knowledge of higher mathematics, while the really interesting fields of nuclear physics and astronomy use group theory, matrix algebra and non-Euclidean geometry.

In other words, no one from a grocer's clerk to the nuclear physicist can do without mathematics—and the study of mathematics can be a great adventure in the methods of quantitative thinking which will provide for everyone a lifetime of better understanding of a technological world.

JOURNEY TO THE SUN

But let us turn now to adventures in the world of physical science rather than mathematics. I should like to start the adventure with a journey to the sun. Adventurers who climb Mt. Everest are pikers; we are going to explore (in our minds at least) what we would find at the center of the sun.

Now the first thing we notice about the sun is that it is hot. It is very hot, in fact. The surface temperature is about 11,000°F.

That is higher than any temperature ever observed on earth except in the burst of an atomic bomb. That is far above the melting point of any material we are familiar with; it is far above the boiling point of most materials. Therefore, the sun is very much like a ball of hot gas.

But the surface of the sun is its coolest part. It is easy for an astrophysicist to prove that, because the sun is so massive and the gravitational forces are therefore so enormous, the sun would promptly collapse into a very much smaller object unless the central part of the sun is at a very high pressure and temperature. In fact, the central temperature is probably about 23,000,000°F. The pressure is so great that the central portion has a density 10 times the density of lead, though it is still a gas—in fact it is mostly hydrogen.

The age-old question about the sun, of course, is what keeps it so hot. We know that the earth has been at roughly its present temperature for 4 billion years or so. The sun must have been at about its present temperature equally long. Where does all that energy come from?

Up until just before World War II—very recently you see—not even the beginnings of a satisfactory answer had been found. We know now that the only source of energy possible is the transmutation of matter—specifically, in the case of the sun, the transformation of hydrogen into helium. The sun, in other words, is a big continuously-operating hydrogen bomb. It would, in fact, explode just like a bomb except that the gravitational forces are so enormous that it is all held together in a very nice balance.

Fortunately, there is a lot of hydrogen still left in the sun— enough to last for another few billion years in fact. Some day, however, it will be gone. What then? Will the sun collapse and cool off? No, it will collapse and get hotter! The gravitational energy developed in contracting generates still more heat, so the interior will get hotter.

And then? Eventually the internal temperature will rise to about 200,000,000°F. at which point something new will happen. The helium which was formed by the conversion of hydrogen will now be at a temperature where it can begin to "burn."

Three atoms of helium can join to make one atom of carbon; four atoms of helium can make one atom of oxygen. In both cases energy is again released so that this source of heat will maintain the internal temperature of the sun at 200,000,000°F. until the helium in turn is all used up. At this stage the sun will start to collapse again; the internal temperature will rise still higher until the point is reached at which the carbon and oxygen atoms will begin to combine to form still heavier atoms, building up eventually to elements in the neighborhood of iron. By this time, the temperature of the center may have reached several billion degrees F.

During these various processes, there are intervals of possible instability and the possibility of an explosion arises. We do not know precisely the conditions under which an explosion might take place, but explosions of distant stars have been observed in the heavens. They are known as supernovae. But at this point our knowledge gets very vague indeed. In fact, it is only in recent months that a detailed quantitative picture of the evolutionary history of the stars and of the process of atom building has been worked out by combining the knowledge of astronomy with knowledge recently acquired in the laboratories of nuclear physics. Again the problems and techniques of mathematics play an important role. Just recently Dr. Fred Hoyle of Cambridge has evolved a project for making detailed computations of the evolutionary history of the stars, a project which will require five years to complete on one of the fastest of modern computing machines. (Incidentally, those who wish to pursue this whole subject more thoroughly could do no better than read Dr. Fred Hoyle's book, *Frontiers of Astronomy,* or the special issue of *Scientific American* for September, 1956.)

A DARING AND INTRICATE ADVENTURE

This, I claim, is one of the greatest of all adventures in science—the most daring, the most intricate. The sun is only one of a billion stars in our galaxy. And there are millions of other galaxies equally large scattered through space. The faintest that can be seen on the plates of the great 200-inch telescope at Palomar are 2 billion light years away. Yet we know that the same elements—the same kinds of atoms and molecules—occur in these distant stars as in our own sun. The same laws of physics apply—the same sources of energy must exist. No doubt there are some stars which are fairly young—are just beginning to "burn" their hydrogen. Others are probably old and hot. Some stars have gone through the explosive phase. Some supernovae are still glowing after many years; some appear to be "decaying" with a half-life of two months or so, like a radioactive element. Indeed there is evidence, recently noted by Fowler, Burbidge and Hoyle at Caltech, that possibly the great explosion did produce a vast quantity of radioactive material —just as does the explosion of a thermonuclear bomb.

This is one of the most exciting aspects of the great adventure of modern astronomy—the intimate way in which it brings together sciences of spectroscopy, of nuclear physics, of electronics, of cosmology, of quantum mechanics—each one helping to fit in some piece of the vast jigsaw puzzle.

RADIO ASTRONOMY

There are other exciting developments in astronomy. Many years ago a radio physicist named Jansky was tracing down some of the sources of noise in a sensitive radio receiver. There were faint hissing sounds which he could not trace to electric motors, spark plugs, thunderstorms, or the other usual sources of "static." He eventually found that these flickering radio waves were coming from the sun! So began the science of radio astronomy.

It was not until 1946, however, that electronic techniques had been developed to allow radio observations to be made consistently and exactly. Today we know of hundreds of objects in the sky which are sources of radio waves. Some are stars like the sun; some are distant galaxies. Possibly the most interesting source is the great cloud of hydrogen gas which exists in the Milky Way galaxy and which gives off radio waves of a frequency of 1420 megacycles—a wave length of 21 centimeters, about 8 inches. In fact, there are parts of our Milky Way which are obscured by clouds of dust in space so that no light gets through. However, the radio waves from the hydrogen clouds do come through and so the only direct knowledge we have of the other side of our own galaxy beyond the dust clouds is supplied by radio waves. And from them we can learn something about the structure and velocity of that part of the galaxy.

Radio waves from the stars! Who would have thought it possible a few years ago? Or who would have thought that obscure studies at Columbia University on the energy levels in hydrogen could have led a couple of physicists (one in Holland and one at Harvard) to guess that hydrogen in space could emit 21-centimeter radio waves—then to look for such waves and find them? Today great radio antennas, radio telescopes—far larger than the 200-inch, but less expensive—are being built all over the world to explore further the nature of the stars as revealed by the radio waves which the racing electrons in their outer atmosphere emit. Since radio waves penetrate air, haze and clouds, a radio observatory does not have to be located in a clear climate, like southern California, or on a mountain top. In fact, the flat plains of Holland and the clouded moors of England and Australia have been primary locations for radio work.

They have there detected waves from sources which are so distant that for their waves to be detected here they must have been projected from a source as strong as a 50-kilowatt broadcasting station—multiplied a *million billion billion billion* times over! The power radiated is the inconceivably large figure of 10^{33} kilowatts. That's as much energy as the total energy from a hundred billion suns. It is lucky indeed that that source is so far away. If it were much closer, the earth would be so blanketed by radio "static" that radio and television broadcasting would be completely impossible. It is possible that radio telescopes may be detecting objects that are so far away that they cannot be seen or photographed, even with the Palomar telescope.

We see then that astronomy, though it is one of the oldest sciences, is being rejuvenated even today. New telescopes have made our distance measurements more accurate; new electronic techniques are extending the power of both optical and radio telescopes; new knowledge of nuclear physics is helping us understand how the energy of stars is produced, how all the different chemical elements are built up from primordial hydrogen, how the stars evolve, how some blow up, condense again and begin a new existence.

THE LANGUAGE OF MODERN SCIENCE

I am told that back in the 15th century so few people could read that millions of young people who were contemporaries of Columbus, Magellan and the other early explorers had never heard of their explorations—never knew that the New World had been discovered or that a ship had sailed clear 'round the earth.

Today we run the danger that because our school children are unable to "read" the language of modern science, they too will miss knowing about the great explorations of this generation—the intellectual examination of the frontiers of space. It is true that some day people may travel out into space beyond the earth. But such excursions will be limited indeed. We could conceivably reach the moon in one day of travel at 10 times the speed of sound. We could reach Mars in 6 months. But to come into the vicinity of even the nearest star would require 100,000 years. Even at 100 times the speed of sound it would take 10,000 years. Hence, the only experience that human beings will have with the far reaches of space will be through the messages brought by light and radio waves. And even these, the fastest of all messengers, have been on the way for millions or billions of years.

So let us make it possible for our new generation to have the fun of understanding these marvelous adventure stories. Just a little familiarity with mathematics and science will help a lot.

The adventures of science are by no means confined to outer space. And the chief practical reason for learning the language of science may not be to understand about distant galaxies, but to understand what is going on right here on earth. There are adventures in each day's routine.

242

You arise in the morning to the ring of an alarm clock—an electric clock, no doubt, synchronized within seconds to millions of other clocks all over the country, all over the world. Synchronization is achieved by the miracle of alternating current in our power lines, connected in a network extending hundreds of miles, and connected by radio to other networks far away. Adventures? Just follow those alternating current impulses back along the wires to a transformer on a pole in the street, to higher voltage lines leading to a substation, to still higher voltage lines strung across the countryside to a power station by a dam in the mountains.

Or maybe the power station burns coal or oil—where man's most primitive discovery, fire, is producing his most modern carrier of energy, electricity. Think of the inventors, engineers, scientists—back through the generations, the centuries—who made that possible. Think of Michael Faraday in a little laboratory thrusting a magnet into a coil of wire and noting that a current was produced; pulling it out, the current was reversed —an alternating current!

A DAY'S ADVENTURE

And so, even before we awake in the morning of each day, our adventure has begun. We get out of bed, put on nylon hose, a dacron shirt or an orlon sweater—fabrics made of coal and air and water. Shades of the alchemists who tried to make gold from lead! They would have been far better off if they had made nylon from air! And as you dress be glad you are not a silk producer of Japan or a wool grower of Australia whose very livelihood is being threatened by synthetic fibers made in America. Yes, adventures in science have their tragedies too.

Your breakfast is another kind of adventure—food brought to you from the far corners of the earth, prepared over a flame which burns gas piped from Texas. And as you eat you read of world events only a few hours old—long stories, and even pictures, which have been flashed with the speed of light from London, or Calcutta, or Cairo. Only a few years ago—less than 100—a famous British physicist, Lord Kelvin, slaved away years of his life supervising the laying of a cable across the Atlantic through which feeble electric impulses (dot-dash-dot) could be pushed—slowly, but thousands of times speedier than the fastest ship.

After breakfast you step then into a real miracle—your car. You seldom look under the hood to witness the bewildering array of examples of the laws of thermodynamics, of mechanics, of electricity, of metallurgy—of almost every science and technology. All we care about is that this device converts a gallon of gasoline into miles of travel—at speeds much faster than we ought to drive.

As your day passes, you will skirt the edge of many adventures: a jet plane will streak above you; you will read that Congress is arguing about guided missiles, about satellites which leave the earth, and you wonder if the congressmen know what they are talking about.

You read that a group of scientists visited Russia—and that they found themselves in full agreement with the Russian physicists on the neutron capture cross-sections of nuclei and also on the best design of a synchrotron. You were not interested of course—but you should have been. It was another example of the fact that adventures in science are international. All countries agree on the laws of physics. We may fight over the writings of Karl Marx—but not over those of Isaac Newton or Albert Einstein. Not even in a dictatorship is it possible to suppress for long the findings of science. A fake genetics promulgated by a certain Lysenko was given official sanction in Russia for a time. But Lysenkoism is now dead; politics cannot for long suppress the facts of nature. We have tried it here too. We thought that nuclear physics could be kept secret; we forgot that scientists in other countries can ask questions of nature too —and get the same answers that we do. We also learned that secrecy in science is very expensive, for secrecy impedes the advance of science and also the advance of technology.

But your day's adventures have only begun. You drive past a TB sanitorium that is being closed—for lack of business. You pass a hospital where once fatal illnesses are cured in a few

244

days. You may see some youngsters getting polio shots and know that another dread disease is on its way to extinction.

INSIDE A LIVING CELL

If the adventures in the stars or the atomic nuclei do not interest you, what about adventures inside a living cell? In recent years giant strides have been made in unraveling the chemistry of living things. The structure of protein molecules has been worked out. And now it is found that viruses, too, are complex molecules built in the form of multiple helices. These virus molecules can be crystallized and kept on a shelf for years, like any other chemical. But when they are given a chance to enter a living cell, they begin the miraculous process of sorting out the substances in that cell and building up a new molecule just like themselves. These molecules can reproduce themselves; they possess one of the essential features of living things.

The properties and behaviors of viruses can be studied now with all the modern techniques of physics and chemistry—not solely by trial and error, but by systematic analytical methods. One by one the different harmful viruses will be isolated, bred and studied until methods of destroying or controlling them are evolved. Beneficial viruses—those that kill harmful bacteria —will also be studied and used in the control of other diseases. The days of bacterial and virus diseases are numbered. It may be years and there will be some exhausting struggles, but these elementary substances now can be understood and controlled.

These then are a few of the thrilling adventures of today's science: the understanding of genes and nuclei and stars; the unraveling of the laws of atomic physics and cosmology and chemical biology. There are also adventures in the application of this understanding to new things to make people healthier, more comfortable, and to improve their way of life.

These adventures are daily getting more exciting. And they are adventures that more and more people will eventually participate in. The fraction of the United States working force engaged professionally in scientific and engineering pursuits has multiplied by 5 in the past 50 years. It can't multiply by 5 again else it would be getting up to 100 percent. But it may well double. The need is great and the opportunities are endless. The great challenge of our school system is to help every child with potential talents to develop them to the utmost.

THE ENJOYMENT OF SCIENCE

But men and women without professional interests in science may still enjoy these adventures of science. The language of the atom can be learned. After all, people enjoy music who do not perform. People enjoy literature who do not write. People enjoy adventure stories who cannot walk. Lawyers and businessmen and English teachers have learned to enjoy science.

For the exciting adventures of science have a great immediacy. From morning alarm to evening TV program we are living in a world which has resulted from adventures in science. Just as the great adventure of Columbus opened a new continent, so the inspired adventures of many scientists—from Galileo to Einstein; from Newton to Bohr; from Faraday to Edison to the thousands of trained men and women working today in laboratories throughout the world—have created on this new continent a new kind of civilization. There are certain things about this civilization that we are not satisfied with. It is far from perfect. But the defects will be fixed by those who understand the nature of the world in which we live. The world will be made better by knowledge, not by ignorance.

But the adventures in science are not only fun; they are an essential part of our everyday intelligent living. I have referred to congressmen who vote on vast technical projects which they cannot possibly understand. But men and women in everyday life, in business, in law, in politics, are experiencing and making decisions on things which they too cannot understand. We spent strenuous efforts in this country to reduce illiteracy, to make it possible for every man, woman and child to read and write. We succeeded—but we face a new type of illiteracy today in which citizens are unable to read and understand the things about which they must make decisions, all the way from spending billions on nuclear energy to investing a few thousand dollars in a new chemical company; decisions as to what to do about smog; about putting fluorine in drinking water; about paying higher salaries to teachers of science. The ability to understand the adventures in science has a real practical value in addition.

But there are certain illusions about science and mathematics that must be eliminated before the adventures of science can be appreciated and advanced more rapidly in America.

The first illusion is that mathematics is too hard for young minds to grasp. That is false. Properly presented and properly taught, mathematics is an exciting adventure—especially for youngsters. What has made it seem hard is the endless procession of dull and useless problems which are normally taught— "How many square rods in 19½ acres?" or "If A has 3 apples and B has twice as many as A and C together . . . ?"—you know the kind. Why crush the glorious excitement of the great principles of algebra, geometry, trigonometry—yes, and calculus—with an avalanche of useless detail? I suggest that to prepare a really first-class series of 7th- to 12th-grade texts on mathematics that really arrest a youngster's imagination, challenge his curiosity, and develop his quantitative reasoning, would be the greatest project that a teachers' group could undertake.

The second illusion that must be eliminated is that mathematics can be taught by teachers who don't know any math— or are only a chapter ahead of the student. As long as teachers of math must take 16 hours of education and only 3 hours of math, mathematics will be badly taught. For it is a subject which becomes really alive only with years of study and can be conveyed in simple and exciting ways to students only by those who have themselves caught its true spirit. In this respect, it is like most other subjects of real intellectual content— it will certainly be taught badly by those who know nothing about it, no matter how much methodology they have learned.

A LIBERAL EDUCATION

A third illusion that needs crushing is that mathematics

and science are narrow, technical or vocational subjects and that only humanities and social science are "liberal" and "broadening" and teach one how to get along with human beings. Nonsense! Mathematics and science are great intellectual adventures that have enlarged and broadened men's intellectual horizons, freed the human spirit from ignorance and fear, and elevated him above a primitive existence. They are a proper part of every liberal education. And if our country is to continue to make progress in evolving the material tools necessary to insure attaining the economic, political and moral goals which we seek, then we as a nation had better re-examine the adequacy of our school curricula in preparing young people to talk the language and understand the problems of *tomorrow*.

For if we are cheating our children of the opportunity of enjoying the adventures in science, we are also cheating our country of the benefits of profiting and prospering from the talents of its people.

L. A. DuBRIDGE

Exploring the Unknown

IN THE END, THIS IS THE WAY WE WILL CONQUER FEAR
—BY CONTINUING TO EXPLORE THE UNKNOWN IN EVERY FIELD
OF HUMAN ENDEAVOR.

Industrial research in America today is, taken all together, an enormous and far-flung enterprise. It must account for the expenditure of between 3 and 4 billion dollars a year, of which the Federal Government supplies about one-half. Hundreds of thousands of scientists, engineers and technical workers are engaged in it. There are products of such research which were unknown 20 years ago but which today account for substantial fractions of the income of many companies—and the entire income of some companies.

Yet, 20 years ago industrial research was still only an adolescent. Forty years ago it was a mere child and 50 years ago it hardly existed at all. Now 50 years is not a very long span in human history. From the long-term view, industrial research has literally exploded into being in a miraculously short period. Why did it not begin sooner?

The answer to that is simple. Industrial research is, I take it, the process of putting scientific knowledge to work for the purpose of developing new industrial products and techniques. Scientific knowledge thus had to exist before the exploitation and use of such knowledge could come about. But the scientific

249

knowledge of, let us say, the theory and structure of atoms and molecules—on which much of the modern chemical industry is based—was only coming into focus 40 years ago. The electron and X-rays were discovered less than 60 years ago; radio waves are 67 years old; the decisive discoveries on the nature and behavior of electricity were made by Faraday only 110 years ago. And, for that matter, modern science itself came into existence less than 300 years ago. It was then that Newton put together the observations of Galileo on rolling marbles, of Tycho Brahe and Kepler on the motions of the planets and deduced the first great theoretical principles of physical science; the laws of motion and of gravitation.

After thousands of years of civilized history, it was not until the 17th century that man finally uncovered the fact that nature operated in accordance with laws that could be discovered; laws that were so exact that they could be used to predict with precision the behavior of physical bodies. And at the same time men were uncovering these startling regularities of nature— the grand and beautifully simple laws which nature obeyed— they also discovered the infinite complexity of nature; that there were undreamed-of phenomena awaiting discovery—for those who were willing and able to explore.

And so it was that during the past 300 years scientific knowledge slowly came into being until, at the beginning of the 20th century the time was ripe for the explosive rise of applied science.

Now this development of applied science has been one of the most spectacular phenomena of our generation. It has revolutionized our way of living—and possibly also our way of dying. It has transformed the lives of millions of people, and has elevated their hopes and ambitions too. Science has become the new "magic"—it is, some people seem to think, capable of doing anything.

And yet there are disquieting notes mixed in with the growth in public acclaim for applied science. The refrigerators and toothpaste are appreciated and enjoyed. But the scientific knowledge which made all these things possible is forgotten or ignored. The latest gadget for better living is promptly purchased on the installment plan. But when someone mentions weapons for defense, a great cry goes up: "The scientists are trying to destroy us." In fact, in these days it has become feasible in some circles to say we have had "too much science"; that "science is the cause of most of the world's troubles"; that we ought to "return to the liberal arts"; that science ought now to wait a while so that social science can "catch up." The idea is, presumably, that social science or the liberal arts or something will then teach us all how to love one another so that human beings won't end up by atom-bombing themselves off the face of the earth!

To hear some people talk, you would think that science causes nothing but unhappiness, conflict, war; that science denies the finer things of life; is too "technical" to have a place of respect in modern education. You would think that the fate of the world rested on the outcome of some sort of a race between scientists on the one hand and all the historians, philosophers, writers, economists, poets, preachers, and political and social scientists on the other, with the implication that if science wins, the human race will be blasted to oblivion.

ANTI-SCIENCE

Some people talk as though they really believe some or all of these things. In fact, there are some very important people who are making it their business to promote these ideas. I think it is time that we, the scientific community, began to do something about the attacks which have been made on science and on scientists. For they are having profound and even terrifying effects. They have already caused an alarming drop, for example, in the number of high school students who take mathematics and physics. They have caused many a serious-minded college or university student to avoid all science courses and to look with disdain on those who major in science fields. They have caused well-meaning people to believe that scientists are necessarily so specialized and blind as to be wholly untrustworthy the moment they step out of the laboratory, and to class all scientists and engineers as "narrow-minded technicians."

How then do we go about meeting these charges, these misunderstandings and prejudices?

First, I want to say that I do not think the way to do it is to brag more about the gadgets and devices and weapons which have come about as a result of the systematic attempts to make use of scientific knowledge. I have great admiration for deep freezes and bulldozers and jet airplanes and detergents and penicillin—and even pink and white Cadillacs. But the values of science really do not lie in these things in themselves. Rather, they lie in the way in which pure and applied science contribute to man's physical, intellectual and spiritual well-being. The true values of science lie not in its by-products, but in its goals; not in its dollar value, but in its human value. The value of science will be judged not by how fast it helps us to travel, but where it helps us to go.

In order to get a better look at this problem, I think we should forget about applied science for a moment and think about basic science, the pure search for knowledge.

First let us ask why men *are* scientists. Why do some men spend their lives in pure science? Well, I can assure you it is not because of any desire to destroy the world or even to harm a single human being, or make him less happy. Quite the contrary! Nor is the scientist usually impelled primarily by a desire to make money—though I am sure he looks forward to receiving the monthly paycheck as much as anyone (especially when the fresh Ph.D. today can go out into his first job at $10,00 a year).

On the other hand, I can't claim either that the scientist's objective is wholly or primarily an altruistic one—trying to make the world over into a Utopia, for example. He simply hopes that his work will be some contribution to human welfare.

Primarily, it seems to me, the scientist is impelled by certain basic human urges. One is the urge to explore. The spirit of Christopher Columbus, of Magellan, of Admiral Byrd; the spirit of all those who have first discovered unknown places or climbed unconquered mountains—such a spirit is in each of us to some extent. It is certainly in every scientist, even though few of them have bothered to recognize it.

Another common human urge is the urge to create. Every human being would like to create something new. Just look at the "do-it-yourself" business! Some people create music or poetry; some create beautiful pictures, fine statues, magnificent buildings, exquisite furniture or jewelry or clothing. So too, a new discovery in science is a creation—and in the eyes of scientists it has a beauty and an elegance all its own. To be able to contribute, even in only a small way, to the building of the magnificent edifice which we call science is a great creative satisfaction.

Add to the urges of exploration and creation the urge of competition—the desire to be the first to find a given piece of knowledge—and one has a good description of a scientist's motivation.

PUBLIC UNDERSTANDING

How can it be then that the structure of science, which results from such almost purely aesthetic motivation and which is admired by the scientist as a thing of beauty and a joy forever, can be looked on by the general public as an ugly, mundane, or even dangerous product? It is true, of course, that some works of art are admired only by the artist, and the artist then complains that the public doesn't "understand" his work. So I guess the scientist also sighs that the public does not understand *him* or what he does. But, if science is to have the surging vitality that it should have in modern America, the public should understand science.

Our usual attempts in this direction, however, are often inadequate. We usually try to explain the value of science not by telling why it is beautiful, but only why it is *useful*. Hence, the public concludes that scientists are materialists, that they are mere technicians, specialists, unaware of the finer things of life!

Now, explaining why a thing is beautiful is much harder than explaining why it might be useful. Yet it is worth trying. We can be encouraged, I think, by the great public interest in astronomy. Everyone knows that the Palomar 200-inch tele-

253

scope has no very "practical" uses. Yet thousands of people journey to Palomar every month to see that magnificent instrument and to hear about the awe-inspiring picture of the universe which it is revealing. Exploring the universe is an adventure which almost anyone envies and admires. And the beauty and grandeur of the universe is at least dimly visible to almost everyone who cares to listen and to look at pictures.

However, I claim there is an equal beauty and grandeur to the picture of an atom of iron or copper or uranium which modern science has revealed. Even more beauty, perhaps, is to be found in the structure of a protein molecule. More still is in the structure of the gene as it is built up of spirals of nucleic acids all so ingeniously designed that the gene can make a copy of itself—can reproduce its kind. With all due respect, I claim there is as much beauty in such things as can be found in great paintings or fine literature or music.

Am I crazy?

ONE OF THE LIBERAL ARTS

In any case, if science were seen and taught in such a light, we would not see the presidents of great universities (not scientists) going around the country saying, "There is too much emphasis on science; let us return to the liberal arts."

Science *is* one of the liberal arts—one of the first and greatest of them. It certainly is one of man's greatest arts and is one which has done the most to *liberate* the human spirit. Science, more than any other subject, has freed men from ignorance and from consequent fear. Consequently, it has elevated man, intellectually and spiritually.

How does it happen that many people have just the opposite conception—that science has been degrading to man; has made him materialistic, unmoral? Apparently it is because scientists are wholly misunderstood.

For example, a distinguished religious leader recently said, "Modern technologists and scientists have come to regard themselves as supreme masters of the universe." Well! That's news to me. Some scientists might have good ideas about some improvements they would make if they were! But the only men in recent times who have thought themselves masters of the universe (Hitler, Mussolini, Stalin) were certainly not scientists! Science is a pursuit that makes men humble—because in learning a few things we come upon so many that we don't know.

But why do these misconceptions of scientists exist?

Personally, I put part of the blame for this on certain misguided philosophers. For example, since the instruments of the scientists have discovered no nonmaterial or nonphysical aspects of the world, therefore the scientist is accused of saying that such immaterial things do not exist. Because the anatomist found no place in the body to house a soul, therefore, says the philosopher, this proves man has no soul! That's nonsense, of course. Physical instruments were never intended to measure nonphysical things and, by their nature, they can never do so. Science thus gives no support to materialism—nor, of course, can it ever disprove it either. Philosophical theories are just not susceptible to experimental proof or disproof.

MISUNDERSTANDING AND MISREPRESENTATION

Again—philosophers have gone wild speculating about the theory of relativity and its philosophical implications. Now the special theory of relativity is simply a theory in physics which describes how the results of observations made on various phenomena will depend on how the observer is moving relative to what he observes. "Aha!" says the philosopher, "that means everything is relative; nothing is absolute. There are no absolutes physically; therefore there are none intellectually or morally either. It all depends on your point of view."

Nonsense again. Aside from the fact that physical theories have no necessary relevance to moral problems, the philosopher totally misunderstands Einstein's relativity theory. Though the relativity theory did show that many observed quantities were changed when there was relative motion (as had always been known), Einstein found that certain things (the velocity of light, for example) were unchanged. They were "relativistically invariant"; they were "absolutes."

A beautiful physical theory thus has been misunderstood and misused; again science has been misrepresented.

Then, too, there were philosophers who said that the theory of evolution denied the existence of God! No scientific theory can either affirm or deny a spiritual existence, of course. But, even so, why does anyone think it is degrading to have God create man by the beautiful processes of organic evolution rather than by making him out of a piece of clay? Especially when He then made Eve by the process of swiping one of Adam's ribs!

To me the whole picture of the universe as revealed by science, as well as the picture of the processes that go on within it and of the life that inhabits it, is one of magnificence, vastness, order, splendor, precision, beauty. It is a picture that exalts the Creator of the Universe—and exalts the dignity of the men He created, the men who can discover and comprehend this majesty of creation.

You see, perhaps, why I can claim that science is one of the "liberalizing arts." You see why it deserves a place of respect along with the humanities, the fine arts and social and behavioral studies as partners and coequals in the intellectual and cultural fields. You see why to dismiss science as too "technical" and too "vocational" is both false and revolting.

However, there are men who say science is still not enough. Of course it isn't! And I do not know any scientist who ever claimed it was. The study of the physical world is *one* important aspect of man's use of his intelligence and his talents. It is one expression of the urge to know, to create. But the studies of the world of human beings, of the world of beauty and the world of moral values are equally essential activities—all are necessary to the educated and civilized man.

SCIENCE IS NOT ENOUGH

Some of those who say science is not enough, however, mean more than that. They mean to reduce science, to eliminate it, to cast it out of a liberal education, to put it in the same class with manual training and shop work. Because science is useful it is dismissed as "mere vocationalism." Because it is exact it is said to be "too technical." There has been created a cult of antiscience—a group of superior beings who read only old books, look only at old pictures, think only old thoughts. They disdain the crass technicalities of algebra, the boring regularities of Newton's laws, the smelly products of chemistry. (However, at the first opportunity they don their nylon shirts and hose and take a Super-Constellation to Paris!)

And why do these antiscientists get so wide a hearing? There are many complex reasons—but partly it is our own fault—the fault of scientists. We have, in times past, not distinguished between the problem of training an automobile mechanic and of educating a mechanical engineer. As late as 20 years ago, there were so-called engineering colleges which trained only the hands and not the mind. There were also schools which had eliminated all educational opportunities except in the scientific and technical fields.

But I know of no such colleges today. The best modern institutes of technology offer superb programs in humanities and social studies—and they insist that the students take them. Overspecialized scientists or engineers are no longer being graduated in any numbers from the American system of higher education—and the number who graduated in the past was not so large as many people pretend. Most of the scientists and engineers that I know—of any age—are well-educated, well-rounded people: many are persons of very extraordinary culture and cultivation. Of course, I also know a few characters who can talk of nothing but their specialty. But I know similar people who are lawyers, doctors, business men and English professors too.

Every now and then even the proponents of the liberal arts realize that some of their members have gone too far and claimed too much. Listen to this wonderful statement by Lynn White, Jr., President of Mills College:

"Spokesmen for the colleges (including me) are constantly trumpeting the importance of the liberal arts as inculcating resourcefulness, spontaneity of spirit, the ability to meet unexpected situations, and that sort of thing. In its extreme form this sound metal contains a certain alloy of nonsense. The Mid-Victorian view that reading Horace at Oxford prepared one to be proconsul over steaming tropical millions overlooked the fact that Oxford in its great days was deftly designed to convince its aristocratic denizens that they were God's anointed, pre-destined to shepherd and shear the less elect portions of the human race. Such massive self-confidence, even when occasionally coupled with stupidity and inefficiency, was irresistible on the banks of the great, gray-green, greasy Limpopo and one may doubt whether the Latin poets had much to do with the diffusion of the Union Jack."

I think it is important then that we think of pure science as a dignifying and edifying—as well as a useful—area of human learning. Possibly then when we come to think of applied science we will think and speak not only of the useful gadgets that we produce, but of the goals of human comfort, leisure, culture and happiness they help us achieve.

Perhaps, however, the most damaging blows struck by the antiscientists are those which prey upon the fears and dangers of the modern world which applied science has helped to build. These dangers are indeed real and terrifying. And scientists will do well to continue making factual statements about what these dangers are. Thermonuclear bombs are really horribly devastating weapons—and don't let anyone tell you otherwise.

FREEDOM FROM DANGER

But the real basis for our fears today is not the human ingenuity that produced terrible weapons, but the human cussedness that threatens to use such weapons against us. The world has never been free from danger. But if we contrast the western world of today with that of 100 years ago, we find much to be proud of. We have eliminated slavery—because our work is now done for us by lumps of coal and pools of oil. We have eliminated much of human suffering caused by ailments and disease —and we will no longer tolerate the existence of suffering caused by human cruelty or neglect.

We have eliminated many evils and many dangers; we face many more of both old and new varieties. But we shall conquer danger not by weeping and wailing, not by stopping or impeding any worthwhile human endeavor, by belittling any noble human aspiration. We shall conquer fear in the end only if we continue to explore the unknown in every field of human endeavor, continue to extend always the frontiers of knowledge, aiming always to elevate the human mind and the human spirit.

RICHARD P. FEYNMAN

The Value of Science

OF ALL ITS MANY VALUES, THE GREATEST
MUST BE THE FREEDOM TO DOUBT.

From time to time, people suggest to me that scientists ought to give more consideration to social problems—especially that they should be more responsible in considering the impact of science upon society. This same suggestion must be made to many other scientists, and it seems to be generally believed that if the scientists would only look at these very difficult social problems and not spend so much time fooling with the less vital scientific ones, great success would come of it.

It seems to me that we do think about these problems from time to time, but we don't put full-time effort into them—the reason being that we know we don't have any magic formula for solving problems, that social problems are very much harder than scientific ones, and that we usually don't get anywhere when we do think about them.

I believe that a scientist looking at nonscientific problems is just as dumb as the next guy—and when he talks about a nonscientific matter, he will sound as naive as anyone untrained in the matter. Since the question of the value of science is not a scientific subject, this discussion is dedicated to proving my point—by example.

The first way in which science is of value is familiar to every-

one. It is that scientific knowledge enables us to do all kinds
of things and to make all kinds of things. Of course if we make
good things, it is not only to the credit of science; it is also to
the credit of the moral choice which led us to good work. Scientific knowledge is an enabling power to do either good or
bad—but it does not carry instructions on how to use it. Such
power has evident value—even though the power may be negated
by what one does.

I learned a way of expressing this common human problem
on a trip to Honolulu. In a Buddhist temple there, the man in
charge explained a little bit about the Buddhist religion for
tourists, and then ended his talk by telling them he had something to say to them that they would *never* forget—and I have
never forgotten it. It was a proverb of the Buddhist religion:
"To every man is given the key to the gates of heaven; the
same key opens the gates of hell."

What then, is the value of the key to heaven? It is true that
if we lack clear instructions that determine which is the gate to
heaven and which the gate to hell, the key may be a dangerous
object to use, but it obviously has value. How can we enter
heaven without it?

The instructions, also, would be of no value without the key.
So it is evident that, in spite of the fact that science could
produce enormous horror in the world, it is of value because it
can produce *something*.

Another value of science is the fun called intellectual enjoyment which some people get from reading and learning and
thinking about it, and which others get from working in it. This
is a very real and important point and one which is not considered enough by those who tell us it is our social responsibility to reflect on the impact of science on society.

Is this mere personal enjoyment of value to society as a
whole? No! But it is also a responsibility to consider the value
of society itself. Is it, in the last analysis, to arrange things so
that people can enjoy things? If so, the enjoyment of science is
as important as anything else.

But I would like *not* to underestimate the value of the world view which is the result of scientific effort. We have been led to imagine all sorts of things infinitely more marvelous than the imaginings of poets and dreamers of the past. It shows that the imagination of nature is far, far greater than the imagination of man. For instance, how much more remarkable it is for us all to be stuck—half of us upside down—by a mysterious attraction, to a spinning ball that has been swinging in space for billions of years, than to be carried on the back of an elephant supported on a tortoise swimming in a bottomless sea.

I have thought about these things so many times alone that I hope you will excuse me if I remind you of some thoughts that I am sure you have all had—or this type of thought—which no one could ever have had in the past, because people then didn't have the information we have about the world today.

For instance, I stand at the seashore, alone, and start to think. There are the rushing waves . . . mountains of molecules, each stupidly minding its own business . . . trillions apart . . . yet forming white surf in unison.

Ages on ages . . . before any eyes could see . . . year after year . . . thunderously pounding the shore as now. For whom, for what? . . . on a dead planet, with no life to entertain.

Never at rest . . . tortured by energy . . . wasted prodigiously by the sun . . . poured into space. A mite makes the sea roar.

Deep in the sea, all molecules repeat the patterns of one another till complex new ones are formed. They make others like themselves . . . and a new dance starts.

Growing in size and complexity . . . living things, masses of atoms, DNA, protein . . . dancing a pattern ever more intricate.

Out of the cradle onto the dry land . . . here it is standing . . . atoms with consciousness . . . matter with curiosity.

Stands at the sea . . . wonders at wondering . . . I . . . a universe of atoms . . . an atom in the universe.

THE GRAND ADVENTURE

The same thrill, the same awe and mystery, come again and again when we look at any problem deeply enough. With more knowledge comes deeper, more wonderful mystery, luring one on to penetrate deeper still. Never concerned that the answer may prove disappointing, but with pleasure and confidence we turn over each new stone to find unimagined strangeness leading on to more wonderful questions and mysteries—certainly a grand adventure!

It is true that few unscientific people have this particular type of religious experience. Our poets do not write about it; our artists do not try to portray this remarkable thing. I don't know why. Is nobody inspired by our present picture of the universe? The value of science remains unsung by singers, so you are reduced to hearing—not a song or a poem, but an evening lecture about it. This is not yet a scientific age.

Perhaps one of the reasons is that you have to know how to read the music. For instance, the scientific article says, perhaps, something like this: "The radioactive phosphorus content of the cerebrum of the rat decreases to one-half in a period of two weeks." Now, what does that mean?

It means that phosphorus that is in the brain of a rat (and also in mine, and yours) is not the same phosphorus as it was two weeks ago, but that all of the atoms that are in the brain are being replaced, and the ones that were there before have gone away.

So what is this mind, what are these atoms with consciousness? Last week's potatoes! That is what now can *remember* what was going on in my mind a year ago—a mind which has long ago been replaced.

That is what it means when one discovers how long it takes for the atoms of the brain to be replaced by other atoms, to note that the thing which I call my individuality is only a pattern or dance. The atoms come into my brain, dance a dance, then go out; always new atoms but always doing the same dance, remembering what the dance was yesterday.

THE REMARKABLE IDEA

When we read about this in the newspaper, it says, "The scientist says that this discovery may have importance in the cure of cancer." The paper is only interested in the use of the idea, not the idea itself. Hardly anyone can understand the importance of an idea, it is so remarkable. Except that, possibly, some children catch on. And when a child catches on to an idea like that, we have a scientist. These ideas do filter down (in spite of all the conversation about TV replacing thinking), and lots of kids get the spirit—and when they have the spirit you have a scientist. It's too late for them to get the spirit when they are in our universities, so we must attempt to explain these ideas to children.

I would now like to turn to a third value that science has. It is a little more indirect, but not much. The scientist has a lot of experience with ignorance and doubt and uncertainty, and this experience is of very great importance, I think. When a scientist doesn't know the answer to a problem, he is ignorant. When he has a hunch as to what the result is, he is uncertain. And when he is pretty darn sure of what the result is going to be, he is in some doubt. We have found it of paramount importance that in order to progress we must recognize the ignorance and leave room for doubt. Scientific knowledge is a body of statements of varying degrees of certainty— some most unsure, some nearly sure, none *absolutely* certain.

Now, we scientists are used to this, and we take it for granted that it is perfectly consistent to be unsure—that it is possible to live and *not* know. But I don't know whether everyone realizes that this is true. Our freedom to doubt was born of a struggle against authority in the early days of science. It was a very deep and strong struggle. Permit us to question—to doubt, that's all—not to be sure. And I think it is important that we do not forget the importance of this struggle and thus perhaps lose what we have gained. Here lies a responsibility to society.

We are all sad when we think of the wondrous potentialities human beings seem to have, as contrasted with their small accomplishments. Again and again people have thought that we could do much better. They of the past saw in the nightmare of their times a dream for the future. We, of their future, see that their dreams, in certain ways surpassed, have in many ways remained dreams. The hopes for the future today are, in good share, those of yesterday.

EDUCATION, FOR GOOD AND EVIL

Once some thought that the possibilities people had were not developed because most of those people were ignorant. With education universal, could all men be Voltaires? Bad can be taught at least as efficiently as good. Education is a strong force, but for either good or evil.

Communications between nations must promote understanding: so went another dream. But the machines of communication can be channeled or choked. What is communicated can be truth or lie. Communication is a strong force also, but for either good or bad.

The applied sciences should free men of material problems at least. Medicine controls diseases. And the record here seems all to the good. Yet there are men patiently working to create great plagues and poisons. They are to be used in warfare tomorrow.

Nearly everybody dislikes war. Our dream today is peace. In peace, man can develop best the enormous possibilities he seems to have. But maybe future men will find that peace, too, can be good and bad. Perhaps peaceful men will drink out of boredom. Then perhaps drink will become the great problem which seems to keep man from getting all he thinks he should out of his abilities.

Clearly, peace is a great force, as is sobriety, as are material power, communication, education, honesty and the ideals of many dreamers.

We have more of these forces to control than did the ancients. And maybe we are doing a little better than most of them could do. But what we ought to be able to do seems gigantic compared with our confused accomplishments.

Why is this? Why can't we conquer ourselves?

Because we find that even great forces and abilities do not seem to carry with them clear instructions on how to use them.

As an example, the great accumulation of understanding as to how the physical world behaves only convinces one that this behavior seems to have a kind of meaninglessness. The sciences do not directly teach good and bad.

Through all ages men have tried to fathom the meaning of life. They have realized that if some direction or meaning could be given to our actions, great human forces would be unleashed. So, very many answers must have been given to the question of the meaning of it all. But they have been of all different sorts, and the proponents of one answer have looked with horror at the actions of the believers in another. Horror, because from a disagreeing point of view all the great potentialities of the race were being channeled into a false and confining blind alley. In fact, it is from the history of the enormous monstrosities created by false belief that philosophers have realized the apparently infinite and wondrous capacities of human beings. The dream is to find the open channel.

What, then, is the meaning of it all? What can we say to dispel the mystery of existence?

If we take everything into account, not only what the ancients knew, but all of what we know today that they didn't know, then I think that we must frankly admit that *we do not know*.

But, in admitting this, we have probably found the open channel.

This is not a new idea; this is the idea of the age of reason. This is the philosophy that guided the men who made the democracy that we live under. The idea that no one really knew how to run a government led to the idea that we should arrange a system by which new ideas could be developed, tried out, tossed out, more new ideas brought in; a trial and error system. This method was a result of the fact that science was already showing itself to be a successful venture at the end of the 18th century. Even then it was clear to socially-minded people that the openness of the possibilities was an opportunity, and that doubt and discussion were essential to progress into the unknown. If we want to solve a problem that we have never solved before, we must leave the door to the unknown ajar.

OUR RESPONSIBILITY AS SCIENTISTS

We are at the very beginning of time for the human race. It is not unreasonable that we grapple with problems. There are tens of thousands of years in the future. Our responsibility is to do what we can, learn what we can, improve the solutions and pass them on. It is our responsibility to leave the men of the future a free hand. In the impetuous youth of humanity, we can make grave errors that can stunt our growth for a long time. This we will do if we say we have the answers now, so young and ignorant; if we suppress all discussion, all criticism, saying, "This is it, boys, man is saved!" and thus doom man for a long time to the chains of authority, confined to the limits of our present imagination. It has been done so many times before.

It is our responsibility as scientists, knowing the great progress and great value of a satisfactory philosophy of ignorance, the great progress that is the fruit of freedom of thought, to proclaim the value of this freedom, to teach how doubt is not to be feared but welcomed and discussed, and to demand this freedom as our duty to all coming generations.

FRED HOYLE

The Place of Technology in Civilization

"TECHNOLOGY CONTROLS CIVILIZATION . . . THE DETAILS
AND VARIATIONS IN SOCIAL ORGANIZATIONS
ARE RELATIVELY UNIMPORTANT . . ."

One of the things that I have found over the years, in discussing matters with my colleagues in humanities, is a profound difference of viewpoint between the scientist and the humanist concerning the organization of society. I've noticed that after discussion into human problems, the humanities side usually ends by saying, "Well, all of these problems are really very complicated; a very large number of factors are involved—and *we* think that you scientists are always looking for explanations that are too simple."

On the other hand, reflecting the scientific point of view, I have maintained what I think is the standard belief, in science, that no matter how complicated a problem one has to deal with, a solution can always be found. Some of our scientific problems are indeed complex, but it is curious how often one finds that things that seemed impossible of solution at one time turn out to have a perfectly straightforward and understandable answer. I have felt for some years that the situation with human affairs may be much the same.

Perhaps I should extend this a little. When our friends in the humanities say that ordinary social affairs are very complicated, there is a sense in which they are perfectly right; human affairs are complicated in the sense that many factors are involved. But this does not really impress a scientist, because, in science, problems with many factors are often quite as easy to deal with as problems with only a few factors. Let me give an example.

Think about the air in this room. We know that the air is composed of a swarm of tiny particles—there are nearly thirty billion billion particles to the cubic centimeter—so you see that the total number is very large. It would be possible to argue that the whole problem of tracing the properties of all these particles is enormously complicated. They are all jostling each other, colliding with each other, and evidently a detailed tracing of their individual motions would be a problem of surpassing complexity. But that is not how the scientist goes about the matter. Instead of worrying about individuals, he tackles the problem of finding how the particles behave *on the average*. And a calculation of the average situation turns out to be simplified, not made more difficult, by the very complexity of the situation. In a word, the very complexity allows us to adopt the powerful methods of statistics.

THE INDIVIDUAL AND SOCIETY

This analogy comes close, I think, to the human situation. If one is concerned to describe the fate of a particular individual, or of a comparatively small group of individuals, then certainly one has a very complex problem on one's hands that probably cannot readily be solved. But if one is concerned to speak of the evolution of human society as a whole, then, just as with the gas problem, matters become comparatively simple. A great deal of what happens in our daily lives averages out when taken statistically. There are only a few factors happening at any given time that are going to have outstanding effects on the future.

To give you a simple example from history, take the case of Napoleon. Apparently he produced enormous disturbances in his day, and everybody thought that the things he did were very important. But by now we can see that present-day society would hardly be any different if Napoleon had never lived. The political and military disturbances that he produced were transitory and did not have a lasting effect. They have averaged out to zero.

SIMPLICITY IN COMPLEXITY

Well, that is the main background for what I am going to say: that, while on the surface human affairs are complex, underneath, on the large scale, things are really quite simple.

Perhaps next I ought to say what factors of the human problem I think to be important, and what factors I believe to be unimportant. First then, what are the things that don't matter? Here are a few of them: The constant striving of one community against another; war; the particular social organizations adopted by different communities. These are the things that we spend a great deal of time on, and these are the things that average out to zero. By contrast, the things that do matter are the making of technological discoveries, and this brings me to the case that I wish to make—that technology controls civilization, and that the details and variations in social organizations are relatively unimportant, except where the social organization in some degree affects technology itself.

Now, shall we look at the evidence for this view? One can readily see the importance of technology by comparing our present situation here today with the position of Stone Age man. Stone Age man had the same earth, he had the same resources as we have today, but he could do little with them. Why? Because he did not have the "know-how." He did not have the technology. Notice that Stone Age man was not lacking in brains. (We have pretty fair indication from certain activities of Stone Age people that their mental stature was not much inferior to ours, if it was at all inferior.) He was lacking in knowledge.

So we can certainly say that technological discoveries make an enormous difference, because, if we didn't have the "know-how," we would be back—right now, at this minute—in the

Stone Age. I often think that the best reply to anyone who affects to despise technology would be: "You despise technology? All right then, back you go to the Stone Age!"

TECHNOLOGY IN THE STONE AGE

Even to the Stone Age people themselves, technology was a very important matter. The Stone Age, which I am speaking of rather loosely now, lasted from about 200,000 years ago to about 6000 years ago. Over that period there were important changes and great inventions. Man had very little 200,000 years ago. He didn't know how to clothe himself; he didn't even know much about how to provide shelter. His tools—his equipment for dealing with situations that might arise in hunting, for example—were no better than odd bits of stones that he had managed to pick up off the ground. Then, over the millennia, people discovered that one could make better tools, not by picking up stones in their natural state, but by shaping them.

It is rather curious that two independent methods of shaping were discovered. In one case people took stones and chipped bits off until the required shape was left. The other technique was to take larger stones and to make tools out of the chippings. In one case it was the core that was wanted, and in the other case it was the bits that were chipped off that were wanted.

A FIGHTING MATTER

The surprising thing is that great areas in Europe and Asia would use one system almost uniformly, and other areas would use the other system. I have no doubt that, when the two groups came in contact with each other, they fought fiercely over which way was best to cut up stones.

Then, men learned how to make more refined tools—axes, spears, the harpoon, and the bow and arrow. Bone needles were used in the making of clothes, and tents were made out of the hides of animals.

Even these crude developments made it possible to provide for more and more people on the earth. But the really great discovery that enabled man to increase enormously in number was, of course, agriculture. Without the invention of agriculture, made some seven or eight thousand years ago—without the deliberate sowing of seeds and the reaping of crops—no large-scale social organization would have been possible at all.

THE ORIGIN OF CIVILIZATION

Agriculture made it profitable for people in certain regions to live together in fairly large numbers, particularly in river valleys, where it was possible to use irrigation methods. In Mesopotamia, for example, productivity was so much increased that a large concentration of population arose. This was the beginning of the type of social organization that we call civilization. So the origin of civilization itself was made possible by a technological discovery—namely, the discovery of agriculture. (You will realize from this remark that I am using the word "technology" in a very wide sense; to cover both the acquisition and the application of knowledge. This includes the activity that we normally call "science.")

The greater number of people that could be supported by the discovery of agriculture led to further discoveries, of which the most important was the discovery of methods of working metals; in particular, of copper and its alloys. Also, because of people coming to live together in increasing numbers, it became important that methods of writing things down should be available, to tell where a man's land started and where it ended, how many cattle he had, and things of that sort. In this way, came the beginnings of the intellectual inventions of writing, and of numbers, and the beginning of calculation.

ACHIEVEMENTS OF ANCIENT CIVILIZATIONS

So we see the technology of agriculture leading to civilization, and, following that, civilization itself producing several far-reaching discoveries. That really, however, is the sum total of what the ancient civilizations achieved, insofar as their achievements have effect on us today. It is true that they formed their different communities, that they had their social organizations, and they fought with each other in a never-ending series of wars—but by now those activities count not a jot. It is only the things they discovered that are of any importance.

When the next important discovery was made, it did not come from civilized people at all; centuries of disturbance and fighting so befuddled the wits of civilized man that he became incapable of making further discoveries. The next discovery, coming from a barbarian tribe, was the discovery of how to smelt iron; an enormous discovery, because iron is a cheap metal as well as a very strong one. Because of its cheapness it became possible for the common people to possess iron tools, in a degree that had not been possible when copper and bronze were the main metals. This meant that farmers no longer had to till the ground with crude stone ploughs, or hack away at it with stone axes. From then on they were able to have iron tools for farming.

CIVILIZATION SWINGS WEST

This had a great effect in swinging civilization away from its origins in the East. It was no longer necessary for men to be congested in the river valleys. The greater territories around the Mediterranean Basin and in Western Europe became available, once iron tools for breaking up the earth were available. So we see the swing of civilization to the Mediterranean Basin. This change was aided by a gradual change of climate that had been going on for several thousand years, which was making the territories occupied by the older civilizations somewhat too arid.

Now I would like to say just a little about the Mediterranean civilizations, and about the Roman civilization in particular, because it was the Roman civilization that led into our own. The Roman society was in essence anti-democratic. It evolved into an aristocracy that controlled everything. The ordinary people were given practically nothing, and they got increasingly less as the civilization went on. Indeed, the aristocracy reached a stage where it could see little point in keeping large numbers of poor people alive, and the condition of the ordinary people was so depressed that the population began to fall, simply because the poorer people were not able to get enough to eat. As time went on, the population declined until the aristocracy even reached the stage where it was not willing to support the Roman army. It was this that caused the collapse of the Roman Empire.

Now the importance of this anti-democratic society, from our point of view, is that it continued on in Europe in the form of the feudal system. Under the feudal system, society moved along on a very low population level. The leaders took most of the productivity and allowed very little for the support of the ordinary people.

A SHORTAGE OF PEOPLE

In such a condition, about a thousand years ago, something rather curious happened. Devastating plagues began to sweep across Europe. In these plagues a very large proportion of the population died; a third or sometimes a half of the people might be wiped out in a matter of a few months. Now, in a population which was already down to a very low level, such a plague was a far more serious matter than it would have been to the overflowing populations of the earlier civilizations. The effects of the plagues turned a low population into a real shortage of people.

This had two important effects; one was the search for machines that would take over the work for humans, so that human muscle-power was no longer required. Thus, we find a tremendous spurt of invention, starting about a thousand years ago. This was the start of modern technology, which has accelerated as the centuries have gone by.

The second effect was a reversal of moral values. The shortage of people led to the basis of our modern ideas of the value of the individual. What had started under the Romans as stark anti-democracy evolved into the most democratic society that the world has ever seen. Our present sense of values, our ideas of liberty, our bills of rights, are a product of Roman anti-democracy—a curious reflection.

This brings me to the last part of my essay. I would like to pin my conclusions down to a sharp form, and then to examine very briefly their implications. Technology decides how much we can produce. If we take the productivity of a community and divide the productivity by the population, then we arrive at what can be described as the average share. The average share decides in a very large measure the evolution of a community.

I would regard the general spirit of activity which is present here in the United States as in a large measure due to the fact that the average share is increasing and has been increasing for some time. In contrast, if we take the opposite case, where the average share decreases, then we have ample historical evidence to show that decadence and collapse is likely to ensue.

I think that the issue of whether a civilization rises or falls is really as simple as this—a rise if the average share is increasing, a fall if the average share is decreasing. If, indeed, I am at all correct in imagining that this is a basic feature of human organization, then we can reach very firm conclusions in regard to the future. We can see that the way into the future is to plan that the average share increases rather than decreases.

Now this is a matter that raises very important questions, because our productivity is something that is not guaranteed to us. It is true that, in a large measure, the earth will continue to yield its agricultural productivity so long as we have the machines with which to deal with our agricultural problems. But if we were suddenly reduced to using stone tools, then, of course, our agricultural productivity would decline enormously. So it is obviously vital that we maintain our industrial technology. The maintenance of our industrial technology is dependent largely on whether we can maintain a large supply of power and of essential metals.

As regards power, the position is not immediately serious. We now derive most of our power from coal and from oil. It is true that supplies are limited—one might say limited to about 500 years—but even if we imagine that we reach the stage where coal and oil become exhausted, then, even so, there remains the possibility of using either atomic power or solar energy.

Speaking personally, I don't think that atomic power is going to be able to take over in the long run from coal and oil. I think it will become a useful addition, but it is hardly an ultimate solution. On the other hand, plenty of energy is falling on the earth's surface every day, being radiated from the sun. Plants manage to use some of this energy. Indeed it is this energy that keeps us going physically; when we eat, we are in effect using the energy supplied to us by the sun. Eventually we shall probably be forced to use the sun's radiation in order to run industrial machinery. This would have the great advantage that effectively no limit exists to the length of time that the sun will make its radiation available. It will remain available for some thousands of millions of years, and that is as long as most of us wish to look ahead.

When we come to metals, the position is more serious, however. Already the lifetime of worked mineral deposits is of the order of fifty years for many metals. It is true that new discoveries may extend this a little, but we can see ahead of us, possibly not in our own lifetime but at least in the lifetime of our children, the day when metal deposits, in the concentration that we now regard as economically useful, will become exhausted.

THE PROBLEMS AHEAD OF US

This doesn't, of course, mean that the total supply of metals will be exhausted, because we can always go to lower and lower grades of ore. But when one goes to lower grades of ore, new processes are required to enable the ore to be smelted in an economical way; that is, by the expenditure of a reasonable amount of energy. Unless such processes can be found the consequences will be serious. If it should become extremely troublesome, for instance, to smelt a very low grade of copper ore, then effectively we shall have lost our supply of copper, which means that we shall have lost the most effective material for use in our electrical machines. So, for this reason, I would say that anyone who discovers how to smelt very low grade ores in an economical way will have a far greater effect on the future of humanity than any of our other apparently more important political activities.

The case of copper is illustrative of the problems that lie before us. Our present technology certainly is not going to be enough. New and important developments will be necessary— and in the not very distant future—if civilization is to avoid running into a period where the average share begins to decline disastrously. And I say again that the time when this problem will overtake us is really not very far away. The time is short, but if we realize the importance of what we are doing, of technological processes, of industrial know-how, then although the time is short, I think it is perhaps sufficient.

LINUS PAULING

The Significance of Chemistry

A PROPOSED PROGRAM FOR THE EDUCATION OF THE CITIZEN IN
SCIENCE, WHICH WOULD START AT THE KINDERGARTEN LEVEL.

It is impossible to deny that science has played a major part in
determining the nature of the modern world. The food that we
eat, the clothes that we wear, the means of transportation that
we use in going from place to place, the medicines that keep
us well, the weapons that we use in killing each other have all
been changed in recent years through scientific discovery.

It may well be contended that the world is now in a dangerous situation because science and its applications have developed
faster than the understanding of the average citizen. It is evidently of great importance to attempt to improve this situation
through a program of education of the citizen in science. The
world in modern times has continued to move toward the ideal
democratic system, in which all important decisions are made
by the people as a whole. In order for this system to operate correctly the citizen must have knowledge enough of the world to
make the right decisions; and in the modern world this means
that the citizen must have a significant understanding of science.

Nearly everyone has some knowledge about science in the
modern world. We know that stockings used to be made from
silk, a fiber spun by the silkworm, and are now made in large
quantities from an artificially spun fiber, nylon. We know that

penicillin, a substance made by a mold, is a very effective medicine for protecting us against bacterial infection, and that chloramphenicol and aureomycin are effective even against some of the virus diseases. We know that power can be transported from one place to another by the flow of electricity along wires, and that this flow of electricity is in fact the movement of charged elementary particles, electrons, along the atoms that constitute the wire. We know that, through the advance of physics during the last half century, man has discovered how to release the immense amounts of energy that are stored up in the nuclei of atoms; and we know that this knowledge is being used in the manufacture of atomic bombs. We know that uranium and thorium could be used to generate electric power, through the release of the energy stored up in the nuclei of the uranium and thorium atoms, and that the known deposits of minerals containing these elements could provide all of the energy required for the world, at the present rate of use, for thousands of years.

It is evident that these are important facts that contribute to the determination of the nature of the modern world. In order to get an idea of how important science is to the modern world, we might ask how many scientific facts are now known, in comparison with the number of nonscientific facts. How great a fraction of all of the knowledge possessed by man is now scientific knowledge?

It is impossible to answer this question precisely, because we have no scale for measuring the comparative importance of a scientific fact and a nonscientific fact. Nevertheless, it may be of interest to consider the rate at which our store of scientific knowledge is being increased. During the year 1949 the journal *Chemical Abstracts,* which attempts to review all of the current publications in chemistry and closely related fields, contained abstracts of 70,000 papers in the field of chemistry. Many of these papers report only one contribution to knowledge, which might be described as one new scientific fact. Some of them report two or more contributions to knowledge that might be described as separate new scientific facts—the subject index of *Chemical Abstracts* for 1949 lists 220,000 items. I believe that we may say, as a rough approximation, that about 100,000 new chemical facts are being discovered each year, at present. Perhaps we may multiply this number by 10, to include other sciences as well as chemistry, and thus reach the rough conclusion that about one million new scientific facts are being discovered each year.

How many significant nonscientific facts are added to man's body of knowledge each year? A nonscientific fact may be a historical event, an artistic creation, a historical, economic, or social correlation, a new general idea published in a paper or book. It is, of course, impossible to define a nonscientific fact rigorously in such a way as to be equivalent to a scientific fact. Nevertheless, we might attempt to estimate how many significant, nonephemeral items of new nonscientific information we have about the world, at the end of 1949, that we did not have at the beginning of the year. It seems to me that the number of these nonscientific facts may well be much less than one million; and that we may accordingly be justified in saying that scientific knowledge is at least roughly equivalent in its significance to the modern world to nonscientific knowledge, at the present time.

CHEMISTRY AND THE AVERAGE MAN

The average citizen has a much better understanding of the nonscientific aspects of the modern world than of its scientific aspects. His knowledge has been obtained in part through his studies in school, and in part through his reading and personal experiences. The great mass of people have not had education extending beyond the elementary school, and have accordingly received no instruction in science at all, or at most one or two years of instruction in geography and general science. The nature of science is such that it is difficult for a man to begin its study without help; accordingly those people, constituting the great mass of the people in the world, who have not studied science in any form in school in general remain ignorant of science throughout their lives, except to the limited extent that scientific information is provided by personal experience.

Because of the nature of chemistry, the average man knows

less about chemistry than about other sciences. He knows about many physical phenomena through his own observation—he knows that objects fall toward the earth, that hot bodies emit light and heat, that an electric spark may pass between two conductors at different potentials, that a body continues to move in a straight line unless acted on by some force (he may recognize that the curved path followed by a projectile reflects the effect of the gravitational attraction of the earth on the projectile), and so on. With this knowledge from personal experience, he is able to understand simple explanations of new discoveries in the field of physics, and to appreciate their significance to him and to the world as a whole. Similarly, he has had personal experience with phenomena in biology, geology, medical sciences, mechanical technology, and other fields which permit him to develop an increased understanding of their nature and their significance in the modern world. His personal experiences with chemical phenomena may, however, be very limited—be limited perhaps to the observation of the chemical reactions that occur in combustion. Chemical phenomena, involving the conversion of substances into other substances which may have entirely different properties, are so surprising in their nature that it is difficult for a man to develop an appreciation of them without instruction. The average man accepts the facts of chemistry that are significant to him, such as the combustion of gasoline with oxygen in an engine to produce mechanical power, as wonders that are not to be understood; and it is not surprising that he may occasionally be led to believe that some new device, offered for sale to him, can be attached to his automobile engine to permit water to be used as fuel in place of gasoline.

This example illustrates one way in which increased scientific knowledge is of value to man in the modern world. The welfare of the individual is determined in considerable part by the decisions that he makes about his own actions; in general, by the way he spends his money. Much of his money is spent in response to advertising appeals that are based on his understanding or misunderstanding of science. The principle of caveat emptor has become far more dangerous to the citizen than it was in the simple, nonscientific world of past centuries. The citizen is asked to buy products containing ozium, arium, durium, —and he is not told what these substances (if they are substances, and not just names) are. Ozium is to be sprayed around within the house, to kill all insects, destroy all cooking odors, protect against disease by killing germs too. Presumably the name ozium was selected because of the hope that the reader of the advertisement would confuse it with ozone, about whose germicidal properties he might have heard. He is asked to buy wonderful new green medicines, containing chlorophyll. Whatever substances, perhaps effective, may be present in the medicines, the advertiser counts on the chlorophyll to sell them. He is banking on the possession of a smattering of scientific information by the reader—and on his lack of possession of more than a smattering. He hopes that the reader will remember that chlorophyll is the wonderful substance, in the leaves of green plants, that purifies the air. He hopes that the reader does not know much more—that he does not know that the only thing that chlorophyll is known to do is to absorb carbon dioxide from the air and to liberate oxygen; and that chlorophyll that has been extracted from the plant has, so far as any scientist has been able to discover, no action as a medicine, no activity whatever. Moreover, he must be hoping that the reader of the advertisement will not even think enough to ask why he does not eat a green leaf, a small spoonful of cooked spinach, or other green vegetable in order to get his chlorophyll, instead of paying a hundred times as much money for inactive chlorophyll in a pill.

In this, and in many similar ways, it is of individual importance to the citizen in the modern world to have an increased understanding of the scientific aspects of the world.

The citizen who is trained in science may also be expected to exercise his political rights more effectively than one not trained in science, both because of his greater understanding of the nature of the modern world and because of his understanding of the scientific method, the way in which conclusions can be drawn from facts. Understanding of the scientific method confers on him the scientific attitude, which gives him an increased chance of reaching the right decision about political and social questions as well as about scientific questions.

One value of training in the scientific method is that it leads to skepticism about all generalizations, "laws of nature." What do we mean by a law of nature? We mean that a number of facts have been seen to be related to one another in such a way as to justify a general statement. For example, when chemical analysis of water was first made it was found that the sample of water that was analyzed contained 11.2 percent hydrogen and 88.8 percent oxygen. When another analysis was carried out, with another sample of water, the same result was obtained, and after a hundred analyses had been made—perhaps after only ten had been made—the general law was proposed that all samples of water contain 11.2 percent hydrogen by weight. This law was accepted for many years; but finally an analysis was made that showed that the percentage of hydrogen in rain water is a little less than 11.2 percent, and the percentage in ocean water is a little greater. This new observation then required that the earlier law of nature be changed in such a way as to take into account the existence of isotopes of hydrogen and oxygen, and the fractionation of water molecules containing different isotopes through the process of evaporation of water from the ocean. A scientific law that is based on only ten facts which agree with one another is not considered to be a very sound one—it has only a limited probability of continuing to remain valid, as more experiments are made. A law that is based on a hundred facts, or a thousand, has greater and greater probability of continuing to be correct. A citizen who understands the nature of scientific generalizations will ask himself what the basis is for generalizations in the field of economics, politics, international relations. How many facts have been used in determining the attitude of one nation toward another nation? Is the number of facts in agreement with one another in supporting the attitude so great that there is no room whatever for skepticism about the national policy on the part of an individual citizen, or is the citizen justified in being skeptical?

THE LAWS OF PROBABILITY

The laws of probability have as much significance in nonscientific fields as in scientific fields. We all understand how a life insurance company calculates its premium payments. The statistician for the life insurance company collects information about the number of people dying at various ages—30, 31, 32, 40, 50, 60, 70, 80, 90, 100, even 110 years of age. From all of these data he calculates the average expectancy of life and thus finds the average number of premiums that will be paid. If he were to say "It is abnormal for a man to live to be 85 years old, or older; therefore I must discard the data about these abnormal people" he would obtain a wrong value about the average expectancy of life, and the life insurance company would go bankrupt. Yet just this foolish procedure is sometimes carried out in the operation of a democratic system of government. The principle upon which a true democratic system operates is that no single man is wise enough to make the correct decisions about the very complex problems that arise, and that the correct decisions are to be made by the process of averaging the opinions of all of the citizens in the democracy. These opinions will correspond to a probability distribution curve, extending from far on the left to far on the right. If, now, we say that all of the opinions that extend too far to the right—beyond the point corresponding to the age 85 in the above example, say—are abnormal, and are to be excluded in taking the average, then the average that we obtain will be the wrong one. An understanding of the laws of probability would accordingly make it evident to the citizen that the operation of the democratic system requires that every one have the right to express his opinion about political questions, no matter what the opinion might be.

It is of the greatest importance to modern man that he understand the modern world. He must have knowledge enough about the world to make the right decisions—and since the modern world is largely scientific in its constitution, the citizen must understand science.

How can the citizen get scientific knowledge? The answer to this question can be drawn from past experience. Hundreds of years ago it was recognized that mathematics is of great value to the individual. Mathematics is a difficult subject; one might be tempted to say that, since it is difficult, the study of it should be put off till the college years. Yet, through experience, we have learned that the way to teach mathematics is to start with the teaching of numbers in kindergarten, arithmetic in the first grade and other elementary grades, and to continue steadily, without interruption, through algebra, geometry, trigo-nometry, calculus. This is the way in which science should be taught.

SCIENCE IN THE KINDERGARTEN

The time has now come for the study of science to be made a part of the curriculum in every grade, at every level. There should be a class in science in the kindergarten, in the first grade, in the second grade, in the third grade, and so on. Every boy and girl who finishes grammar school should know science, in the same way that he now knows arithmetic, languages, and history. Every boy and girl who finishes high school should know still more about science. Every college student should begin his college work with a sound knowledge of the whole of science—comparable to the knowledge that he now has, at this stage, of mathematics—in order that he might devote his years in college to the more advanced aspects of the subject. Only in this way can we train citizens for life in the modern world. Only in this way can we develop a citizenry able to solve the great social and political problems that confront the world.

In suggesting that the study of science should be carried on throughout the period of school training, I have in mind that it should occupy one class hour every day—that is, one instructional period of thirty or forty minutes in the beginning grades, and forty or fifty minutes in the higher grades. At the present time in many primary schools elementary instruction is given in geography, usually at some time between the fourth and the eighth grade. In addition, it is customary in many parts of the world for a course lasting for one year to be given in general science, usually the last year of primary school work, the eighth grade. In a relatively few schools a small amount of information about the nature of the physical and biological world is presented to the students during the first few years of primary school work. If one classroom period per day were devoted to science throughout the years of primary school instruction, the work might begin with very simple discussions of the physical world, including simple demonstrations. The fields of knowledge covered would be largely descriptive in nature, in all branches of science—physics, chemistry, biology, geology, astronomy, geography, etc., but in addition there could be, even in the earliest years, instruction in the scientific method and the scientific attitude.

UNDERSTANDING CERTAIN SCIENTIFIC CONCEPTS

The concepts of chemical change and of atomic structure and other concepts of modern science are no more difficult to understand than the concept that the earth is round. We teach students in the elementary schools that the earth is round, even though convincing proof is so difficult that the fact has been generally accepted only during the last few centuries. In the same way the important basic principles of atomic science could now be taught to beginning students, in the elementary schools, with rigorous proof of the truth of the concepts deferred until a later time.

The principal practical problem accompanying the introduction of instruction in science for one class period each day in all school grades is that of deciding what activities the instruction in science should replace. This decision is not an easy one to make, and presumably the subjects to be replaced or on which decreased emphasis is to be laid would be somewhat different in different schools and in different parts of the world.

There has been just as great reluctance to introduce extensive teaching of science into the field of adult education as into the field of elementary education. The best methods to be used in giving scientific information and instruction in the scientific method to mature individuals who have only an extremely limited background in science probably still need to be discovered. It is likely that a thorough study of existing alternative methods and a search for new ones would yield very important results.

The argument might be presented that it is hopeless to attempt to give the average citizen an understanding of science, because of the complexity of science at the present time and the enormous rate of increase in scientific knowledge. How can even the foremost scientist keep abreast of the rapidly advancing front of knowledge when millions of new facts are being discovered every year? I believe that this pessimism is not justified, and that, indeed, science as a whole is becoming simpler rather than more difficult. Many parts of physics have already passed through the stage of greatest complexity—the stage at which the body of knowledge in the field consists of an aggregate of largely disconnected facts. With the recognition of relationships among these facts, great numbers of them can be encompassed within a single principle. An understanding of the field as a whole can then be obtained by the process of understanding the general principles. It is not necessary for every fact to be learned; instead, a few of the facts can be considered, in order to discover their relationship to the general principles, and thereafter other facts that, for practical or accidental reasons, come to the attention of the individual can immediately be correlated by him with the general principles. At the present time chemistry is making rapid progress toward the ultimate goal of theoretical simplification; chemistry too has passed through the stage of maximum complexity. In biology and the medical sciences much of the fundamental investigational work now going on consists of a search for the fundamental general principles; we may feel confident that before many years have gone by the most significant of these principles will be discovered, and these subjects too will from that time on become progressively simpler.

One way in which an increased knowledge of the nature of the physical and biological world can be of value to the individual citizen is through the conferring on him of an increased equanimity, an increased confidence in natural law and order. The well-being of an individual may be greatly impaired by his fear of the unknown, which may far exceed the fear that he would have of a known danger, which he might prepare to meet in a rational way. In a world in which human beings have achieved extreme powers of destruction of one another, through the use of an astounding new source of energy, the nonunderstanding individual might well become extremely apprehensive, in such a way as to prevent him from making the correct personal and political decisions and to cause him to accede without a trace of protest to suggestions or orders from a dictatorial leader.

An incidental advantageous result of scientific education for all people which is of more than negligible significance is the personal satisfaction and pleasure that accompany pure knowledge and understanding. The physical and biological world in which we live is truly astounding and wonderful. No matter what the extent of his general education or the caliber of his mental abilities, every human being might achieve satisfaction and increased happiness through an increased knowledge and understanding of the world. The sources of happiness in life are not so bountiful that mankind can afford to neglect such an important one. If the ever-present oppressing danger of world war can ultimately be averted and the world can enter into a continuing period of peace and friendliness, the intellectual activities of the average man may become a source of happiness to him comparable to that provided by his emotions.

IRA S. BOWEN

Astronomy In a Changing World

A NOTED ASTRONOMER ANSWERS THE QUESTION—"WHAT GOOD
DOES ASTRONOMY DO THE AVERAGE MAN?"

Why investigate and teach astronomy? How can we justify the
very large expenditure of funds for great research telescopes,
for laboratories and classrooms for instruction, and for salaries
of large staffs of instruction and research?

When questions of this type are under discussion we have been
asked many times, "What is the practical value of astronomy?
Can any past or expected astronomical discoveries be used to
make better radios, automobiles or atomic bombs?" To such
questions we must answer that the direct application of recent
astronomical observations to practical affairs is very small. There
are exceptions, such as the use of observations of sunspots and
solar flares for the prediction of radio transmission, but these
cases are rare.

But does this mean that astronomy is of little value to the
average man, in comparison to some of the sciences that have
found great direct application to technology? I would go even
further and raise the question of whether we are as sure as we
once were of the enormous human value of the great scientific
and technological development of our present civilization. Thus
present historians of civilization point with a certain amount of
contempt at Greek and Roman philosophers and scientists be-

cause they attempted to reach an understanding of the world
about them from reasoning alone and failed to develop the
experimental method. We are told therefore that these early
efforts led chiefly up a blind side road rather than along the
great highway of scientific and technological advance of modern
civilization.

But if our own civilization should follow these of the past,
and be replaced by another a millenium or two hence, can we
be certain as to how the historians of this new civilization will
evaluate the scientific efforts of our own age? Will our efforts be
considered a real advance along the road to a better world for
mankind—or will they be listed as but another diversion up a
blind alley? Obviously we are too close to our own period to
have the necessary perspective for such an evaluation of our
own science and technology. Lest we be too complacent about
our present position, however, let us examine a very few effects
of the impact of science and technology on our civilization.

A century or two ago most of the world had an agricultural
economy. A large fraction of the people were small land-owners
producing their own necessities of life. While many examples
of tyranny and abuse of power could be found, various groups
—notably in America, Switzerland, and to a large extent in
England—had developed social and political institutions in which
great individual freedom and security had been attained.

To this agricultural economy our great scientific and technological advances were added during the last century. To exploit
these advances great industries were developed and an increasingly large fraction of the population left their farms and
became factory workers. But as factory workers they no longer
retained the security of being able to produce their own food
and other necessities. The continuance of their livelihood depended on the goodwill of their employer and the stability of
demand in their particular industry.

The insecurity and hardship that this situation can produce
was acutely brought home to all of us during the depression of
the 1930's. In an effort to counteract this insecurity the govern-
ments of most industrial nations have, by popular demand,

moved rapidly toward job insurance, old age pensions, the detailed control of industry and many other steps toward state socialism. These steps, along with the attendant large increase in taxation, have already gone a long way toward eliminating individual freedom of action and incentive to individual effort.

Even more directly we have seen in the past decade many of the beneficial effects of technological advance nullified by the application of these advances to the destructive purposes of warfare, often with truly appalling results.

Undoubtedly the early application of science to technology brought many physical comforts and freedom from drudgery and disease. On the other hand it is rapidly becoming evident that these technological advances are more and more being accompanied by the loss of security, freedom, and incentive and are in many cases unleashing destructive forces which, unless controlled, may become a real menace to our civilization.

These questions are not raised in a spirit of pessimism and disillusionment. They are raised to emphasize that mankind may still have failed to find the one sure road to a better and happier world in the uncontrolled advance of science and technology. We still may profitably look for other criteria of value besides the applicability of a given discovery to technology.

THE VALUE OF ASTRONOMY

What, then, may be some of the important values of astronomical discovery? Before attempting an answer let me review very briefly some of the concepts that have come from astronomy.

Until the time of Copernicus men thought of the universe as consisting of a stationary earth around which the sun, moon, planets and stars revolved in a complicated series of cycles. As the one intelligent inhabitant of the only tangible part of the universe, man and his doings were of very fundamental importance in this universe.

But Copernicus moved the center of the universe to the sun. His immediate successors found this newly-devised solar system to have dimensions measured in billions of miles. In 1838 refined instruments allowed Bessel to fix the distance of a nearby star.

The next half century saw this and similar direct trigonometric measurements of the distances of the nearer stars push out the diameter of the measured universe to a few hundred light years. (It will be recalled that a light year is six million million miles.)

The measurement of still greater distances awaited the development of new methods in the present century. These methods depend on the comparison of the absolute and the apparent brightness of a given object, and were based on the discovery that the absolute brightness of a star can be determined from its spectra or, in the case of certain variable stars, from the period of its light variation. Using these methods the dimensions of our own Milky Way system were outlined during the first quarter of the present century. These investigations showed that the Milky Way contains some billions of stars, many of them larger than our own sun, arranged in a flat disk-like structure some 100,000 light years in diameter.

Previous to this, astronomers had noticed a large number of faint nebulous objects often having a spiral structure. With the advent of the 100-inch telescope on Mount Wilson it was possible to resolve a few of the nearest of these into stars and apply these same methods for the determination of the distances and dimensions of these objects. These measurements showed that each of these spiral galaxies is another system made up of many millions of stars, and is comparable in size and structure to our own Milky Way system. It is estimated that the 200-inch Hale telescope could photograph about 100,000,000 of these galaxies extending out to distances of over one billion light years.

Further studies show that all of these galaxies are moving away from us at velocities which increase proportionally with their distances. The most distant objects thus far measured are receding at a velocity of 38,000 miles per second. If these measurements are correctly interpreted it means that all of these objects started from one place about six billion years ago. It is interesting to speculate that the universe, as we know it, may therefore have started off with a huge atomic explosion at that time which imparted to these objects their present velocity.

Other studies, particularly those using a spectrograph, have told us about the temperatures and the chemical compositions of the stars. Some of the surface temperatures are over one hundred thousand degrees, while in the interiors temperatures of several tens of millions of degrees are reached. At these interior temperatures nuclear reactions occur, similar to those that give the atomic bomb its tremendous power. This provides the sun and most of the stars with the enormous energy which they require to enable them to continue to shine with their great brilliance. From the determination of the chemical composition of the stars we can estimate the amount of fuel remaining to keep these nuclear fires burning. Again we arrive at stellar lifetimes measured in billions of years.

All of this has obviously had a very great and very humbling effect on our concepts of man's place in the universe. Thus, instead of man's home—the earth—being the center of the universe, we now find it to be a minor planet moving about one of the smaller of some billions of stars that make up our galaxy— which in turn is only one of many millions of such galaxies. Likewise, instead of man dominating the earth throughout its existence, we find that the history of civilized man has only extended for a few thousand years out of the billions of years that the universe has been developing.

A MATTER OF PERSPECTIVE

This, I believe, is the great value of astronomy: More than any other science it has given us a true perspective of man's place in the universe. Possibly this is illustrated in a simple way by a request that came to the Mount Wilson Observatory shortly after the war. It came from a civilian high up in the War Department. He asked for one of our photographs of a spiral galaxy. In explaining his request he said in effect, "These days of reconversion are very hectic, particularly here in the War Department. In a continually tense situation it is often very difficult not to take ourselves and our immediate problems very seriously. I would like to have this photograph of a galaxy to frame and hang in my office opposite my desk so that, when the going gets tough and the immediate problem seems unusually important and urgent, I can just take a look."

I wonder whether we would not find some of our present problems and tensions somewhat relieved if a few more heads of states, and labor and industrial leaders were in a position to take an understanding look now and then.

Certainly, if our civilization is to continue to prosper and advance, it is evident that man must obtain a much broader understanding than he now has of the technological, social, and political structures that are most conducive to his continued happiness and well-being. Furthermore he must have not only the knowledge but the will to attain this goal. I cannot help but believe that the understanding of man's true place in the universe which we are slowly obtaining from astronomy is a significant step toward this end.

ALFRED STERN

Why Do We Laugh and Cry?

A PHILOSOPHER THROWS FRESH LIGHT ON
THE SOCIAL MEANING OF LAUGHTER AND TEARS.

In trying to answer the question, "Why do we laugh and cry?"
I do not want to inquire into the psychological motives of people's laughter and tears. The meaning of my question is: How can
the psychological phenomena of laughing and crying be interpreted philosophically? How can we conceive rationally these
two polar manifestations of our psychism, which are so typically
human and, nevertheless, so deeply irrational?

In my theory, laughter is interpreted as a value judgment,
an instinctive, negative value judgment concerning a degradation of values. This judgment is not expressed in words, but in
the inarticulate sounds we call laughter.

Laughter, however, is not only our *reaction* towards a degradation of values. Sometimes it is also an *action* provoking a
degradation of values or, at least, trying to provoke it. When we
laugh at a person, or a thing done by a person, although no
value degradation can be found in them, we try to degrade their
value. And often we succeed.

There is a French saying, *le ridicule tue,* the ludicrous kills.
Of course, it does not kill physically, but it may kill morally,
axiologically;* it may kill values, and then laughter may have
tragic consequences.

---

* *Axiology* is the technical term, derived from the Greek, to designate the
theory of values.

If we laugh at a serious person or his work, this person is offended. And he is right to be offended, for instinctively he recognizes in this laughter an attempt to degrade his value or that of his work in the eyes of other people.

The phenomenon of weeping is closely related to that of laughing. The basic difference between the two became obvious to me when I tried to interpret two souvenirs of my childhood. I remember a walk with my father and one of his colleagues, Mr. F., in an Austrian summer resort. I was about seven years old. A torrential rain had just ceased, and the ways were soaked and muddy. Suddenly, Mr. F. slipped and fell into a dirty puddle. He rose immediately, wet and full of mud, while my father roared with laughter.

I did not understand this laughter at the time, nor the fact that Mr. F. became very offended. Years later I learned that my father did not like Mr. F., who indeed, was not very worthy of affection.

Now, interpreting my father's laughter axiologically, I come to the following conclusion: Falling into a puddle and rising wet and covered with mud, the human personality, supposedly the source of all spiritual values, changes for a moment into a simple thing, into a physical object, subjected to gravity and other mechanical forces, like all unintelligent passive objects of a nature exempt from values and hierarchies. By this change from an evaluating subject into a value-free object, the human person suffers a transitory degradation of his value, and the laughter he provokes by behaving like a dull lifeless thing is an instinctive negative value judgment, criticizing and chastising that degradation.

Perhaps my father would not have laughed if he had had some affection for and sympathy with Mr. F., for, as Emerson remarks, affection and sympathy may prevent us from noticing the ludicrous. Axiologically speaking, this means that some affection would have prevented my father from seeing in Mr. F., fallen in the puddle, only a passive object, subjected to value-free mechanical forces, degrading the value of what man is supposed to be: the center of emanation of spiritual values. If

Mr. F. was offended, he recognized in my father's laughter an instinctive negative value judgment, prejudicial to his human dignity.

The philosophical significance of the phenomenon of crying was revealed to me by the analysis of another childhood souvenir. One day—I was about nine years old—my mother brought me to school. On the way we saw a man stumbling and falling on the paving stones. Some passers-by laughed, but immediately ceased laughing, because the man did not rise again. My mother asked me to wait a moment in a doorway, in order to spare me afflicting impressions, and went, with other persons, to help the unknown man. A few minutes later she returned, crying. The man had fractured his skull and was dead.

Only now do I understand, philosophically, the difference between these two events.

What had aroused my father's laughter had been a *degradation of values*. What had caused my mother's tears had been a *loss of values*. Even without knowing the man, my mother, instinctively, must have interpreted his death as a loss of values, for every human life represents an ensemble of values: moral values, intellectual values, esthetic values, religious and social values—in short, spiritual values. And death means a loss of those specific values united in a certain human person. Not only a loss of values, but also the fact that they are threatened or unattainable may provoke our tears.

In a general way, we may affirm:

We *laugh* at *degraded values,* or in order to degrade values, but we *weep* about *threatened, lost,* and *unattainable values.* If the laughter about the comic is the instinctive expression of a *negative* value judgment concerning a degradation of values, weeping is the instinctive expression of a *positive* value judgment on threatened, unattainable, and lost values. Weeping, thus, always refers to things positively appreciated.

We may say that the tears of fear and anxiety express positive value judgments on values considered as threatened, while the tears of nostalgia, affliction, and mourning express positive value judgments on lost values. The tears of frustration, anger, and rage express positive value judgments on unattainable values.

This situation seems to involve a paradoxical element, for although expressing *positive* value judgments, weeping is considered a *negative* vital value, and we don't like to weep. And although expressing *negative* value judgments, laughing is considered a *positive* vital value, and we like to laugh. As far as weeping is concerned, this paradox is easily solved. Although we express by our tears that we appreciate certain things in a positive way, it is evident that what we weep about is the menace, the unattainableness, or the loss of those positive values. The menace, the unattainableness, and the loss of positive values are evidently negative values. Therefore, weeping is considered a negative value, and we don't like to weep.

THE PARADOX OF LAUGHTER

But how about laughter? We like to laugh and consider it a *positive* vital value, although it expresses a *negative* appreciation. This seems paradoxical. But we have to admit that we do not dislike uttering negative value judgments from time to time. He who expresses a negative value judgment—be it rationally or instinctively, as in laughter—criticizes a degradation of values, committed by somebody else—except in the cases where we laugh at ourselves, chastising ourselves for a degradation of values *we* have committed.

The word "to criticize" comes from the Greek *krités,* meaning judge. He who criticizes, uttering a negative value judgment —either in rational concepts and articulate words or in the irrational, inarticulate sounds we call laughter—considers himself the judge of the one he criticizes; and this gives him an agreeable feeling of superiority.

But this is only one of the reasons we like to laugh, and certainly not the most flattering for *homo sapiens.* I think there are other reasons, which seem to me more important. They are linked to the double character of laughter: laughter as a criticism of society with respect to the individual, on the one hand, and, on the other hand, as a criticism of the individual with respect to society. From this latter angle laughter would appear as a kind of self-liberation of the individual from the coercive influence which the social group exerts on him, by virtue of its imperious system of values.

Society laughs at human weaknesses expressed in individuals, for human weaknesses are degradations of human forces, which have a positive value and which society tries to preserve. Therefore, society chastises by its laughter those human weaknesses whose degradation the individual could avoid.

If our fellow men laugh when we commit a stupidity, this laughter is a mild punishment and a warning, by which society wishes to tell us: "Be careful, you just degraded *intellectual* values, which are the privilege of man. Watch yourself, be more attentive and industrious, and you will avoid such humiliating incidents."

We view here a pedagogical aspect of laughter—its corrective function, which serves to show its social usefulness.

Society also chastises by laughter any minor degradation of *moral* values committed by its members, such as roguery, cheating, boasting. But we would not laugh at any moral default of a more serious character, like unfaithfulness, hypocrisy, calumniation, or treason, because they no longer constitute *degradations* of moral values, but *losses* of moral values, which may provoke tears.

Most rarely and only with uneasiness do we laugh at degradations of *esthetic* values, as they appear in ugly persons. When laughing at an ugly person, that is, a person who, by his mere physical appearance, degrades certain esthetic and sometimes vital values, we have a bad conscience, because the person is not responsible for his ugliness. It escapes his will, it is his nature.

Thus, the criticism expressed in laughter would not exert its corrective function. When laughter, a social and axiological manifestation, clashes with nature, it is an empty blow. Nature is stronger. Being pedagogically and socially useless, laughter about the degradation of esthetic values as it appears in human ugliness is not sanctioned by society. It is even condemned and rejected as indecent. And this, too, can be explained axiologically. For in laughing at the expense of an ugly person, we risk hurting him morally and provoking a loss of his self-confidence.

In this case, our punishment of the *degradation* of *esthetic* values, as it appears in his ugliness, would provoke a *loss* of *moral* values, and tears may be the reaction of the victim. This would be especially true with respect to ugly girls or women, for in the hierarchy of values of the feminine sex the esthetic value of physical beauty occupies a higher place than in that of the male, since the personal destiny of a woman depends to a large extent on her physical appearance.

"INDECENT" LAUGHTER

But if, for these reasons, society condemns as "indecent" our laughter about human ugliness, it encourages our laughter at any degradation of esthetic values which results not from nature but from willful human activity. Society encourages us, for instance, when we chastise by our laughter those true or pretended degradations of esthetic values which it calls "degenerate art." It allows us also to laugh at the clown.

In order to understand the axiological relations between the individual and society we have to distinguish among individual, collective, and universal values. It has been contended that, since they are relations between objects and appreciating subjects, *all* values are individual. But this contention is short-sighted, for it overlooks the fact that only those values are individual which depend on the individual peculiarities of the appreciating subjects, while the values which are independent of the individual peculiarities of those who affirm them may be termed objective values.

Among the latter I distinguish between collective and universal values, defining as collective those values which depend upon the collective peculiarities of the group that upholds them —for instance, a class or a political party; and as universal those values which are independent both of the individual and the collective peculiarities of those who affirm them.

The majority of individuals, collective groups within society, and society as a whole tend to present their individual or collective values as universal values. This explains the state of axiological warfare which exists between the individual and the society, the individual and particular collective groups, the individual and the individual, and among the different collective groups within society. Laughter is one of the most powerful weapons in this axiological warfare. In order to protest against the claim of universality of a merely individual or collective value, the adversary has only to degrade, that is, to ridicule it.

SOCIETY'S SYSTEM OF VALUES

The majority of individual and collective values are dictated by particular interests and tastes. But in society the different particular interests and tastes compensate one another, so that what comes up to the surface consists of only the most general appreciations. This is why the system of values of society implies most of the universal values, and especially those which are necessary for the conservation of society. Hence, society tries to preserve them and to protect them with special sanctions. The mildest of these sanctions is the laughter with which society punishes whoever degrades values belonging to the system of values that it is interested in preserving and protecting.

The ideal society would be that one whose system of values would include nothing but values of universal validity. However, any actual society is always more or less distant from that ideal. During periods of degeneracy, the number of collective values of a ruling party, or of the individual values of a dictator, exceeds that of the universal values in the axiological system of a given society. This society is not always an honest administrator of universal values.

The criticism of society is mostly directed against the collective values of certain particularistic groups within itself and against the individual values of certain original persons. Wishing to preserve its own system of values intact, wanting to increase its authority, and trying to impose it upon everybody, society uses laughter in order to degrade any competing system of values, that is the systems of collective values of certain particularistic groups or the systems of individual values of certain too individualistic persons.

In order to escape this punishment of laughter, which would isolate them socially, the particularistic groups and individuals may give up their specific value conceptions, too ostensibly different from those of the majority. By its laughter or even by the menace of this laughter society will then have exerted an *assimilatory* function.

This dangerous character of the laughter of society at the cost of individuals and particular groups explains the reaction of the individual and of the particular groups toward society, the revenge they take in laughing at society, in trying, by their laughter, to degrade the system of values of society by which they feel themselves oppressed.

This is the second basic aspect of laughter I have mentioned: that of a criticism of the individual toward society. From this angle laughter would appear as a kind of spiritual liberation of the individual from the coercive influence society exerts on him, by virtue of its imperious system of values. In laughing at certain values sustained by society, the individual tries to degrade them, and thus affirms his personal sovereignty towards society. The positive value we ascribe to this laughter would then be derived from the freedom of appreciation, reconquered by the individual from an axiologically oppressive society.

The specific weapon the individual forges in this warfare of laughter against society is the joke. There exist as many classes of jokes as classes of values. There are jokes degrading intellectual values, others degrading moral values, esthetic values, religious values, vital values, instrumental values, economic values, etc.

THE OFF-COLOR JOKE

The number of anecdotes drawing their comic effects from a degradation of those moral values which characterize the erotic life is especially noticeable. On the one hand, we have the vigorous sexual passions; on the other hand, the rigorous restrictions of these passions by ethics, religion, social conventions, and penal prohibitions. The individual cannot escape the social pressure exerted by these conventions and taboos. He can violate them only at the risk of social and sometimes even of penal sanctions. The individual takes his revenge in trying, by means of jokes and anecdotes, to degrade those moral values of erotic life which the social and moral conventions and legal prohibitions try to protect. The laughter resulting from those degradations is for the individual a kind of symbolic liberation from a social pressure from which he suffers.

When the individual ceases to suffer from the effect of those conventions and prohibitions, he is no longer so eager to degrade their value. Therefore, it is neither the old ladies nor the old gentlemen who tell us the most piquant stories.

There are many kinds of laughter which have nothing to do with the comic. Let me mention here only two of them: the laughter of joy, closely linked with tears of joy, and the smiles of modesty, politeness, etc. These kinds of laughter beyond the comic can be explained not by degradation, but by another phenomenon which I call devaluation. By devaluation I mean any quantitative diminution of a positive or negative value, which does not necessarily imply a qualitative degradation. In diminishing, for instance, the negative character of a negative value, I do not degrade it, because it does not suffer any deterioration of its quality. I simply devaluate it quantitatively.

THE SMILE OF MODESTY

There is a great variety of smiles: the smile of modesty, of courtesy, of welcome, of encouragement, of pity, of irony, of embarrassment, and so on. I have tried to explain all of them by using the concept of devaluation.

Let me only take the example of the smile of modesty. If one pays a compliment to a pretty lady, to a great artist or scientist, these persons react, in general, with a smile. Is it a smile of joy? Rarely, unless the lady is in love with the man who pays her the compliment, and the artist or scientist considers the flatterer a true connoisseur. But in general the smile by which we respond to a compliment is a smile of modesty, expressing a social convention rather than a true feeling. I have tried to understand this phenomenon axiologically and found that whoever responds with a smile of modesty to the compliment of another person tries to devaluate his own value, to minimize it in the eyes of the partner or partners.

In general, the smile of modesty is not sincere, it is a social fiction, but it is an important one in human relations. Whoever refuses to respond with a smile of modesty to a compliment is immediately considered as arrogant. People say of him: "This man is very sure of his value."

And if it is a lady who accepts a compliment without a smile of modesty, she is immediately condemned, especially by the feminine witnesses of the scene. Refusing to devaluate by a smile—at least fictitiously—the esthetic value which was ascribed to her by the compliment, the lady certainly exposes herself to all kinds of criticism.

"Look at her!" the other ladies will say. "She takes this seriously; she really believes in her superiority!"

And the ladies who are less pretty than she will comment: "Besides, her legs are far from perfect!"

But in allowing a smile of modesty to glide over her lips, the lady makes "as if" she devaluated the esthetic value of her beauty, and thus she will be pardoned for possessing it.

I said earlier that we weep about threatened, lost, and unattainable values. But how about the tears we may shed in reading or attending the performance of a tragedy? Since the events presented in a tragedy are purely fictitious, the values involved in it do not seem to be really lost or threatened or unattainable.

Aristotle was right in insisting on the fictitious character of the events presented in the tragedy and of the *dramatis personae*. But in my opinion we have to realize that the *values* involved in the tragedy are not fictitious at all. The mode of existence of values is that of validity, and this is a domain beyond the distinction between the real and the fictitious. Values which proved their validity in the fictitious experiment of artistic imagination have at the same time proved their validity in life, for an ideal validity is, at the same time, a real one. From this springs the gravity of the fictitious experiences of the artistic play, for its axiological results are valid for life itself.

If the tragedy shows, in an imaginary realm, that certain values are threatened, unattainable, or lost, if it shows the precariousness of these values on an ideal plane, then their precariousness is also demonstrated on the plane of reality. Thus, the tears we may shed at a tragedy are justified, axiologically.

We may say with Kant that man is a citizen of two worlds. Not of a metaphysical and an empirical world, as Kant affirmed, but of the world of values and the world of value-free physical, causal occurrences. I think that during his whole life man balances on the edge between these two worlds. He sacrifices a good deal of his energies to the effort to remain well equilibrated within the world of values, so that he may not fall into the axiological emptiness of the natural world of blind causes, toward which he is pulled by a kind of gravity, since, with a part of his being man belongs to this natural world of physical things and causes. This effort is justified, for the laughter he provokes by degrading human values sounds badly to the ears of the victim of such a fall into the axiological emptiness of brute nature.

LIVING IN TWO WORLDS

We are citizens of these two worlds also as far as the tragic is concerned: for the collisions between the spiritual world of values and the world of value-free natural occurrences are responsible for most of the losses of values which characterize our tragic existence and thus make us cry. The causal world of natural occurrences is totally indifferent toward values; it destroys them, without taking into account their positive or negative character, their superiority or inferiority. In the clashes between the worlds of natural occurrences and of spiritual values, the highest positive values often perish on the field, and the negative values survive.

Since man is a citizen of two worlds—that of values and that of natural, causal occurrences—he is the battlefield of their terrible collisions. If there is in the world an inexhaustible source, it is that of tears. The clashes among antagonistic values and their collisions with the world of natural occurrences never cease to nourish that source of the bitterest of all liquids.

RICHARD P. FEYNMAN

The Relation of Science and Religion

SOME NEW OBSERVATIONS ON AN OLD CONTROVERSY.

In this age of specialization men who thoroughly know one field are often incompetent to discuss another. The great problems of the relations between one and another aspect of human activity have for this reason been discussed less and less in public. When we look at the past great debates on these subjects we feel jealous of those times, for we should have liked the excitement of such argument. The old problems, such as the relation of science and religion, are still with us, and I believe present as difficult dilemmas as ever, but they are not often publicly discussed because of the limitations of specialization.

But I have been interested in this problem for a long time and would like to discuss it. In view of my very evident lack of knowledge and understanding of religion (a lack which will grow more apparent as we proceed), I will organize the discussion in this way: I will suppose that not one man but a group of men are discussing the problem, that the group consists of specialists in many fields—the various sciences, the various religions and so on—and that we are going to discuss the problem from various sides, like a panel. Each is to give his point of view, which may be molded and modified by the later discussion. Further, I imagine that someone has been chosen by lot to be the first to present his views, and I am he so chosen.

I would start by presenting the panel with a problem: A

young man, brought up in a religious family, studies a science, and as a result he comes to doubt—and perhaps later to disbelieve in—his father's God. Now, this is not an isolated example; it happens time and time again. Although I have no statistics on this, I believe that many scientists—in fact, I actually believe that more than half of the scientists—really disbelieve in their father's God; that is, they don't believe in a God in a conventional sense.

Now, since the belief in a God is a central feature of religion, this problem that I have selected points up most strongly the problem of the relation of science and religion. Why does this young man come to disbelieve?

The first answer we might hear is very simple: You see, he is taught by scientists, and (as I have just pointed out) they are all atheists at heart, so the evil is spread from one to another. But if you can entertain this view, I think you know less of science than I know of religion.

Another answer may be that a little knowledge is dangerous; this young man has learned a little bit and thinks he knows it all, but soon he will grow out of this sophomoric sophistication and come to realize that the world is more complicated, and he will begin again to understand that there must be a God.

I don't think it is necessary that he come out of it. There are many scientists—men who hope to call themselves mature—who still don't believe in God. In fact, as I would like to explain later, the answer is not that the young man thinks he knows it all—it is the exact opposite.

A third answer you might get is that this young man really doesn't understand science correctly. I do not believe that science can disprove the existence of God; I think that is impossible. And if it is impossible, is not a belief in science and in a God—an ordinary God of religion—a consistent possibility?

Yes, it is consistent. Despite the fact that I said that more than half of the scientists don't believe in God, many scientists *do* believe in both science and God, in a perfectly consistent way. But this consistency, although possible, is not easy to attain, and I would like to try to discuss two things: Why it is not easy to attain, and whether it is worth attempting to attain it.

When I say "believe in God," of course, it is always a puzzle —what is God? What I mean is the kind of personal God, characteristic of the Western religions, to whom you pray and who has something to do with creating the universe and guiding you in morals.

For the student, when he learns about science, there are two sources of difficulty in trying to weld science and religion together. The first source of difficulty is this—that it is imperative in science to doubt; it is absolutely necessary, for progress in science, to have uncertainty as a fundamental part of your inner nature. To make progress in understanding we must remain modest and allow that we do not know. Nothing is certain or proved beyond all doubt. You investigate for curiosity, because it is *unknown*, not because you know the answer. And as you develop more information in the sciences, it is not that you are finding out the truth, but that you are finding out that this or that is more or less likely.

That is, if we investigate further, we find that the statements of science are not of what is true and what is not true, but statements of what is known to different degrees of certainty: "It is very much more likely that so and so is true than that it is not true"; or "such and such is almost certain but there is still a little bit of doubt"; or—at the other extreme—"well, we really don't know." Every one of the concepts of science is on a scale graduated somewhere between, but at neither end of, absolute falsity or absolute truth.

It is necessary, I believe, to accept this idea, not only for science, but also for other things; it is of great value to acknowledge ignorance. It is a fact that when we make decisions in our life we don't necessarily know that we are making them correctly; we only think that we are doing the best we can—and that is what we should do.

ATTITUDE OF UNCERTAINTY

I think that when we know that we actually do live in un-uncertainty, then we ought to admit it; it is of great value to realize that we do not know the answers to different questions. This attitude of mind—this attitude of uncertainty—is vital to the scientist, and it is this attitude of mind which the student must first acquire. It becomes a habit of thought. Once acquired, one cannot retreat from it any more.

What happens, then, is that the young man begins to doubt everything because he cannot have it as absolute truth. So the question changes a little bit from "Is there a God?" to "How sure is it that there is a God?" This very subtle change is a great stroke and represents a parting of the ways between science and religion. I do not believe a real scientist can ever believe in the same way again. Although there are scientists who believe in God, I do not believe that they think of God in the same way as religious people do. If they are consistent with their science, I think that they say something like this to themselves: "I am almost certain there is a God. The doubt is very small." That is quite different from saying, "I know that there is a God." I do not believe that a scientist can ever obtain that view—that really religious understanding, that real knowledge that there is a God—that absolute certainty which religious people have.

Of course this process of doubt does not always start by attacking the question of the existence of God. Usually special tenets, such as the question of an after-life, or details of the religious doctrine, such as details of Christ's life, come under scrutiny first. It is more interesting, however, to go right into the central problem in a frank way, and to discuss the more extreme view which doubts the existence of God.

Once the question has been removed from the absolute, and gets to sliding on the scale of uncertainty, it may end up in very different positions. In many cases it comes out very close to being certain. But on the other hand, for some, the net result of close scrutiny of the theory his father held of God may be the claim that it is almost certainly wrong.

BELIEF IN GOD—AND THE FACTS OF SCIENCE

That brings us to the second difficulty our student has in

trying to weld science and religion: Why does it often end up
that the belief in God—at least, the God of the religious type—
is considered to be very unreasonable, very unlikely? I think
that the answer has to do with the scientific things—the facts or
partial facts—that the man learns.

For instance, the size of the universe is very impressive, with
us on a tiny particle whirling around the sun, among a hundred
thousand million suns in this galaxy, itself among a billion
galaxies.

Again, there is the close relation of biological man to the
animals, and of one form of life to another. Man is a latecomer
in a vast evolving drama; can the rest be but a scaffolding for
his creation?

Yet again, there are the atoms of which all appears to be
constructed, following immutable laws. Nothing can escape it;
the stars are made of the same stuff, and the animals are made
of the same stuff, but in such complexity as to mysteriously appear alive—like man himself.

It is a great adventure to contemplate the universe beyond
man, to think of what it means without man—as it was for the
great part of its long history, and as it is in the great majority
of places. When this objective view is finally attained, and the
mystery and majesty of matter are appreciated, to then turn
the objective eye back on man viewed as matter, to see life as
part of the universal mystery of greatest depth, is to sense an
experience which is rarely described. It usually ends in laughter, delight in the futility of trying to understand. These scientific views end in awe and mystery, lost at the edge in uncertainty, but they appear to be so deep and so impressive that the
theory that it is all arranged simply as a stage for God to watch
man's struggle for good and evil seems to be inadequate.

So let us suppose that this is the case of our particular student, and the conviction grows so that he believes that individual prayer, for example, is not heard. (I am not trying to
disprove the reality of God; I am trying to give you some idea
of—some sympathy for—the reasons why many come to think
that prayer is meaningless.) Of course, as a result of this doubt,

the pattern of doubting is turned next to ethical problems, because, in the religion which he learned, moral problems were connected with the word of God, and if the God doesn't exist, what is his word? But rather surprisingly, I think, the moral problems ultimately come out relatively unscathed; at first perhaps the student may decide that a few little things were wrong, but he often reverses his opinion later, and ends with no fundamentally different moral view.

There seems to be a kind of independence in these ideas. In the end, it is possible to doubt the divinity of Christ, and yet to believe firmly that it is a good thing to do unto your neighbor as you would have him do unto you. It is possible to have both these views at the same time; and I would say that I hope you will find that my atheistic scientific colleagues often carry themselves well in society.

COMMUNISM AND THE SCIENTIFIC VIEWPOINT

I would like to remark, in passing, since the word "atheism" is so closely connected with "communism," that the communist views are the antithesis of the scientific, in the sense that in communism the answers are given to all the questions—political questions as well as moral ones—without discussion and without doubt. The scientific viewpoint is the exact opposite of this; that is, all questions must be doubted and discussed; we must argue everything out—observe things, check them, and so change them. The democratic government is much closer to this idea, because there is discussion and a chance of modification. One doesn't launch the ship in a definite direction. It is true that if you have a tyranny of ideas, so that you know exactly what has to be true, you act very decisively, and it looks good—for a while. But soon the ship is heading in the wrong direction, and no one can modify the direction any more. So the uncertainties of life in a democracy are, I think, much more consistent with science.

Although science makes some impact on many religious ideas, it does not affect the moral content. Religion has many aspects; it answers all kinds of questions. First, for example, it answers questions about what things are, where they come from, what man is, what God is—the properties of God, and so on. Let me call this the metaphysical aspect of religion. It also tells us another thing—how to behave. Leave out of this the idea of how to behave in certain ceremonies, and what rites to perform; I mean it tells us how to behave in life in general, in a moral way. It gives answers to moral questions; it gives a moral and ethical code. Let me call this the ethical aspect of religion.

Now, we know that, even with moral values granted, human beings are very weak; they must be reminded of the moral values in order that they may be able to follow their consciences. It is not simply a matter of having a right conscience; it is also a question of maintaining strength to do what you know is right. And it is necessary that religion give strength and comfort and the inspiration to follow these moral views. This is the inspirational aspect of religion. It gives inspiration not only for moral conduct—it gives inspiration for the arts and for all kinds of great thoughts and actions as well.

INTERCONNECTIONS

These three aspects of religion are interconnected, and it is generally felt, in view of this close integration of ideas, that to attack one feature of the system is to attack the whole structure. The three aspects are connected more or less as follows: The moral aspect, the moral code, is the word of God—which involves us in a metaphysical question. Then the inspiration comes because one is working the will of God; one is for God; partly one feels that one is with God. And this is a great inspiration because it brings one's actions in contact with the universe at large.

So these three things are very well interconnected. The difficulty is this: that science occasionally conflicts with the first of the three categories—the metaphysical aspect of religion. For instance, in the past there was an argument about whether the earth was the center of the universe—whether the earth moved around the sun or stayed still. The result of all this was a terrible strife and difficulty, but it was finally resolved—with religion retreating in this particular case. More recently there was a conflict over the question of whether man has animal ancestry.

The result in many of these situations is a retreat of the religious metaphysical view, but nevertheless, there is no collapse of the religion. And further, there seems to be no appreciable or fundamental change in the moral view.

After all, the earth moves around the sun—isn't it best to turn the other cheek? Does it make any difference whether the earth is standing still or moving around the sun? We can expect conflict again. Science is developing and new things will be found out which will be in disagreement with the present-day metaphysical theory of certain religions. In fact, even with all the past retreats of religion, there is still real conflict for particular individuals when they learn about the science and they have heard about the religion. The thing has not been integrated very well; there are real conflicts here—and yet morals are not affected.

As a matter of fact, the conflict is doubly difficult in this metaphysical region. Firstly, the facts may be in conflict, but even if the facts were not in conflict, the attitude is different. The spirit of uncertainty in science is an attitude toward the metaphysical questions that is quite different from the certainty and faith that is demanded in religion. There is definitely a conflict, I believe—both in fact and in spirit—over the metaphysical aspects of religion.

In my opinion, it is not possible for religion to find a set of metaphysical ideas which will be guaranteed not to get into conflicts with an ever-advancing and always-changing science which is going into an unknown. We don't know how to answer the questions; it is impossible to find an answer which someday will not be found to be wrong. The difficulty arises because science and religion are both trying to answer questions in the same realm here.

SCIENCE AND MORAL QUESTIONS

On the other hand, I don't believe that a real conflict with science will arise in the ethical aspect, because I believe that moral questions are outside of the scientific realm.

Let me give three or four arguments to show why I believe this. In the first place, there have been conflicts in the past between the scientific and the religious view about the metaphysical aspect and, nevertheless, the older moral views did not collapse, did not change.

Second, there are good men who practice Christian ethics and who do not believe in the divinity of Christ. They find themselves in no inconsistency here.

Thirdly, although I believe that from time to time scientific evidence is found which may be partially interpreted as giving some evidence of some particular aspect of the life of Christ, for example, or of other religious metaphysical ideas, it seems to me that there is no scientific evidence bearing on the golden rule. It seems to me that that is somehow different.

Now, let's see if I can make a little philosophical explanation as to why it is different—how science cannot affect the fundamental basis of morals.

The typical human problem, and one whose answer religion aims to supply, is always of the following form: Should I do this? Should we do this? Should the government do this? To answer this question we can resolve it into two parts: First— If I do this, what will happen?—and second—Do I want that to happen? What would come of it of value—of good?

Now a question of the form: If I do this, what will happen? is strictly scientific. As a matter of fact, science can be defined as a method for, and a body of information obtained by, trying to answer only questions which can be put into the form: If I do this, what will happen? The technique of it, fundamentally, is: Try it and see. Then you put together a large amount of information from such experiences. All scientists will agree that a question—any question, philosophical or other—which cannot be put into the form that can be tested by experiment (or, in simple terms, that cannot be put into the form: If I do this, what will happen?) is not a scientific question; it is outside the realm of science.

I claim that whether you want something to happen or not— what value there is in the result, and how you judge the value of the result (which is the other end of the question: Should I do this?)—must lie outside of science because it is not a question that you can answer only by knowing what happens; you still have to *judge* what happens—in a moral way. So, for this theoretical reason I think that there is a complete consistency between the moral view—or the ethical aspect of religion—and scientific information.

Turning to the third aspect of religion—the inspirational aspect—brings me to the central question that I would like to present to this imaginary panel. The source of inspiration today—for strength and for comfort—in any religion is very closely knit with the metaphysical aspect; that is, the inspiration comes from working for God, for obeying his will, feeling one with God. Emotional ties to the moral code—based in this manner—begin to be severely weakened when doubt, even a small amount of doubt, is expressed as to the existence of God; so when the belief in God becomes uncertain, this particular method of obtaining inspiration fails.

I don't know the answer to this central problem—the problem of maintaining the real value of religion, as a source of strength and of courage to most men, while, at the same time, not requiring an absolute faith in the metaphysical aspects.

THE HERITAGES OF WESTERN CIVILIZATION

Western civilization, it seems to me, stands by two great heritages. One is the scientific spirit of adventure—the adventure into the unknown, an unknown which must be recognized as being unknown in order to be explored; the demand that the unanswerable mysteries of the universe remain unanswered; the attitude that all is uncertain; to summarize it—the humility of the intellect. The other great heritage is Christian ethics—the basis of action on love, the brotherhood of all men, the value of the individual—the humility of the spirit.

These two heritages are logically, thoroughly consistent. But logic is not all; one needs one's heart to follow an idea. If people are going back to religion, what are they going back to? Is the modern church a place to give comfort to a man who doubts God—more, one who disbelieves in God? Is the modern church

THE RELATION OF SCIENCE AND RELIGION

a place to give comfort and encouragement to the value of such doubts? So far, have we not drawn strength and comfort to maintain the one or the other of these consistent heritages in a way which attacks the values of the other? Is this unavoidable? How can we draw inspiration to support these two pillars of Western civilization so that they may stand together in full vigor, mutually unafraid? Is this not the central problem of our time?

I put it up to the panel for discussion.

317

ELTING E. MORISON

A Case Study of Innovation

A DISTINGUISHED HISTORIAN DISCUSSES THE INTRODUCTION OF
A SINGLE TECHNOLOGICAL CHANGE IN THE UNITED STATES NAVY
—AND COMES TO SOME PROVOCATIVE CONCLUSIONS ABOUT THE
PROCESS OF CHANGE IN GENERAL.

In the early days of the last war, when armaments of all kinds
were in short supply, the British, I am told, made use of a ven-
erable field piece that had come down to them from previous
generations. The honorable past of this light artillery stretched
back, in fact, to the Boer War. In the days of uncertainty after
the fall of France, these guns, hitched to trucks, served as useful mobile units in the coast defense. But it was felt that the
rapidity of fire could be increased. A time-motion expert was,
therefore, called in to suggest ways to simplify the firing procedures. He watched one of the gun crews of five men at practice in the field for some time. Puzzled by certain aspects of
the procedures, he took some slow-motion pictures of the sol-
diers performing the loading, aiming, and firing routines.

When he ran these pictures over once or twice, he noticed
something that appeared odd to him. A moment before the firing, two members of the gun crew ceased all activity and came
to attention for a three-second interval, extending throughout
the discharge of the gun. He summoned an old colonel of artillery, showed him the pictures, and pointed out this strange

behavior. What, he asked the colonel, did it mean? The colonel, too, was puzzled. He asked to see the pictures again. "Ah," he said when the performance was over, "I have it. They are holding the horses."

This story, true or not, and I am told it is true, suggests nicely the pain with which the human being accommodates himself to changing conditions. The tendency is apparently involuntary and immediate to protect oneself against the shock of change by continuing in the presence of altered situations the familiar habits, however incongruous, of the past.

Yet, if human beings are attached to the known, to the realm of things as they are, they also, regrettably for their peace of mind, are incessantly attracted to the unknown and to things as they might be. As Ecclesiastes glumly pointed out, men persist in disordering their settled ways and beliefs by seeking out many inventions.

The point is obvious. Change has always been a constant in human affairs; today, indeed, it is one of the determining characteristics of our civilization. In our relatively shapeless social organization, the shifts from station to station are fast and easy. More important for our immediate purpose, America is fundamentally an industrial society in a time of tremendous technological development. We are thus constantly presented with new devices or new forms of power that, in their refinement and extension, continually bombard the fixed structure of our habits of mind and behavior. Under such conditions, our salvation, or at least our peace of mind, appears to depend upon how successfully we can in the future become what has been called in an excellent phrase a completely "adaptive society."

It is interesting, in view of all this, that so little investigation, relatively, has been made of the process of change and human responses to it. Recently psychologists, sociologists, and cultural anthropologists have addressed themselves to the subject with suggestive results. But we are still far from a full understanding of the process, and still farther from knowing how we can set about simplifying and assisting an individual's or a group's accommodation to new machines or new ideas.

With these things in mind, I thought it might be interesting and perhaps useful to examine historically a changing situation within a society; to see if from this examination we can discover how the new machines or ideas that introduced the changing situation developed; to see who introduces them, who resists them, what points of friction or tension in the social structure are produced by the innovation, and perhaps why they are produced and what, if anything, may be done about it. For this case study, the introduction of continuous-aim firing in the United States Navy has been selected. The system, first devised by an English officer in 1898, was introduced into our Navy in the years 1900-1902.

I have chosen to study this episode for two reasons. First, a navy is not unlike a society that has been placed under laboratory conditions. Its dimensions are severely limited; it is beautifully ordered and articulated; it is relatively isolated from random influences. For these reasons the impact of change can be clearly discerned, the resulting dislocations in the structure easily discovered and marked out. In the second place, the development of continuous-aim firing rests upon mechanical devices. It, therefore, presents for study a concrete, durable situation. It is not like many other innovating reagents—a Manichean heresy, or Marxism, or the views of Sigmund Freud—that can be shoved and hauled out of shape by contending forces or conflicting prejudices. At all times we know exactly what continuous-aim firing really is. It will be well now to describe, as briefly as possible, *what* it is.

The governing fact in gunfire at sea is that the gun is mounted on an unstable platform—a rolling ship. This constant motion obviously complicates the problem of holding a steady aim. Before 1898 this problem was solved in the following elementary fashion. A gun pointer estimated the range of the target—ordinarily about 2800 yards. He then raised the gun barrel to give the gun the elevation to carry the shell to the target at the estimated range. This was accomplished by turning a small wheel on the gun mount that operated the elevating gears. With the gun thus fixed for range, the gun pointer peered through open sights, not unlike those on a small rifle, and waited until the roll of the ship brought the sights on the target. He then pressed the firing button that discharged the gun. There were, by 1898, on some naval guns, telescope sights which naturally enlarged the image of the target for the gun pointer. But these sights were rarely used by gun pointers. They were lashed securely to the gun barrel and, recoiling with the barrel, jammed back against the unwary pointer's eye. Therefore, when used at all, they were used only to take an initial sight for purposes of estimating the range before the gun was fired.

Notice now two things about the process. First of all, the rapidity of fire was controlled by the rolling period of the ship. Pointers had to wait for the one moment in the roll when the sights were brought on the target. Notice also this: There is in every pointer what is called a "firing interval"—the time lag between his impulse to fire the gun and the translation of this impulse into the act of pressing the firing button. A pointer, because of this reaction time, could not wait to fire the gun until the exact moment when the roll of the ship brought the sights onto the target; he had to will to fire a little before, while the sights were off the target. Since the firing interval was an individual matter, varying obviously from man to man, each pointer had to estimate, from long practice, his own interval and compensate for it accordingly.

These things, together with others we need not here investigate, conspired to make gunfire at sea relatively uncertain and ineffective. The pointer, on a moving platform, estimating range and firing interval, shooting while his sight was off the target, became in a sense an individual artist.

In 1898, many of the uncertainties were removed from the process—and the position of the gun pointer radically altered—by the introduction of continuous-aim firing. The major change was that which enabled the gun pointer to keep his sight and gun barrel on the target throughout the roll of the ship. This was accomplished by altering the gear ratio in the elevating gear to permit a pointer to compensate for the roll of the vessel by rapidly elevating and depressing the gun. From this change another followed. With the possibility of maintaining the gun always on the target, the desirability of improved sights became immediately apparent. The advantages of the telescope sight, as opposed to the open sight, were for the first time fully realized. But the existing telescope sight, it will be recalled, moved with the recoil of the gun and jammed back against the eye of the gunner. To correct this, the sight was mounted on a sleeve that permitted the gun barrel to recoil through it without moving the telescope.

These two improvements—in elevating gear and sighting—eliminated the major uncertainties in gunfire at sea and greatly increased the possibilities of both accurate and rapid fire.

You must take my word for it that this changed naval gunnery from an art to a science, and that gunnery accuracy in the British and our Navy increased about 3000 percent in six years. This doesn't mean much except to suggest a great increase in accuracy. The following comparative figures may mean a little more. In 1899 five ships of the North Atlantic Squadron fired five minutes each at a lightship hulk at the conventional range of 1600 yards. After twenty-five minutes of banging away 2 hits had been made on the sails of the elderly vessel. Six years later one naval gunner made 15 hits in one minute at a target 75 x 25 feet at the same range; half of them hit in a bull's eye 50 inches square.

Now with the instruments (the gun, elevating gear, and telescope), the method, and the results of continuous-aim firing in mind, let us turn to the subject of major interest: how was the idea, obviously so simple an idea, of continuous-aim firing developed; who introduced it; and what was its reception?

INTRODUCTION OF AN IDEA

The idea was the product of the fertile mind of the English officer, Admiral Sir Percy Scott. He arrived at it in this way, while, in 1898, he was the captain of H.M.S. *Scylla*. For the previous two or three years he had given much thought, independently and almost alone in the British Navy, to means of improving gunnery. One rough day when the ship, at target practice, was pitching and rolling violently, he walked up and down the gun deck watching his gun crews. Because of the heavy weather they were making very bad scores. Scott noticed, however, that one pointer was appreciably more accurate than the rest. He watched this man with care and saw, after a time, that he was unconsciously working his elevating gear back and forth in a partially successful effort to compensate for the roll of the vessel. It flashed through Scott's mind at that moment that here was the sovereign remedy for the problems of inaccurate fire. What one man could do partially and unconsciously, perhaps all men could be trained to do consciously and completely.

Acting on this assumption, he did three things. First, in all the guns of the *Scylla*, he changed the gear ratio in the elevating gear, previously used only to set the gun in fixed position for range, so that a gunner could easily elevate and depress the gun to follow a target throughout the roll. Second, he rerigged his telescopes so that they would not be influenced by the recoil of the gun. Third, he rigged a small target at the mouth of the gun, which was moved up and down by a crank to simulate a moving target. By following this target as it moved, and firing at it with a subcalibre rifle rigged in the breech of the gun, the pointer could practice every day. Thus equipped, the ship became a training ground for gunners. Where before the good pointer was an individual artist, pointers now became trained technicians, fairly uniform in their capacity to shoot. The effect was immediately felt. Within a year the *Scylla* established records that were remarkable.

At this point I should like to stop a minute to notice several things directly related to, and involved in, the process of innovation. First, the personality of the innovator. I wish there were space to say a good deal about Admiral Sir Percy Scott. He was a wonderful man. Three small bits of evidence must suffice, however. First, he had a certain mechanical ingenuity. Second, his personal life was shot through with frustration and bitterness. There was a divorce, and a quarrel with the ambitious Lord Charles Beresford—the sounds of which, Scott liked to recall, penetrated to the last outposts of empire. Finally, he possessed, like Swift, a savage indignation directed ordinarily at the inelastic intelligence of all constituted authority—especially the British Admiralty.

There are other points worth mention here. Notice first that Scott was not responsible for the invention of the basic instruments that made the reform in gunnery possible. This reform rested upon the gun itself, which as a rifle had been in existence on ships for at least forty years; the elevating gear, which had been, in the form Scott found it, a part of the rifled gun from the beginning; and the telescope sight, which had been on shipboard at least eight years. Scott's contribution was to bring these three elements, appropriately modified, into a combination that made continuous-aim firing possible for the first time. Notice also that he was allowed to bring these elements into combination by accident, by watching the unconscious action of a gun pointer endeavoring through the operation of his elevating gear to correct partially for the roll of his vessel.

THE PREPARED MIND IS NOT ENOUGH

Scott, as we have seen, had been interested in gunnery; he had thought about ways to increase accuracy by practice and improvement of existing machinery; but able as he was, he had not been able to produce on his own initiative and by his own thinking the essential idea and to modify instruments to fit his purpose. Notice here, finally, the intricate interaction of chance, the intellectual climate, and Scott's mind. Fortune (in this case the unaware gun pointer) indeed favors the prepared mind, but even fortune and the prepared mind need a favorable environment before they can conspire to produce sudden change. No intelligence can proceed very far above the threshold of existing data or the binding combinations of existing data.

All these elements that enter into what may be called "original thinking" interest me as a teacher. Deeply rooted in the pedagogical mind often enough is a sterile infatuation with "inert ideas"; there is thus always present in the profession the tendency to be diverted from the *process* by which these ideas, or indeed any ideas, are really produced. I well remember with what contempt a class of mine, which was reading Leonardo da Vinci's *Notebooks*, dismissed the author because he appeared to know no more mechanics than, as one wit in the class observed, a Vermont Republican farmer of the present day. This is perhaps the result to be expected from a method of instruction that too frequently implies that the great generalizations were the result, on the one hand, of chance—an apple falling in an orchard or a teapot boiling on the hearth—or, on the other hand, of some towering intelligence proceeding in isolation inexorably toward some prefigured idea, such as evolution, for example.

This process by which new concepts appear—the interaction of fortune, intellectual climate, and the prepared imaginative mind—is an interesting subject for examination offered by any case study of innovation. It was a subject that momentarily engaged the attention of Horace Walpole, whose lissome intelligence glided over the surface of so many ideas. In reflecting upon the part played by chance in the development of new concepts, he recalled the story of the three princes of Serendip who set out to find some interesting object on a journey through their realm. They did not find the particular object of their search, but along the way they discovered many new things simply because they were looking for *something*. Walpole believed this intellectual method ought to be given a name—in honor of the founders—Serendipity; and Serendipity certainly exerts a considerable influence in what we call original thinking. There is an element of Serendipity, for example, in Scott's chance discovery of continuous-aim firing in that he was, and had been, looking for some means to improve his target practice and stumbled upon a solution, by observation, that had never entered his head.

EDUCATING THE NAVY

It was in 1900 that Percy Scott went out to the China Station as commanding officer of H.M.S. *Terrible*. In that ship he continued his training methods and his spectacular successes in naval gunnery. On the China Station he met up with an American junior officer, William S. Sims. Sims had little of the mechanical ingenuity of Percy Scott, but the two were drawn together by temperamental similarities that are worth noticing here. Sims had the same intolerance for what is called spit-and-polish and the same contempt for bureaucratic inertia as his British brother officer. He had for some years been concerned, as had Scott, with what he took to be the inefficiency of his own Navy. Just before he met Scott, for example, he had shipped out to China in the brand new pride of the fleet, the battleship *Kentucky*. After careful investigation and reflection he had informed his superiors in Washington she was not a battleship at all—"but a crime against the white race."

The spirit with which he pushed forward his efforts to reform the naval service can best be stated in his own words to a brother officer: "I am perfectly willing that those holding views different from mine should continue to live, but with every fibre of my being I loathe indirection and shiftiness, and where it occurs in high place, and is used to save face at the expense of the vital interests of our great service (in which silly people place such a childlike trust), I want that man's blood and I will have it no matter what it costs me personally."

From Scott in 1900 Sims learned all there was to know about continuous-aim firing. He modified, with the Englishman's active assistance, the gear on his own ship and tried out the new system. After a few months' training, his experimental batteries began making remarkable records at target practice. Sure of the usefulness of his gunnery methods, Sims then turned to the task of educating the Navy at large. In 13 great official reports he documented the case for continuous-aim firing, supporting his arguments at every turn with a mass of factual data. Over a period of two years, he reiterated three principal points: First, he continually cited the records established by Scott's ships, the *Scylla* and the *Terrible*, and supported these with the accumulating data from his own tests on an American ship; second, he described the mechanisms used and the training procedures instituted by Scott and himself to obtain these records; third, he explained that our own mechanisms were not generally adequate without modification to meet the demands placed on them by continuous-aim firing. Our elevating gear, useful to raise or lower a gun slowly to fix it in position for the proper range, did not always work easily and rapidly enough to enable a gunner to follow a target with his gun throughout the roll of the ship. Sims also explained that such few telescope sights as there were on board our ships were useless. Their cross wires were so thick or coarse that they obscured the target, and the sights had been attached to the gun in such a way that the recoil system of the gun plunged the eyepiece against the eye of the gun pointer.

This was the substance not only of the first but of all the succeeding reports written on the subject of gunnery from the China Station. It will be interesting to see what response these met with in Washington. The response falls roughly into three easily indentifiable stages.

First stage: no response. Sims had directed his comments to the Bureau of Ordnance and the Bureau of Navigation; in both bureaus there was dead silence. The thing—claims and records of continuous-aim firing—was not credible. The reports were simply filed away and forgotten. Some indeed, it was later discovered to Sims' delight, were half eaten away by cockroaches.

Second stage: rebuttal. It is never pleasant for any man to have his best work left unnoticed by superiors, and it was an unpleasantness that Sims suffered extremely ill. In his later reports, beside the accumulating data he used to clinch his argument, he changed his tone. He used deliberately shocking language because, as he said, "They were furious at my first papers and stowed them away. I therefore made up my mind I would give these later papers such a form that they would be dangerous documents to leave neglected in the files." To another friend he added, "I want scalps or nothing and if I can't have 'em I won't play."

SIMS GETS ATTENTION

Besides altering his tone, he took another step to be sure his views would receive attention. He sent copies of his reports to other officers in the fleet. Aware, as a result, that Sims' gunnery claims were being circulated and talked about, the men in Washington were then stirred to action. They responded—notably through the Chief of the Bureau of Ordnance, who had general charge of the equipment used in gunnery practice—as follows: (1) Our equipment was in general as good as the British; (2) since our equipment was as good, the trouble must be with the men, but the gun pointer and the training of gun pointers were the responsibility of the officers on the ships; (3) and most significant—continuous-aim firing was impossible. Experiments had revealed that five men at work on the elevating gear of a six-inch gun could not produce the power necessary to compensate for a roll of five degrees in ten seconds. These experiments and calculations demonstrated beyond peradventure or doubt that Scott's system of gunfire was not possible.

Only one difficulty is discoverable in these arguments; they were wrong at important points. To begin with, while there was little difference between the standard British equipment and the standard U.S. equipment, the instruments on Scott's two ships, the *Scylla* and the *Terrible*, were far better than the standard equipment on our ships. Second, all the men could not be trained in continuous-aim firing until equipment was improved throughout the fleet. Third, the experiments with the elevating gear had been ingeniously contrived at the Washington Navy Yard—on solid ground. It had, therefore, been possible in the Bureau of Ordnance calculation, to dispense with Newton's first law of motion, which naturally operated at sea to assist the gunner in elevating or depressing a gun mounted on a moving ship. Another difficulty was of course that continuous-aim firing was in use on Scott's and some of our own ships at the time the Chief of the Bureau of Ordnance was writing that it was a mathematical impossibility. In every way I find this second stage, the apparent resort to reason, the most entertaining and instructive in our investigation of the responses to innovation.

Third stage: name calling. Sims, of course, by the high temperature he was running and by his calculated overstatement, invited this. He was told in official endorsements on his reports that there were others quite as sincere and loyal as he and far less difficult; he was dismissed as a crack-brain egotist; he was called a deliberate falsifier of evidence.

SIMS GETS ACTION

The rising opposition and the character of the opposition was not calculated to discourage further efforts by Sims. It convinced him that he was being attacked by shifty, dishonest men who were the victims, as he said, of insufferable conceit and ignorance. He made up his mind, therefore, that he was prepared to go to any extent to obtain the "scalps" and the "blood" he was after. Accordingly he, a lieutenant, took the extraordinary step of writing the President of the United States, Theodore Roosevelt, to inform him of the remarkable records of Scott's ships, of the inadequacy of our own gunnery routines and records, and of the refusal of the Navy Department to act. Roosevelt, who always liked to respond to such appeals when he conveniently could, brought Sims back from China late in 1902 and installed him as Inspector of Target Practice, a post the naval officer held throughout the remaining six years of the Administration.

With this sequence of events (the chronological account of the innovation of continuous-aim firing) in mind, it is possible now to examine the evidence to see what light it may throw on our present interest—the origins of and responses to change in a society.

First, the origins. We have already analyzed briefly the origins of the idea. We have seen how Scott arrived at his notion. We must now ask ourselves, I think, why Sims so actively sought, almost alone among his brother officers, to introduce the idea into his service. It is particularly interesting here to notice again that neither Scott nor Sims invented the instruments on which the innovation rested. They did not urge their proposal because of pride in the instruments of their own design.

THE ENGINEER AND THE ENTREPRENEUR

The telescope sight had first been placed on shipboard in 1892 by Bradley Fiske, an officer of great inventive capacity.

329

In that year Fiske had even sketched out on paper the vague possibility of continuous-aim firing, but his sight was condemned by his commanding officer, Robley D. Evans, as of no use. Instead of fighting for his telescope Fiske turned his attention to a range finder. But six years later Sims took over and became the engineer of the revolution.

I would suggest, with some reservations, this explanation: Fiske, as an inventor, took his pleasure in great part from the design of the device. He lacked not so much the energy as the overriding sense of social necessity that would have enabled him to *force* revolutionary ideas on the service. Sims possessed this sense. In Fiske we may here find the familiar plight of the engineer who often enough must watch the products of his ingenuity being organized and promoted by other men. These other promotional men, when they appear in the world of commerce, are called entrepreneurs. In the world of ideas they are still entrepreneurs.

Sims was one, a middle-aged man caught in the periphery (as a lieutenant) of the intricate webbing of a precisely organized society. Rank, the exact definition and limitation of a man's capacity at any given moment in his own career, prevented Sims from discharging all his exploding energies into the purely routine channels of the peacetime Navy. At the height of his powers he was a junior officer standing watches on a ship cruising aimlessly in friendly foreign waters. The remarkable changes in systems of gunfire to which Scott introduced him gave him the opportunity to expend his energies quite legitimately against the encrusted hierarchy of his society. He was moved, it seems to me, in part by his genuine desire to improve his own profession but also in part by rebellion against tedium, against inefficiency from on high, and against the artificial limitations placed on his actions by the social structure, in his case junior rank.

RESPONDING TO CHANGE

Now having briefly investigated the origins of the change, let us examine the reasons for what must be considered the

330

weird response we have observed to this proposed change. Here was a reform that greatly and demonstrably increased the fighting effectiveness of a service that maintains itself almost exclusively to fight. Why then this refusal to accept so carefully documented a case, a case proved incontestably by records and experience? Why should virtually all the rulers of a society so resolutely seek to reject a change that so markedly improved its chances for survival in any contest with competing societies?

There are the obvious reasons that will occur to everyone—the source of the proposed reform was an obscure junior officer 8000 miles away; he was, and this is a significant factor, criticizing gear and machinery designed by the very men in the bureaus to whom he was sending his criticisms. And furthermore, Sims was seeking to introduce what he claimed were improvements in a field where improvements appeared unnecessary. Superiority in war, as in other things, is a relative matter, and the Spanish-American War had been won by the old system of gunnery. Therefore, it was superior even though of the 9500 shots fired, at varying but close ranges, only 121 had found their mark.

A less obvious cause appears by far the most important one. It has to do with the fact that the Navy is not only an armed force; it is a society. In the forty years following the Civil War, this society had been forced to accommodate itself to a series of technological changes—the steam turbine, the electric motor, the rifled shell of great explosive power, case-hardened steel armor, and all the rest of it. These changes wrought extraordinary changes in ship design and, therefore, in the concepts of how ships were to be used: that is, in fleet tactics, and even in naval strategy. The Navy of this period is a paradise for the historian or sociologist in search of evidence of a society's responses to change.

To these numerous innovations, producing as they did a spreading disorder throughout a service with heavy commitments to formal organization, the Navy responded with grudging pain. It is wrong to assume, as civilians frequently do, that this blind reaction to technological change springs exclusively from some causeless Bourbon distemper that invades the military

331

mind. There is a sounder and more attractive base. The opposition, where it occurs, of the soldier and the sailor to such change springs from the normal human instinct to protect oneself and more especially one's way of life. Military organizations are societies built around and upon the prevailing weapon systems. Intuitively and quite correctly the military man feels that a change in weapon portends a change in the arrangements of his society.

Think of it this way. Since the time that the memory of man runneth not to the contrary, the naval society has been built upon the surface vessel. Daily routines, habits of mind, social organization, physical accommodations, conventions, rituals, spiritual allegiances have been conditioned by the essential fact of the ship. What then happens to your society if the ship is displaced as the principal element by such a radically different weapon as the plane? The mores and structure of the society are immediately placed in jeopardy. They may, in fact, be wholly destroyed. It was the witty cliché of the 20's that those naval officers who persisted in defending the battleship against the apparently superior claims of the carrier did so because the battleship was a more comfortable home. What, from one point of view, is a better argument?

This sentiment would appear to account in large part for the opposition to Sims; it was the product of an instinctive protective feeling, even if the reasons for this feeling were not overt or recognized. The years after 1902 proved how right, in their terms, the opposition was. From changes in gunnery flowed an extraordinary complex of changes: in shipboard routines, ship design, and fleet tactics. There was, too, a social change. In the days when gunnery was taken lightly, the gunnery officer was taken lightly. After 1903, he became one of the most significant and powerful members of a ship's company, and this shift of emphasis naturally was shortly reflected in promotion lists. Each one of these changes provoked a dislocation in the naval society, and with man's troubled foresight and natural indisposition to break up classic forms, the men in Washington withstood the Sims onslaught as long as they could. It is

332

very significant that they withstood it until an agent from outside
—outside and above—who was not clearly identified with the
naval society, entered to force change.

This agent, the President of the United States, might reasonably and legitimately claim the credit for restoring our gunnery
efficiency. But this restoration by *force majeure* was brought
about at great cost to the service and men involved. Bitternesses,
suspicions, wounds were caused that it was impossible to conceal or heal.

Now this entire episode may be summed up in five separate
points:

1. The essential idea for change occurred in part by chance,
but in an environment that contained all the essential elements
for change, and to a mind prepared to recognize the possibility
of change.

2. The basic elements—the gun, gear, and sight—were put in
the environment by other men; men interested in designing
machinery to serve different purposes, or simply interested in
the instruments themselves.

3. These elements were brought into successful combination
by minds not interested in the instruments for themselves but in
what they could do with them. These minds were, to be sure,
interested in good gunnery, overtly and consciously. They may
also, not so consciously, have been interested in the implied
revolt that is present in the support of all change. Their temperaments and careers indeed support this view. From gunnery,
Sims went on to attack ship designs, existing fleet tactics, and
methods of promotion. He lived and died, as the service said,
a stormy petrel, a man always on the attack against higher
authority, a rebellious spirit.

4. He and his colleagues were opposed on this occasion by
men who were apparently moved by three considerations: honest
disbelief in the dramatic but substantiated claims of the new
process; protection of the existing devices and instruments with
which they identified themselves; and maintenance of the existing society with which they were identified.

5. The deadlock between those who sought change and those

who sought to retain things as they were was broken only by an appeal to superior force; a force removed from and unidentified with the mores, conventions, devices of the society. This seems to me a very important point. The naval society in 1900 broke down in its effort to accommodate itself to a new situation. The appeal to Roosevelt is documentation for Mahan's great generalization that no military service should or can undertake to reform itself. It must seek assistance from outside.

Now, with these five summary points in mind, it may be possible to seek, as suggested at the outset, a few larger implications from this story. What, if anything, may it suggest about the general process by which any society attempts to meet changing conditions?

NO SOCIETY CAN REFORM ITSELF?

There is, to begin with, a disturbing inference half concealed in Mahan's statement that no military organization can reform itself. Certainly civilians would agree with this. We all know now that war and the preparation of war is too important, as Clemenceau said, to be left to the generals. But military organizations are really societies—more rigidly structured, more highly integrated than most communities, but still societies. What then if we make this phrase to read, "No society can reform itself"? Is the process of adaptation to change, for example, too important to be left to human beings? This is a discouraging thought, and historically there is some cause to be discouraged.

This is a subject to which we may well address ourselves. Our society, especially, is built, as I have said, just as surely upon a changing technology as the Navy of the 90's was built upon changing weapon systems. How then can we find the means to accept with less pain to ourselves and less damage to our social organization the dislocations in our society that are produced by innovation? I cannot, of course, give any satisfying answer to these difficult questions. But in thinking about the case study before us, an idea occurred to me that at least might

334

warrant further investigation by men far more qualified than I.

A primary source of conflict and tension in our case study appears to lie in this great word I have used so often in the summary—the word *identification*. It cannot have escaped notice that some men identified themselves with their creations—sights, gun, gear, and so forth—and thus obtained a presumed satisfaction from the thing itself, a satisfaction that prevented them from thinking too closely on either the use or the defects of the thing; that others identified themselves with a settled way of life they had inherited or accepted with minor modification and thus found their satisfaction in attempting to maintain that way of life unchanged; and that still others identified themselves as rebellious spirits, men of the insurgent cast of mind, and thus obtained a satisfaction from the act of revolt itself.

This purely personal identification with a concept, a convention, or an attitude would appear to be a powerful barrier in the way of easily acceptable change. Here is an interesting primitive example. In the years from 1864-1871 ten steel companies in the country began making steel by the new Bessemer process. All but one of them at the outset imported from Great Britain English workmen familiar with the process. One, the Cambria Company, did not. In the first few years those companies with British labor established an initial superiority. But by the end of the 70's, Cambria had obtained a commanding lead over all competitors.

The Bessemer process, like any new technique, had been constantly improved and refined in this period from 1864-1871. The British laborers of Cambria's competitors, secure in the performance of their own original techniques, resisted and resented all change. The Pennsylvania farm boys, untrammeled by the rituals and traditions of their craft, happily and rapidly adapted themselves to the constantly changing process. They ended by creating an unassailable competitive position for their company.

How then can we modify the dangerous effects of this word *identification*? And how much can we tamper with this identifying process? Our security, much of it, after all, comes from

335

giving our allegiance to something greater than ourselves. These are difficult questions to which only the most tentative and provisional answers may here be proposed for consideration.

THE DANGER OF LIMITED IDENTIFICATIONS

If one looks closely at this little case history, one discovers that the men involved were the victims of *severely limited* identifications. They were presumably all part of a society dedicated to the process of national defense, yet they persisted in aligning themselves with separate parts of that process—with the existing instruments of defense, with the existing customs of the society, or with the act of rebellion against the customs of the society. Of them all, the insurgents had the best of it. They could, and did, say that the process of defense was improved by a gun that shot straighter and faster, and since they wanted such guns, they were unique among their fellows—patriots who sought only the larger object of improved defense. But this beguiling statement—even when coupled with the recognition that these men were right, and extremely valuable and deserving of respect and admiration—cannot conceal the fact that they were interested too in scalps and blood. They were so interested, in fact, that they made their case a militant one and thus created an atmosphere in which self-respecting men could not capitulate without appearing either weak or wrong or both. So these limited identifications brought men into conflict with each other, and the conflict prevented them from arriving at a common acceptance of a change that presumably, as men interested in our total national defense, they would all find desirable.

It appears, therefore, if I am correct in my assessment, that we might spend some time and thought on the possibility of enlarging the sphere of our identifications from the part to the whole. For example, those Pennsylvania farm boys at the Cambria Steel Company were, apparently, much more interested in the manufacture of steel than in the preservation of any particular way of making steel. So I would suggest that in studying innovation we look further into this possibility: the possibility that any group that exists for any purpose—the family, the factory, the educational institution—might begin by defining for itself its grand object, and see to it that that grand object is communicated to every member of the group. Thus defined and communicated, it might serve as a unifying agent against the disruptive local allegiances of the inevitable smaller elements that compose any group. It may also serve as a means to increase the acceptability of any change that would assist in the more efficient achievement of the grand object.

There appears also a second possible way to combat the untoward influence of limited identifications. We are, I may repeat, a society based on technology in a time of prodigious technological advance, and a civilization committed irrevocably to the theory of evolution. These things mean that we believe in change; they suggest that if we are to survive in good health we must become an "adaptive society." By the word "adaptive" is meant the ability to extract the fullest possible returns from the opportunities at hand; the ability of Sir Percy Scott to select judiciously from the ideas and material presented both by the past and present and to throw them into a new combination. "Adaptive," as here used, also means the kind of resilience that will enable us to accept fully and easily the best promises of changing circumstances without losing our sense of continuity or our essential integrity.

We are not yet emotionally an adaptive society, though we try systematically to develop forces that tend to make us one. We encourage the search for new inventions; we keep the mind stimulated, bright, and free to seek out fresh means of transport, communication, and energy; yet we remain, in part, appalled by the consequences of our ingenuity and, too frequently, try to find security through the shoring up of ancient and irrelevant conventions, the extension of purely physical safeguards, or the delivery of decisions we ourselves should make into the keeping of superior authority like the state. These solutions are not necessarily unnatural or wrong, but historically they have not been enough, and I suspect they never will be enough to give us the serenity and competence we seek.

A NEW VIEW OF OURSELVES

If the preceding statements are correct, they suggest that we might give some attention to the construction of a new view of ourselves as a society which in time of great change identified itself with and obtained security and satisfaction from the wise and creative accommodation to change itself. Such a view rests, I think, upon a relatively greater reverence for the mere *process* of living in a society than we possess today, and a relatively smaller respect for and attachment to any special *product* of a society—a product either as finite as a bathroom fixture or as conceptual as a fixed and final definition of our Constitution or our democracy.

Historically such an identification with *process* as opposed to *product,* with adventurous selection and adaptation as opposed to simple retention and possessiveness, has been difficult to achieve collectively. The Roman of the early republic, the Italian of the late fifteenth and early sixteenth century, the Englishman of Elizabeth's time appear to have been most successful in seizing the new opportunities while conserving as much of the heritage of the past as they found relevant and useful to their purpose.

We seem to have fallen on times similar to theirs, when many of the existing forms and schemes have lost meaning in the face of dramatically altering circumstances. Like them we may find at least part of our salvation in identifying ourselves with the adaptive process and thus share with them some of the joy, exuberance, satisfaction, and security with which they went out to meet their changing times.

J. ROBERT OPPENHEIMER

Talk to Undergraduates

A NOTED SCIENTIST SPEAKS TO THE YOUTH OF TODAY
ABOUT THE MEANING AND USES OF
KNOWLEDGE IN A COMPLEX WORLD.

I have a few thoughts on the situation we face in the world in
which we live that I would like to discuss. What I say is not
only incomplete and partial, but there is a very special ground
for some humility in what I do say. Between your generation
and mine there are differences that neither of us is likely fully
to understand. I am aware of this gulf and I don't underestimate it.

There is another reason for humility: What you have to deal
with is partly the heritage of what the generations your senior
have left you. I think we have no great reason for pride in the
heritage. The problems seem to me very grave, and the measures and means for dealing with them and resolving them nothing to write home about.

PECULIARITIES OF THE TIME

Before talking about the specific problems of learning
and ignorance—as they appear here, and as they appear in
a larger sense for all of us—it may not be too bad to remind
ourselves of some of the peculiarities of the time. It seems
to me an extremely peculiar age. All ages are; but I am in

some doubt as to whether there is any valid historical analog to this time.

I was reminded today of a story; and before outlining some of the traits of the mid-twentieth century, I may repeat it. It has a kind of moral. A friend of mine signed up in the Army, after Pearl Harbor. He is a Greek philologist and philosopher, and the Army understood that he was a clever man and put him to work in Intelligence. Part of his job, in preparation for the invasion of Europe, was to interview men who had participated in the Canadian raid and in the evacuation from Dunkirk, and one day he talked to a fellow who had been the communications officer for his outfit. This fellow had come moderately late to Dunkirk and there were great masses of men on the beach waiting to be evacuated. So he dug down in the sand and turned on his radio and listened. There was a little bit of music—and that was all right—and then he got a BBC broadcast. The broadcast described how the ships were standing off to sea, waiting, and the men were waiting in long lines, and the Germans were approaching, and overhead there were dogfights—and the fellow said, "It was much too horrible; I had to turn it off."

So it is whenever we take an appraisal of our situation. One of the features of this time is that we live under a palpable threat of an apocalypse. I don't regard this as inevitable; on the contrary, I think that for anyone who has an opportunity of working to avert it, that is a valid full-time job. It isn't like the apocalypse that was expected in the year 1000, but it is very much at the back of our minds in everything we do.

It is a strange time, too, in that never in the history of the world has there been as rapid a growth of knowledge, as rapid a growth in understanding, or as great changes. I suppose that, in the 18th century, men talked about how knowledge doubled every 50 years. I think we could make a case for saying that it doubles every 10 years now.

This creates problems which I will discuss here. But it also creates problems of the use of that knowledge, of the vast powers that it seems to make available, of the choices. It creates a world of incredibly rapid change. Almost nobody can look back to a schooling with a feeling that it is entirely relevant to the problems that he is now dealing with. Almost everyone has to have the sense that he goes to school all his life.

In some ways this situation, which I think is a natural continuation of the fluidity and openness of American society—an openness now not with regard to the physical frontier but with regard to the frontier of knowledge—has given this country a strange destiny. I cannot believe that other parts of the world will not also very rapidly be caught up in changes comparable to those in which we live. They are not prepared for it; they have remained in relatively steady, relatively quiet, relatively enduring forms. And how we deal with this certainly will not be an example that other peoples will inevitably or rightly follow. But how we deal with it cannot be irrelevant to the future of the whole world.

A CHARACTERISTIC IRONY

This is also a time when the very rapidity of change seems to me to underline the irony that is so characteristic of history —the irony which makes the event, the outcome, so different from the human purpose.

Think of the communist movement; it began in compassion, and now it is probably the least compassionate of any major political force the world has seen for a long, long time. Think of China, with its pattern of respect and love for the family and the past, its addiction to reflection, and almost private beauty. Think what the Chinese have embraced in the way of forced, quick, violent, brilliant change—and how little they are prepared for it. Think of India, if you will, and a government in India which is a direct consequence of Cambridge, of Oxford, and of London—these symbols of two centuries of oppression. And think of us, who founded ourselves in independence, and who are inextricably stuck in the most monstrous kind of interdependence—both here, where the vastness of all our affairs makes the individual's wink invisible, and even interdependent with very remote parts of the globe. Think of the irony of the great weapons, which, developed to give a military answer to the problem of security, have assumed such proportions that they almost cannot be used and have produced for the general staffs that evoked them a nightmare of almost total insecurity.

All these things—and there are many more—could easily, it seems to me, make in the times a kind of bitterness and a kind of feeling that the individual had better see to his own delight and to heck with society, to heck with virtue. That is not so different from the way it was in the decade when I grew up, after the first world war, where a kind of revolt was characteristic in the colleges and in the arts. It was a revolt which said that what we have had from the past was not much of a guide for the future, a revolt where there was a hope of improvising something gay and new, where the bitter fruit of that terrible war seemed to call for a kind of new, fresh departure.

It isn't really quite like that now. I think that today, if I know you and your friends through the country, you hold very close to the ancient imperatives—the imperatives of Christianity, of our traditions, of our country. I think you are not after novelty and improvisation in art or politics or philosophy, or manners. I think that, even if the end of our time should come, you are quite content that we live out these days faithful to the gospels, faithful to the ethic, faithful to the sense of responsibility which we have from times past.

These are some of the things that are in the background. Of course, the present problem of young people at college is the same everywhere. They are finding their way into an enormous cognitive jungle, the jungle of everything there is to know. They are finding their way into it with very little guide, either from synoptic kinds of knowledge, like philosophy, which say: This is important; this is unimportant; this fits in here; this fits in there—or from the state of the world, which doesn't, in any very clear or loud voice, say: Learn this; ignore that; learn this well; skip over that lightly.

IMPOSSIBLE CHOICES

There is, in most places, the vast trouble of impossible

342

choices. I have talked with and been among undergraduates—and schoolboys and graduate students as well—in some places around the country, and a typical agony is: "What do I do? Where am I headed?" The complement of that, of course, is to be told what to do, and in a measure, that is what goes on here. I think it varies from place to place, and there is no doubt that Caltech is far on one side of the spectrum—of the spectrum between openness and permissiveness on the one hand and rather strict and specific guidance on the other; between knowledge as an end in itself, something to study because of the joy of it and the beauty of it, and knowledge as an instrument, as a way of getting on in the future. I think Caltech is very much on the instrumental side, and very much on the predetermined side.

But the sense of loss which I hear in you—I don't know whether it is exaggerated in our talk but I'm sure it's there—of the things which you are not studying; the sense of loss at all that you might be learning, and aren't; the slight fear that this might not be easy to make up at a later time; this is a much larger thing, a quite general part of human life. There is much more that one might know than any of us are ever going to know. There is much more to know than any of us are ever going to catch up with; and this is not just the trivial fact that we don't work hard enough; it is not the trivial fact that things are difficult to learn. It is that any form of knowledge really precludes other forms; that any serious study of one thing cuts out some other part of your life. Narrowness is not an accident of one place but a condition of knowledge.

I think myself that, with the growth of knowledge—the immense perplexity, the pervasive mutual relevance of different things to each other—all we can do is to accept the state of affairs, to affirm it and to accept it deeply. It is not that some courses are not better than others and some worse, some even good and some evil; it is that, in the balance between ignorance and loss on the one hand and knowledge and richness of experience on the other, we have to keep the affirmative love of the knowledge and the richness very close and never deny that most of what men can know, we don't know; that much of what man can know, nobody knows.

Of course, in a certain sense this is trivial and people have always known it. When it comes to the will, the element of choice has always been clear. The fact that you had one course which precluded another; you could take a job or you could continue to study; you could marry or you could say goodbye; everybody knows that. But I think it has not been quite as clear how, in the very conditions of knowledge, choice is built in and exclusion is part of depth.

I don't want to try to derive this from anything in science because it seems to me quite deep and quite commonsensical, and very much a part of all our experience. But I do want to give three examples from three different areas in science which illustrate it rather sharply. One is from the physiology of perception, one is from the psychology of learning, and one is from physics.

The philosophers like to talk about sense data as though they were something that came to all men who were properly constituted, a replica, a picture, a sign of something outside; and all philosophers have always been very confident that the sense datum was something very solid to build on. But, in being able to perceive, we take a far more active part and not necessarily a conscious one.

A SIMPLE EXPERIMENT

There is, for instance, an experiment of great simplicity having to do with hearing. The nerves running from the hair cells in a dog's ear toward the cortex can be tapped, and one can see what kind of electrical impulses travel along them. If you take a dog so "hooked up," you will soon learn to recognize the electrical pattern of the signal that comes along when the dog hears a bell ring. If you put a piece of meat in front of the dog, that signal disappears. The way this happens is that, along with the afferent nerve fibers, there are finer nerve fibers which, so to speak, tell the nerves what to do, what to hear,

344

and what signals to send. This is not understood in detail. But the coding which we always assume characterizes the human brain—the organization of material, the focusing of attention, animadversion, concentration, memory—this coding pervades the most primitive parts of the cognitive system, and the dog may or may not hear the bell. It isn't something that he fixes up inside himself; it is a question of what he is attuned to.

There are very similar experiments having to do, for instance, with language—a whole series of them reported from the Harvard Cognition Project. It is astonishing what people will notice and what they will ignore. For instance, if you take some sounds that have some variations in them and say them, then an American who is attuned only to our language will hear differences— but only those differences which correspond to the way we spell and write, to our phonetic elements. Of course, we don't spell and write very accurately, but we recognize *a* as distinct from *e*, and *r* as distinct from *n* and so on. If you take a Navaho who doesn't know English, he will hear quite different things. He won't distinguish our vowels, but he will distinguish by the length of the vowel. You can teach the Navaho to notice the English differences and the American to notice the Navaho differences, but he doesn't normally do it. The possibility of communicating, of course, rests on the fact that we don't hear too much. You hear someone talk, but only that part of it which really has meaning in English. All the rest of it—the rumble and roar that goes with it—you don't hear. It isn't that you hear it and ignore it.

Of the incredibly many examples, one of the most striking comes to anyone who tries to translate the words for colors from one language to another, even two languages that are Indo-Germanic. The English words for color distinguish spectrally what we call color, by the hue. The Greek words have to do almost entirely with depth and brightness, and you can't find a Greek word for blue. You can find one that sometimes means blue. All these questions of animadversion are extremely primitive.

AN EXAMPLE FROM PHYSICS

And what is the example from physics? It is the one that I talk about much too much. Of course, if one is now learning atomic theory, one learns Schroedinger's equation in quantum mechanics, and it all seems very unphilosophical and practical. It is a wonderful way of describing atomic phenomena, and one tries to get the techniques and get it over with. But to anyone who lived with the development of this, it was quite a different story, because what one had to get through his head was something quite odd.

We are used to a world in which we can find out anything of interest about a large physical system without in any way questioning the means by which we can find it out. The classical examples are that we can tell where a planet is and, by observing it successively, we can tell how fast it is moving. The question whether this observation could have any paradoxical features in it never arises. But in atomic mechanics we had to learn that, although experiments in some ways like finding where a planet is and in some ways like finding out its velocity are indeed possible and are indeed a part of describing what is going on, the kind of arrangement that is suitable for doing one of these experiments not only makes it impossible to do the other but also makes it logically contradictory to assume that the other quantity has a value or has one of a number of values. In other words, we came to realize that, in the atomic scale, one can realize, by the way one goes about it in the laboratory, that there is some free choice—not free in the sense of an ethical problem, but free in that the physicist can decide what he is interested in or what he wants to study. Having made that choice, one has closed out the chance of doing the other thing so that both are valid measurements or so that one can even imagine that he has done both and that each has had a given result. If he imagines thus and starts to draw the consequences, he will get a prediction for the future of that atom that has no relation to what he will find in the laboratory.

These are examples of the pervasiveness with which, in all

scientific things, one meets again the fact that knowledge, by the very techniques, powers, and facts of its acquisition, by its organizing the chaos that is the world around us, precludes other knowledge.

A NEW PICTURE OF THE COGNITIVE WORLD

This makes a picture of the cognitive world which, in many ways, is not the one we have inherited. It is not as though we can be in a room, just looking at it, and could then, if we wanted to know some more, look some more, exhausting all the properties of it and being able to talk about it all—or as though we were in a temple and could go back over and over again, studying the peculiarities of the temple until there was nothing more to know, and then make a description of this room or this temple which was total and global.

It is much more as though we had deep, not always connected, parts of knowledge—knowledge of physics, knowledge of life, knowledge of man, knowledge of history. Between these things that are known to any one of us there is always potential relevance, so that one can never say, even of the most implausibly abstract kind of mathematics: This will not be relevant to psychology or physics. But the image that comes to my mind is not that of the chamber that can be exhausted but of an essentially infinite world, knowable in many different ways; and all these paths of knowledge are interconnectable, and some are interconnected, like a great network—a great network between people, between ideas, between systems of knowledge—a reticulated kind of structure which is human culture and human society.

This means that I am very suspicious of statements that refer to totality or completeness, that I am very suspicious of our ability to have more than partial knowledge, in the very real sense that it can be supplemented and that it doesn't close. It means that I am very suspicious also of order which is hierarchical in the sense that it says that some things are more important than others—that some things are so important that you can derive everything else from them. These were great hopes of

347

man, and philosophical systems are their monuments. I don't
think that the prospects of their being realized look very good.

THE COLLAR

Now, one could take an attitude of real horror toward this
and say that one can't live with it—that this is to offer man
not knowledge, but chaos. I don't think that is right. We have
all had the experience of seeing the relevance of something
that we hadn't known before, of learning at all times in our
lives something deep and new and wonderful that had been
hidden before. We have all had the experience of what companionship and intercourse and an open mind can do, and I
don't think the absence of global traits to our knowledge is a
cause for despair. But I'd like to quote a poem that seems to
me to fit a little not only with this general situation but also
perhaps even with the local situation. It is not a new poem; it
is three centuries old and the language is archaic, and I can't
be sure that everyone will like it—but I can say I like it. It is
called "The Collar," and it is by a devout Anglican named
George Herbert.

> I struck the board, and cry'd No more;
>   I will abroad.
> What? Shall I ever sigh and pine?
> My lines and life are free; free as the road.
> Loose as the wind, as large as store.
>   Shall I be still in suit?
> Have I no harvest but a thorn
> To let me blood, and not restore
> What I have lost with cordial fruit?
>   Sure there was wine,
> Before my sighs did dry it: there was corn,
>   Before my tears did drown it.
> Is the year only lost to me?
>   Have I no bays to crown it?
> No flowers, no garlands gay? all blasted?
>   All wasted?
> Not so, my heart: but there is fruit,
>   And thou hast hands.

348

Recover all thy sigh-blown age
On double pleasures: leave thy cold dispute
Of what is fit, and not forsake thy cage,
    Thy rope of sands,
Which petty thoughts have made, and made to thee
Good cable, to enforce and draw,
    And be thy law.
While thou didst wink and wouldst not see.
    Away: take heed:
    I will abroad.
Call in thy deaths head there: tie up thy fears.
    He that forebears
    To suit and serve his need,
      Deserves his load.
But as I raved and grew more fierce and wild,
    At every word,
Methought I heard one calling, Child;
    and I reply'd, My Lord.

Having spoken so, and tried to measure what the flowering, changing, rich, but only partially ordered world of the mind means for us, it may not be inappropriate to stress what seem to me a few of the things that will be useful in living with it. They are certainly not new things; they have always been useful.

The first is to have a kind of deep reverence, not, certainly, for the learned man or the stuffed shirt, but for learning, for knowledge and skill, and to hold tight to it, and not to be talked out of it by any superficial parody of what it is—the kind of thing we learn in school where we learn to do and create and understand, and where we learn really to act with the knowledge we get.

This is something that is not easy to come by. It has not been easy for man; it is not being easy now, and it is incredibly precious; and the world is full of it. Accounts of this—stories (whether in general education or in *Life* magazine), short cuts, and synopses—miss most of the point. It is just the technique and the wonder of one's own ability to do it that is part of the value of it. And in ourselves and in other people this is, I think, to be held on to very tight. If you have learned how to be something, how to be a competent professional, you will know a great deal about what is good in this world. You will have a bond in common with every other man who is a scholar or a scientist.

The greatest of all protections against narrowness, and the greatest relief and opening, is comradeship and that ability to learn from others of what their world is like. Learn from books for sure; learn from people, but learn with a kind of sense that every man enriches you and enlarges you if you only have the strength, the wit, the openness, the fortitude to learn what he is all about and what he knows.

THE OTHERNESS OF PEOPLE

And very much we need tolerance. We are all incredibly different. I think sometimes that one of the unexpected fruits of biological research may be that we can, on occasion, be made to feel more like somebody else than we normally do and so get some impression of the immense diversity in human experience. But, of course, as it is, we don't have that. Through art, through affection, we have some sense of a global kind of what other people are like, of what life means to them, of what makes them tick, and of what their learning and their understanding is. But an immense sense of the otherness of people and the otherness of possible worlds and ideas is, I guess, the basis of tolerance. I don't mean, in any simple way, tolerance of evil in one's self but rather a recognition that even two people, hearing the same words, living together, seeing the same things, have some measure of gulf between them; and a recognition that when we are dealing with remote peoples, remote traditions, we need to bring an overpowering humility to our estimate of what they are, and our measure of them.

I have the impression that if we, in this time and this age, manage properly to live with the wealth of knowledge, the wealth of change, the responsibility, and the traits of impotence which these times dish up, we will really be quite something, and that perhaps there will be people in places and times that come after who will have reason to be grateful to us.

Biographical Notes on the Contributors

GEORGE W. BEADLE has been Chairman of the Biology Division at Caltech since 1946, when he came to the Institute from Stanford University, where he had been Professor of Biology. Dr. Beadle is identified mainly with the discovery (by the use of the bread mold *Neurospora*) that genes control chemical reactions. This discovery opened up a whole new field of research, leading to new knowledge of genes themselves, to new knowledge in biochemistry and even in bacteriology for study of bacterial genes.

HUGO BENIOFF, Professor of Seismology, has been an authority on the design of earthquake instruments since 1931, when the first Benioff seismograph was put into service. In recent years he has been interested in the mechanism of earthquakes and aftershocks and crustal strains and crustal structure, as defined by earthquake sequences. During the IGY, Dr. Benioff directed studies in South America of secular, tidal, and seismic strains.

JAMES BONNER, Professor of Biology, was trained in chemistry and interested in biology; logically, he took his Ph.D. at Caltech in plant physiology. This was in 1934, and he was the first graduate student to receive a degree in this field. He was an early participant in the Caltech research on plant growth hormones that led to the isolation of the growth substance indoleacetic acid, or auxin.

HENRY BORSOOK, Professor of Biochemistry, is an M.D. who chose biochemistry as a career. His current research is concerned with the biological synthesis of proteins, but he is equally well known for his work on nutrition. He conducted some of the early studies on vitamins and is the author of *Vitamins—What They Are and How They Can Benefit You* (1940).

IRA S. BOWEN, Director of the Mount Wilson and Palomar Observatories, came to Caltech as an instructor in 1921 and received his Ph.D. there in 1926. He served as a professor of physics from 1931 to 1946, when he became director of the Observatories. Spectroscopy is one of his special fields, as well as research into the nature of substances in gaseous nebulae. "Astronomy in a Changing World" has been adapted from a talk given at the Bracket Observatory of Pomona College.

HARRISON BROWN joined the Caltech faculty in 1951 to establish its geochemistry laboratories in the division of geological sciences, after five years at the University of Chicago's Institute for Nuclear Studies. He has made key contributions to the development of the atomic bomb, first on the Plutonium Project at Chicago and later as Assistant Director of Chemistry at the Clinton Laboratories in Oak Ridge, Tennessee. His special fields are investigations of the age of rocks, the abundance of elements in the universe, and the composition of the earth and meteorites—all problems that involve the fields of chemistry, physics, and astronomy as well as geology. Dr. Brown, who received his Ph.D. from Johns Hopkins in 1941, is the author of *The Challenge of Man's Future* and *Must Destruction be our Destiny?* and co-author with John Weir and James Bonner of *The Next Hundred Years*.

MARGARET and GEOFFREY BURBIDGE are a husband-and-wife team from Cambridge University who, in 1956-1957, worked at Caltech on a new theory of the synthesis of elements in stars. Mrs. Burbidge, an observational astronomer, and Dr. Burbidge, a theoretical astrophysicist, received their Ph.D.s from the University of London, she in 1943, he (in applied mathematics) in 1951. Both are now at Yerkes Observatory, Mrs. Burbidge as a research fellow and her husband as Assistant Professor of Astronomy.

ROBERT B. COREY, Professor of Structural Chemistry, works with Dr. Linus Pauling on one of the most important problems in the fields of biochemistry—finding out how proteins, the principal building blocks of the body, are put together. Dr. Corey, a graduate of the University of Pittsburgh, took his Ph.D. at Cornell University in 1924. After several years with the Rockefeller Institute for Medical Research he came to Caltech in 1937 as a senior research fellow. His current research concerns the determination of the structure of crystalline proteins from X-ray diffraction patterns.

SIR CHARLES DARWIN is the grandson of the author of *On the Origin of Species*. Now retired, Sir Charles was a pioneer in nuclear studies and, from 1938 to 1949, was Director of the National Physics Laboratory in England. "Forecasting the Future" was presented at a physics seminar during Sir Charles's visit to Caltech in 1956. No stranger to the Institute, Sir Charles served there as a visiting professor in 1922.

L. A. DUBRIDGE has been president of Caltech since 1946, when he succeeded Robert A. Millikan. A native of Indiana, Dr. DuBridge was graduated from Cornell College, Iowa, in 1922 and received his Ph.D. at the University of Wisconsin in 1926. From 1926 to 1928 he did research in physics at Caltech as a National Research Council fellow, then joined the faculty of Washington University in St. Louis. In 1934 he became Professor of Physics and chairman of the department at the University of Rochester, where he remained until 1940, when he took a leave of absence to direct the Radiation Laboratory (radar research) of the National Defense Research Committee at M.I.T. during the war.

There are three DuBridge essays in this book: "The Inquiring Mind" has been adapted from a talk at the national meeting of the Institute of Food Technologists; "Exploring the Unknown" from one given to the Industrial Research Institute; and "Science—The Endless Adventure," from a speech made at the annual convention of the National Education Association.

RICHARD P. FEYNMAN, Professor of Theoretical Physics, is known best for his work on the quantum theory of electricity and magnetism and for his current research in the field of low temperature physics. He received his Ph.D. from Princeton in 1942. During the war he worked at the Los Alamos Laboratory, then served as a member of the Laboratory of Nuclear Studies at Cornell University from 1945 to 1950, when he joined the Caltech faculty. In 1954 he received the Albert Einstein Award, one of the highest honors in science, for his "outstanding contributions to knowledge in the mathematical and physical sciences." His essay "The Value of Science" has been adapted from a public lecture at a meeting of the National Academy of Sciences held on the Caltech campus; "The Relation of Science and Religion" is a direct transcription of a talk given to the Caltech YMCA Forum.

LYMAN FRETWELL, who received his B.S. in physics from Caltech in 1956, is now in his second year of graduate study there, on a National Science Foundation fellowship. He is working on the construction of a large heavy liquid bubble chamber in the Caltech synchrotron, to be used for experiments on the physics of elementary particles.

ARTHUR W. GALSTON, formerly Associate Professor of Biology at Caltech, is now Professor of Plant Physiology at Yale. A graduate of Cornell University, he received his Ph.D. from the University of Illinois. Dr. Galston's research activities have concerned the actions of enzymes in plant cell growth.

NORMAN H. HOROWITZ, Professor of Biology, has been concerned in recent years with learning how genes govern the chemistry of the body through their control over the synthesis of enzymes and, through them, the synthesis of vitamins, amino acids, and other important constituents of living matter. Dr. Horowitz received his Ph.D. from Caltech in 1939 and joined the Caltech faculty in 1946.

FRED HOYLE, Fellow of St. Johns College and Lecturer in Mathematics at Cambridge University, is also a visiting professor of astrophysics at Caltech and a staff member of the Mount Wilson and Palomar Observatories. Furthermore, he was recently appointed Plumian Professor of Astronomy and Experimental Philosophy at Cambridge. A prolific writer (including popular science books and articles and science fiction), he is represented twice in this collection.

EDWARD HUTCHINGS, JR., is a nonscientist who has been editor of *Engineering and Science* magazine since 1948. A graduate of Dartmouth (1933), he has worked on the editorial staffs of *The Literary Digest, Tide, Business Week, Look, Liberty,* and *Science Illustrated* magazines.

JAMES M. KENDALL, a graduate of The Carnegie Institute of Technology, received both his M.S. and Ph.D. degrees from Caltech. He is now a senior research engineer working in supersonic aerodynamics at the Caltech Jet Propulsion Laboratory.

HUNTER MEAD, Professor of Philosophy and Psychology, is a native Californian and an alumnus of Pomona College. He took his Ph.D. at the University of Southern California in 1936, then taught in American colleges in Turkey and Greece for two years, returning to the United States to take a teaching fellowship at U.S.C. He joined the Caltech faculty in 1947. Dr. Mead is the author of *Introduction to Philosophy* and *Aesthetics.*

ELTING E. MORISON, Professor of Industrial History in the Sloan School of Industrial Management at M.I.T., gave "A Case Study of Innovation" as a lecture at the faculty club (the Athenaeum) during a visit to Caltech. Professor Morison has been a consultant for the Research and Development Board of the Department of Defense, and during World War II he was Director of the Historical Section in the Office of the Chief of Naval Operations. He is the author of *Admiral Sims and the Modern American Navy* and editor of *The Letters of Theodore Roosevelt.*

J. ROBERT OPPENHEIMER visited the Caltech campus as one of the Caltech YMCA "Leaders of America." As such, he spent most of his time in informal discussions with students. "Talk to Undergraduates" is a direct transcription of the one formal talk he gave during his visit. Dr. Oppenheimer, who is Director of the Institute for Advanced Study in Princeton, N.J., was a member of the Caltech faculty from 1928 to 1948.

LINUS PAULING, Chairman of the Division of Chemistry and Chemical Engineering at Caltech, was awarded the 1954 Nobel Prize in chemistry for his research into the nature of the chemical bond and its application to the elucidation of the structure of complex substances. He is represented twice in this volume; "The Significance of Chemistry in the Modern World" originally written for UNESCO, concerns another of Dr. Pauling's myriad interests. A graduate of Oregon State College, Linus Pauling has been at Caltech since 1922. He received his Ph.D. in 1925 and became a full professor in 1931. In 1933 he was elected to the National Academy of Sciences; he is also an honorary member of the Royal Society of London, the Royal Institution of Great Britain, the French Academy of Sciences, the French Academy of Medicine, and other academies in Belgium, Italy, Sicily, Portugal, Norway, and India. Under his direction, a team of Caltech scientists is now exploring the molecular chemistry of mental disease.

FRANK PRESS came to Caltech in 1955 as Professor of Geophysics and in 1957 became Director of the Institute's Seismological Laboratory. He taught previously at Columbia University, where he received his Ph.D. in 1949. "Volcanoes, Ice and Destructive Waves" was one of Caltech's Friday Evening Demonstration Lectures, a series of talks given by the Caltech faculty for the general public. A member of the IGY Continental Committee which is in charge of all research projects on this continent, Dr. Press is also a member of the Technical Panel on Glaciology and the Technical Panel on Seismology for the IGY. He is best known for his geophysical investigations of the crustal structure of the continents and ocean basins and for theoretical and experimental work on elastic wave propagation.

HARRY RUBIN, Senior Research Fellow in Biology, received his Doctor of Veterinary Medicine degree at Cornell in 1947, then spent a year doing field work in Mexico on hoof-and-mouth disease in cattle. In 1949 he joined the U.S. Public Health Service, where for 3½ years he did research on virus diseases in animals which were transmissible to man. In 1952 he joined the virus group, under Wendell Stanley, at the University of California. He has been at Caltech since 1953, and his work there on the Rous sarcoma virus may eventually lead to a better understanding of the nature of cancer.

FRANK SALISBURY received his Ph.D. in biology from Caltech in 1955. A plant physiologist who is equally interested in plant ecology, he calls himself an "ecological physiologist," is now teaching plant physiology at Colorado State University.

ALLAN SANDAGE, staff member of the Mount Wilson and Palomar Observatories, received his Ph.D. in astronomy at Caltech in 1953 —which makes him one of the youngest members of the Observatories staff. Dr. Sandage is noted for his work on the current measurements of the extragalactic distance scale—the number of light years from here to distant galaxies. "The Birth and Death of a Star" was originally given as a talk before the trustees and staff of the Carnegie Institution of Washington.

R. W. SPERRY, Hixon Professor of Psychobiology, has been at Caltech since 1954. He received his Ph.D. from the University of Chicago in 1941. Active for many years in the fields of neurology and psychology, he came to Caltech from a joint appointment at the University of Chicago and the National Institutes of Health in Bethesda, Md.

JOHN S. STAMM began his scientific career as a working electrical engineer, then went back to school and took a Ph.D. in psychology at the University of Southern California. From 1950 to 1955 he was at Caltech studying the physiological and behavioral functions of the brain and the recording of brain waves. He is now a research associate in experimental psychology at the Institute of Living in Hartford, Connecticut.

ALFRED STERN, Associate Professor of Languages and Philosophy, is a native of Austria and received his Ph.D. from the University of Vienna. A volunteer in the French Infantry in World War II, he escaped to Mexico in 1942, after France was overrun by the Nazis, and later entered the United States. His work has earned him the insignia of a Knight of the Legion of Honor as well as the Academic Palms and the title Officer of the Academy of France. Dr. Stern has taught at the University of Paris, the Institute of High Studies of Belgium in Brussels, the National University of Mexico, the French College in Mexico City, the French University in New York, and the University of Southern California. He came to Caltech in 1947. "Why Do We Laugh and Cry?" has been adapted from *Philosophie du Rire et des Pleurs,* published in Paris in 1949 but not translated into English.

A. H. STURTEVANT, Professor of Genetics, has been on the Caltech faculty since 1928. Working with the small fruit fly, *Drosophila,* he first established that the genes are distributed in the chromosomes as are beads on a string. In his essay, Dr. Sturtevant explains why science considers the medical use of X-rays and irradiation from atomic explosions potentially dangerous to future generations.

ALBERT G. WILSON, now Director of the Lowell Observatory in Flagstaff, Arizona, was previously at the Mount Wilson and Palomar Observatories. Dr. Wilson reecived his M.S. and Ph.D. degrees in astronomy at Caltech and was actively concerned with the National Geographic Society-Palomar Observatory Sky Survey—one of the most comprehensive photographic records of the skies ever made. While working on this project he was the co-discoverer, with Dr. Rudolph Minkowski, of a small planet which has now been officially named Geographos.

Index

numbers, importance of, 235
nutrition, 80

oil, supplies of, 113
Opik, E. J., 208
Oppenheimer, J. Robert, 221, 339
origin of species, 125

Pasteur, Louis, 20, 22, 24
Pauling, Linus, 14, 28, 221, 278
peptides, 29
perception (*see* brain; mind)
Phillips, Horatio, 152
photosynthesis, 38, 88, 175, 176, 178
physical sciences, 122
planetary systems, formation of, 127
plants, 15
  growth of, 88, 95
  (*see also* chlorophyll)
pleated-sheet configuration, 35
polypeptide chains, 28
population
  food for, 80, 108, 112, 117, 222
  genetic effects of radiation on
    (*see* radiation)
  growth of, 17, 100, 107, 110, 117, 222
  limitation of, 109, 111, 118, 120, 223
  shortage of, 274
Population Division of the United Nations, 76
postulates, 217
Press, Frank, 141
presuppositions, 117
proteins, 82
  from algae, 108
  amount required by humans, 83
  sources of, 84
  structure of, 28
  synthesis of, 14

Pure Food and Drugs Administration, 42
Putnam, P. C., 110

radiation, high-energy
  from bomb fall-out, 74, 78
  direct effects of, 70
  genetic effects of, 70, 71
  maximum permissible exposure to, 77
  and mutation rate, 17, 71
  natural background, 76
radio waves, from stars, 240
reactors, nuclear, 17, 77, 114
reflexes, reversal of, 51
relativity, special theory of, 255
religion, and science, relationship of, 256, 263, 307
replication, 9, 13
reproduction, self, 24
Reynolds number, 153
ribonucleic acid (RNA), 12, 14
Roentgen unit, 72
Rous sarcoma, 16, 43
Rubin, Harry, 16, 43
Runes, D. D., 215

Salisbury, Frank, 128, 168
Saltpeter, E. E., 181
Sandage, Allan, 188, 202, 210
Schardt, A. W., 180
Schiaparelli, Giovanni, 169
Schlieren apparatus, 156
Schwarzschild, Martin, 185, 210
Schwarzschild, Martin, Mrs., 185
science
  anti-, 251, 254, 257
  applied, 250
  and communism, 312
  developments in, 233
  education in, 242, 246, 257, 278
  enjoyment of, 246, 261
  evaluation of, 290
  goals of, 224